150

GUIDANCE
FROM MEN
OF GOD

GUIDANCE FROM MEN OF GOD

JOHN A. REDHEAD

ABINGDON PRESS   NEW YORK   NASHVILLE

GUIDANCE FROM MEN OF GOD

Copyright © 1965 by Abingdon Press

Library of Congress Catalog Card Number: 65–20365

Scripture quotations unless otherwise noted are
from the Revised Standard Version of the Bible,
copyrighted 1946 and 1952 by the Division
of Christian Education, National Council
of Churches, and are used by permission.

The poetry on page 12 is by G. A. Studdert-
Kennedy and is used by permission of Hodder
and Stoughton, Ltd. The verse of the hymn on
page 89 is from "I Know Not How That
Bethlehem's Babe" by Harry Webb Farrington.
The poem "Outwitted" by Edwin Markham on
page 108 is reprinted by permission of Virgil
Markham.

SET UP, PRINTED, AND BOUND BY THE
PARTHENON PRESS, AT NASHVILLE,
TENNESSEE, UNITED STATES OF AMERICA

CONTENTS

ADAM: MIRROR OF HUMAN NATURE

The story of Adam is told in the early chapters of the book of Genesis. The story says that God formed Adam of the dust of the ground; then he put Adam to sleep, took a rib from his side, and from the rib he made Eve to be his wife. They lived in a place called Eden, but soon a serpent came along and spoiled things for them. And because they broke the rules, God drove them out from the garden and closed the gates behind them; and ever since that time life has been anything but a picnic.

You can take this story in one of two ways. You can think of it as literal fact, as stating that our first ancestor was a man named Adam who succumbed to his wife's tempting offer and ate the forbidden fruit. Thus Adam committed the original sin; and because we are all his children, we have inherited his guilt and stand under the condemnation of God. If you see it that way, you will think of Adam's fall as something which happened many years ago. You will hate him for getting us all into trouble, and you will hold it against God for blaming you for something which somebody else did.

But suppose you learn that Adam is a Hebrew word which means "man," in the sense of mankind; then what you have is not so much a story of what happened to one man, but a brilliant pictorial representation of the way things are with you and me. Adam is a mirror of human nature; and when you look at him, you are looking at yourself.

In Irving Stone's *The Agony and the Ecstasy*, you will remember that one day Michelangelo was talking with a friend about two pieces of sculpture he had been commissioned to carve for the Medici Chapel. The friend says: "You're not going to carve the portraits for the niches?" And the artist replies: "Assuredly not. Who will know a hundred years from now whether my marbles are good likenesses of young Lorenzo and Guiliano? I'm going to carve universal figures . . . . They will be nobody, yet everybody."

That is what we have here in the early chapters of Genesis. This story is not a piece of ancient history which is buried in the dead past; it is a candid camera shot of you and me in the act of being ourselves. When you look into the mirror that is man, what do you see?

I

The first thing you see is that human nature is a mixture, a mixture of both the good and bad. Pascal hit the nail on the head when he called man at one and the same time, "The glory and the scum of the universe." And both facts are a part of the mirror that is Adam.

For example, "God created man in his own image, in the image of God he created him." This means that man shares with God "the power of understanding truth, of creating what is beautiful and doing what is right." Man has capacity for the true, the beautiful, and the good; and as such he differs from every other living creature upon the earth. More than that, man enjoys an intimate fellowship with his maker. God is pictured here "walking in the garden in the cool of the day"—come down, as it were, to take a stroll with Adam and Eve. And furthermore, man's world is like a garden, the garden of Eden. The word "Eden" means "delight," "enchantment," "pleasure"; it is a veritable paradise, a garden of delight. It would appear that Adam and Eve had it made.

But, of course, there is a fly in the ointment, and along with the good there is the bad. Right here in the garden of Eden there is a serpent, which means that in this human nature, which is made in the image of God, there is something else too that we call a snake in the grass. This serpent gets busy and begins to give Eve notions; she brings Adam in on the business; and before you know it, both of them have eaten the forbidden fruit and lost their paradise, and are shut out to earn their bread by the sweat of their brow.

The story is told in pictures, but its truth is plain enough: Original goodness and original sin are both a part of human nature, and they create the split personality that you know so well. Dr. Jekyll and Mr. Hyde are one and the same man. When Goethe's Faust wakes up to the fact he cries, "Two souls, alas, are lodged within my breast." And Studdert-Kennedy puts it:

11

> I'm a man, and man's a mixture
> Right down from his very birth,
> For part of 'im comes from 'eaven
> And part of 'im comes from earth.
> There's summat as draws 'im upward,
> And summat as drags 'im down,
> And the consequence is he wobbles
> 'Twixt muck and a golden crown.

Somewhere I have read about a scientist who took two kinds of insects in their early development and grafted them together. One of his experiments was to graft a spider with a butterfly. You can imagine what the result was. It was a creature that wanted to fly and crawl at once, to seek the sunshine and hide in the black shadows, to feast off the flowers of spring and feed on the food of spiders.

That is what you see when you look at yourself in the mirror that is Adam: part angel and part devil, a creature made in the image of God, and at the same time poisoned by the serpent's fang.

II

Move on and notice, in the second place, that we have here a picture of the nature of the thing which causes all the trouble.

The story is very simple indeed. The serpent came to the woman and said to her, "Did God say, 'You shall not eat of any tree in the garden'?" And the woman told him: "We may eat of the fruit of the trees of the garden; but God said, 'You shall not eat of the fruit of the tree which is in the midst of the garden, neither shall you touch it, lest you die.' " But the serpent said to the woman: "You will not die. For God knows that when you eat of it your eyes will be opened, and you will be like God, knowing good and evil." So the woman took of the fruit and ate; and she also gave some to her husband, and he ate.

This is the famous story of the forbidden fruit. Notice that it does not say anything about sex. What it says is that a man and woman were given a certain command by God; that there was something in their natures like a snake in the grass, which suggested to them that God did not know what he was talking about; that they succumbed to that suggestion, defied the word of God, and ended by asserting their own wills over the will of God. They took God off his throne of power and authority and put themselves in his place. They made gods of themselves; and in the light of the Bible, that is the granddaddy of all sin.

Take the word and spell it out: S-i-n. The middle letter is the letter "I," and this is the best way of putting the matter that I know: Sin is taking God out of his central place and putting the self in the center. Some years ago there was a movie called *The Man Who Played God*. That is a picture of every man. What this story is saying is not that thousands of years ago there were a man and a woman, our first parents, who made this mistake and we have been paying for their guilt ever since. What it is saying is that Adam is a picture of human nature, that every new life that is born is born with a bent to do the same thing, that you cannot get into the world without bringing with you a will which attempts to take over in the place of God.

For example, you mothers know that every newborn infant comes into this world with himself as the center of his universe. He is concerned only with his own well-being and demands that everybody and everything cater to his own wishes. Sometimes you meet an adult who is more than ordinarily the same way, and you say that he is immature, still just a child. He thinks of himself as the center of the universe. As one wife said to me about her husband, "The whole trouble in our home is that he thinks he is God Almighty." A distinguished lecturer spoke to our men on the life of that great soldier, Stonewall Jackson. One of the things which a contemporary said about him stuck in my mind: "General Jackson was a man who gave God's place to God." The original sin, the root sin, the essence of all sin, is to give God's place to self.

Joseph Sizoo says that some years ago a friend of his was visiting Rome with his wife, and late one afternoon they went to St. Peter's Cathedral. They walked leisurely through the long nave until they came to the high altar, and they stood facing it with a sense of reverence. As his wife wandered away to examine something which interested her, he turned around and stood with his back to the altar to take in the vast cathedral. It happened that many devout people were walking through the church, nuns and priests, and others of the faithful. As they approached the altar, they bowed solemnly and with great dignity. The man thought they were curtsying to him, so he bowed in return to them. This went on for some time until his wife saw it, walked rapidly to where he was, tugged on his sleeve, and said, "My dear, you are suffering from an omnipotence complex."

That was the trouble with Adam and Eve. That is the main trouble with you and me. We are suffering from an omnipotence complex. We refuse to give God's place to God, but demand it for ourselves.

III

The story goes on to say a third thing. When Adam and Eve took for themselves the role of deity, they brought trouble to themselves—trouble which comes from estrangement.

When they heard the sound of the Lord God walking in the garden in the cool of the day, the man and his wife hid themselves from the presence of the Lord God among the trees of the garden. God called to Adam and said, "Where are you?" And Adam answered, "I heard the sound of thee in the garden, and I was afraid, . . . and I hid myself." God said, "Have you eaten of the tree of which I commanded you not to eat?" And Adam said, "The woman whom thou gavest to be with me, she gave me of the fruit of the tree, and I ate." Then God said to the woman, "What is this that you have done?" The woman said, "The serpent beguiled me, and I ate." Therefore the Lord God sent them forth from the garden of Eden, to till the ground from which Adam was taken. When the man and the woman who had lived in such happy and intimate fellowship with God tried to take over and put themselves in his place, then they were driven out, cut off, separated, estranged from God.

Once again Adam becomes a mirror of your human nature because one thing life has taught you is this: The moment you defy the will of God, the sense of guilt fills you with fear, and you try to hide from the divine presence. Doctors' offices are filled with men and women all over our land who are sick because they are running away from God. "Thou hast made us for thyself," said Augustine, "and our hearts are restless till they find their rest in thee." There is no rest for the sons of Adam who put themselves in the place of God.

The trouble does not stop with their estrangement from God. In the course of time two sons are born to Adam and Eve. Their names are Cain and Abel, and one day Cain said to his brother, "Let us go out to the field." And when they were in the field, Cain rose up against his brother Abel and killed him.

The sin of putting yourself in the place of God not only causes estrangement from the divine presence, but it causes trouble between you and other people. Why did Cain kill Abel? Because he was angry with him. And why was he angry with him? Because he was jealous of him: Because "the Lord had regard for Abel and his offering, but for Cain and his offering he had no regard." Cain simply could not stand to see Abel get ahead of him and to let God have the last word, so he took things in his own hands and killed his brother. And isn't that the source of all family trouble: envy, anger, jealousy, rebellion, and selfishness—the demand that I have my way over your way, and the refusal to let God have his way?

When you stop to think about it, here is the basis also of our race problem. In the face of a God who is no respecter of persons and in the light of a gospel which says that in Christ all human distinctions are wiped out, still we cling to our doctrine of white supremacy. Our omnipotence complex dies hard; and as long as the courts will let us, we keep on playing God.

Even a blind man can see the estrangements between the larger groups known as nations. A few years ago a certain wise man said to a friend, "The whole trouble with our world is the lack of an apostrophe." When the friend wanted to know what he meant, he said: "Look at Hitler and Mussolini and Stalin and Tojo, and what you see is this: men trying to be gods, g-o-d-s, instead of men trying to be God's—G-o-d apostrophe s."

And then of course this estrangement goes on beyond that between you and God, and you and other people: It estranges you from yourself. Here is a man who went to see his doctor because he thought he was suffering from certain allergies. The doctor made a series of tests; and when the patient went back

to get his report, the doctor staid to him: "Sir, I am afraid you
are allergic to yourself."

Sin is rebellion, and rebellion brings civil war; this civil war
not only divides a man against his Maker and against other
people, but against himself.

IV

There is one further fact which you see in the mirror that
is Adam and which makes it possible to end this story on a note
of encouragement. Before the drama is ended, God promises
to heal the breach brought on by man's rebellion.

After the serpent had done his dirty work, God had a hard
word for him too. The Lord said to the serpent, "I will put
enmity between you and the woman, and between your seed
and her seed; he shall bruise your head, and you shall bruise
his heel."

This is what biblical scholars call the protevangelium: the
first announcement of a Savior. All the way back at the very
beginning man is given the confidence that sin will not have
the last word: The seed of the woman shall bruise the head of
the serpent, and the coming Son of man will slay completely
and forever the power of evil.

Paul speaks of Christ as the Second Adam; and his idea is
that while the first Adam was the father of the old humanity
marred by sin, the Second Adam is the creator of a new humanity. "As in Adam all die, so also in Christ shall all be made
alive."

And so the story of human nature, which begins on a low
note in the mirror that is Adam, ends in promise; and your
gospel and my gospel is the good news that "if any man be in
Christ, he is a new creation."

ISAAC: A GUIDE TO GETTING GUIDANCE

This chapter comes from the biography of Isaac, and it deals with a problem familiar to us all. The name Isaac means "laughter," and it reminds us of the circumstances of his birth: His parents were still childless in their old age; and when God told them they were going to have a son, the idea was so ludicrous that they laughed at it. The place of Isaac is a minor one, and apparently the only reason he is mentioned is that he serves as a necessary link between two great men: his father Abraham and his son Jacob. There are only two episodes which are commonly remembered about him: his brush with death as a boy when he was almost sacrificed by his father and the choice of his wife Rebekah. In both instances he is seen as a passive person with no initiative, and one of my preacher friends says he reminds him more of a tame house cat than anything else. He had so little initiative that he was willing to allow the family butler to pick out his wife for him, and it is to that story that we turn now.

The problem which it poses is the problem of guidance. You know that one of the most difficult things you ever have to do is to make a decision. That fact is true all the way from the small questions which come up in day-by-day living to the larger affairs like the choice of the person you will marry. And you know too the agony of indecision: to go or not to go; to accept or to decline; to turn this way or that? To stand at the crossroads and look in vain for the sight of a beckoning hand or to listen in vain for the sound of a guiding voice—the uncertainty of being torn between two opinions is one of the hardest things you have to bear.

Now the question is, are we justified in our times of perplexity in expecting guidance? "It is not in man who walks," says the Bible, "to direct his steps"; but can we look to someone else for the guiding hand? If we say No, then our faith is failing to measure up at a point of critical need. And if we say Yes, then what is the source of our guidance, and how do we go about finding it?

Nothing is ever settled until it is settled right, and what determines whether or not a thing is right is the will of God. Once you are sure that your choice is in line with the will of God, then you can give yourself to it with full steam ahead. But how can you discern that will? That is the problem; and it is here that the story concerning Isaac can speak to our need.

The situation is this: Abraham believes that God has a purpose for him and for his descendants. In line with that conviction he left his own home in the East and moved into a country called Palestine. But now he is old, and his son Isaac is still a bachelor; so what does he do to find a wife for Isaac?

I

The first thing he does is to show a willingness to follow God's will, and not his own in the matter. He is confident that God wills for Isaac a wife who will share his faith and be sympathetic with the purpose to which his life is dedicated. He knows that the marriage will work better if there is some similarity of family background. And so he tells his servant to leave the local girls behind and go back to his old home in Mesopotamia where such a person is likely to be found, even though it involves a long journey. Consequently, we see that the first step in getting guidance from God is a willingness to do his will.

You will understand this necessity when you see it as a law which applies in all search for truth. Before you can learn anything, you must give up all preconceived notions and desires. For instance, the scientist Julian Sorell Huxley says, "Science seems to me to teach in the highest and strongest manner the great truth which is embodied in the Christian conception of entire surrender to the will of God. Sit down before a fact as a little child, be prepared to give up every preconceived notion, follow humbly wherever and to whatever abysses nature leads, or you shall learn nothing."

Just so. If you refuse to open, or to yield, your eyes to a beautiful picture, you cannot see it. If you refuse to open, or to yield, your mind to a certain thought, you cannot understand it. And by the same token, if you refuse to open, or yield, your will to the will of God, you cannot find the guidance you are seeking. Willingness to do God's will is the first condition for knowing his will.

During a recent vacation I reread the life of John Calvin, and I was reminded again of one of the turning points in his life. When he had been exiled from the city of Geneva and the people had repented and sought to bring him back, he tried to discover God's will in the matter. It is plain that he did not want to go. "There is no place in the world," he wrote to one of his friends, "that I fear more." Yet the big thing with Calvin was not what he wanted; it was what God wanted. He left it all to the divine will. That was his north star. What he said was this: "When I remember that in this matter I am not my own master, I present my heart as a sacrifice and offer it up unto the Lord." There is a seal of Calvin bearing this motto. The emblem is a hand presenting a heart to God, and the inscription says this: "My heart I give thee, Lord, eagerly and sincerely." No wonder the working of the divine will is so evident in the life of John Calvin. He made a place for it. He opened the way for it. He sought to bring his life parallel to it, and God always meets a man on the spot of self-surrender! "Not my will, but thine."

II

The first thing done then to find a wife for Isaac was to determine to follow God's will in the matter. That called for a long trip from Palestine back to Mesopotamia. So the servant took ten of his master's camels and all sorts of choice gifts and set out and reached the city of Nahor. It was late in the afternoon when he arrived, the time when the women go to the well for water, and so he stopped by the well where he had his camels kneel. Then he said to himself: "Behold, I am standing by the spring of water, and the daughters of the men of the city are coming out to draw water. Let the maiden to whom I shall say, 'Pray let down your jar that I may drink,' and who shall say, 'Drink, and I will water your camels'—let her be the one whom thou hast appointed for thy servant Isaac."

What that seems to say is this: The wise old servant had made up his mind that God wants a man to use his own brains in seeking a knowledge of the divine will. When you think about it, this sign which he set for himself makes sense. Had he said, the first girl who comes along with blond hair is the one I shall choose; or, let it be the one with brown eyes; or, the one wearing a red dress—then this would show no use of intelligence. It would be like flipping a coin and saying, Heads, I'll speak to this one or, Tails, to that one. Such a sign would give no indication of what the girl was like. But since the servant knew Isaac's lack of initiative and resources, the girl who would both comply with his request for a drink of water and then offer to water the camels was the type of outgoing and self-reliant woman whom Isaac needed to marry. If willingness to do God's will is the first prerequisite for knowing it, then readiness to use your own intelligence is the second.

In the light of that fact, it is amazing how many otherwise intelligent people will let a decision hinge upon the outcome of some event which has absolutely no relation to reason. A man told me once that he was trying to make up his mind about what God wished him to do in a certain matter, and he could not get any clear answer. Then one September morning the weather turned cool, and he had to go to the basement to start the fire in his furnace. On the way upstairs he made God the proposition that if the fire burned, he would do one thing; but if the fire went out, he would do the other. There was no connection at all between the test he proposed and rational judgment; it showed nothing about the will of God, only whether he was any good at making a fire.

At the other end of the line is the expectation that God will split the heavens open and visit you with some supernatural voice or vision. Some years ago there was a young man named John McDowell who was a student at Princeton. He was debating the question of the Christian ministry, and he said that for a long time he was expecting God to walk across the campus and stand beneath his window and call up to him: "John McDowell, stick your head out; I want you for the ministry." He said it never happened like that and that later he discovered that the reason God had put a head on his shoulders was to use it.

What that means is this: If you have some decision to make, like going to this college or to that one, choosing this vocation or that one, marrying this person or that one, taking this job or that one—then God wants you to use your brains. Take a piece of paper, draw a line down the middle, write at the top of one column the word *For* and at the top of the other the word *Against*. Then list all the reasons you can think of, both pro and con. You will find that it helps to clear your thinking by putting your thoughts into words; and when they are written down, you can get a more composite picture.

A further method of using your head in seeking guidance is to consult your friends or family. You may be hesitant in revealing your thoughts in delicately personal matters like your decision for marriage, but in so many cases our friends know us better than we know ourselves. There is a young woman who was discussing marriage with her mother and who was using the argument that opposites attract. It must have been that she was interested in a man in many ways unlike herself. And her mother, knowing the danger in too many dissimilarities, said to her: "My dear, the fact that you are a woman and he is a man is opposite enough."

The command to love God with all your mind surely means

that it is right to use your head in finding his will, and that is what Isaac's advocate did.

III

The third thing the servant did was to keep his mind open to receive light by praying about the matter. He said, "O Lord, God of my master Abraham, grant me success today, I pray thee. . . . Behold, I am standing by the spring of water and the daughters of the men of the city are coming out to draw water." It is just plain common sense that if you expect to receive light from a certain direction, you will keep looking in that direction. And that is what prayer is: It is keeping your eyes glued on God and your ears open for his guiding voice.

I cannot forget that the thing which helped me most in a moment of major decision was what a teacher of vocational guidance said to a group of us high school boys at Blue Ridge: "God has a plan for your life; and if you will listen, he will tell you what it is." That is what prayer is: It is the listening ear. There is an old saying to the effect that the reason you have two ears and one mouth is that it is better to listen twice as much as you talk. This surely is the case when you are seeking guidance. It is difficult to say something to a person unless he listens, and prayer is the listening ear. So the servant of Abraham not only showed a willingness to follow God's will and a readiness to use his own head, but he made prayer a part of his plan.

And when you do the same, you will find in prayer a useful corrective in making your decisions. For one thing, if you follow the plan of consulting your friends about the choice you have to make, often one will say one thing and one another; and you will need some means of testing their opinions. A wise man put it to me like this once, and his word has often stood me in good stead: "Beware," he said, "of allowing other people to interpret providence for you." When you check their interpretation by the will of God in going directly to headquarters, you will know which is the right one.

Furthermore, prayer is the best means of getting your own wishes out of the way and giving the right-of-way to the higher will. There in Gethsemane, for example, our Lord faced the most important decision of his life, the choice of the Cross; and it does no discredit to him to point out that he had his own wish in the matter. He definitely did not want the cross, and if you happen to be a young man of thirty-three, you have only to put yourself in his place to understand why. And so the first time he prayed, he said this: "My Father, if it be possible, let this cup pass from me." Three times he prayed, and all the while he was rearranging his own wishes in their relation to the higher will; so that finally he said this: "My father, if this cup may not pass unless I drink it, thy will be done."

As far as Jesus was concerned, the prayer of the listening ear was the very heart of the thing; and it cannot be otherwise with his followers.

IV

The fourth and final step in the servant's search for guidance was his waiting for the feeling of certainty. Having put himself in line with God's will, having used his own judgment to the best of his ability, having opened his mind in prayer for the entrance of divine light, he waited for an inward assurance of certainty. "And he looked steadfastly on Rebekah, holding his peace, to know whether the Lord had made his journey prosperous or not."

Those of you who are accustomed to seeking God's guidance at the crossroads will know the feeling for which this faithful man was waiting. You say concerning some choice: "Everything seemed to point in that direction, but I just could not feel right about it; and then all of a sudden I had a hunch that this was it." When our Lord went into Gethsemane, his mind was torn in the agony of indecision; but before he left, he reached that certainty which spoke in a commanding voice to his friends: "Get up, men, let's be going." And the presence or absence of that certainty is the difference between light and darkness.

So we come right back to the place where we started: One of the hardest things you have to do is to make decisions, and yet everybody has to make them. The promise of the word of God goes like this: "In all your ways acknowledge him, and he will make straight your paths." And the formula which fits them all goes like this: Make sure you are willing to follow the way the will of God points; put your own best thought on the problem, and give God a chance to speak through your mind; keep your eye open in the direction from which you expect light to come; then wait on the Lord for assurance. And when you have the certainty that you are in the way of the will of God, then you will know too the power and the peace of God.

BALAAM: ON BEING TEMPTED

Sometime ago I clipped from our daily paper an interesting story concerning a town in England. The name of the village in Cornwall is Veryan, and the distinguishing characteristic of the place is several conically roofed round houses. Local tradition says that they were so constructed in order to discourage the devil. The first five were built at the beginning of the last century by a former rector of the parish as an endowment for his five daughters. They will tell you there that he ordered the walls to be circular in order to allow Satan no corner in which to hide and to make him dizzy as he goes around searching for one. The story goes on to say that as recently as 1955 two more such houses were built under the bequest of a certain woman, who left money for building homes for the widows of seamen.

The story is useful because it brings to focus a problem common to our humanity: namely, the necessity of dealing with the devil. Temptation is the name given to this experience, and a firsthand acquaintance belongs to everybody from the Son of God on down. It finds dramatic demonstration in the life of a man named Balaam, and we make him our theme now. Balaam lived a long time ago, but the story of his life is as modern as the morning paper; and he stands before us as a picture of how *not* to deal with the devil.

I

The first mistake he made was to tamper with temptation. The situation was this, as described in Numbers 22. The people of Israel were moving out of Egypt toward the Promised Land. In the course of their journey on the east side of Jordan they had met and conquered a nation known as the Amorites, and the next stage on their march was the land of Moab. The king of the Moabites was Balak, and he did not wish to suffer the fate of his neighbors. All of a sudden he had a bright idea. He knew a prophet named Balaam, and there was a belief in that far-off time that a prophet could bring good fortune or ill fortune merely by pronouncing a blessing or a curse. And so he went to Balaam and said, "Come now, curse this people for me; . . . perhaps I shall be able to defeat them and drive them from the land." And of course the king was willing to pay for this service and to cross the prophet's palm with silver; the story says his messengers carried the rewards for divination in their hands.

When the message came to Balaam, he did what any good man will do when he has to make a decision: He took it to the Lord in prayer. He told the messengers to spend the night, and he would bring back the word given him by God. And that word was as clear as daylight. God said to Balaam: "You shall not go with them; you shall not curse the people, for they are blessed." So Balaam went to them and gave them this plain answer: "The Lord has refused to let me go with you."

Here is a fact of human nature which is useful to nail down: Your first reaction to moral evil is likely to be the right one. In worldly matters you can think twice before you act; but in questions of right and wrong, your first thoughts are probably your best. The instant recoil which an honest student feels when cheating is first suggested to him; the first flush of shame which a decent girl knows when an unscrupulous man proposes that she violate her conscience; the disgust which a four-square business man feels when he is asked to pull a shady deal—these first reactions are sound and can best be trusted. It was so with Balaam, and it would have been better for him had he had the good sense to see it. But he didn't; he made the fatal mistake of tampering with temptation.

When Balaam refused, the messengers went back to the king and told him their mission had failed. But Balak was a keen student of human nature and a persistent sort, and he tried again. He sent another deputation of still more important people with larger gifts and a promise of a post of honor in the country. And now listen to Balaam's answer: "Though Balak were to give me his house full of silver and gold, I could not go beyond the command of the Lord. . . . Pray, now, tarry here this night also, that I may know what more the Lord will say to me."

And with that Balak knew he had him hooked. Once you are willing to say to some unworthy suggestion: "Let me think it over, let me sleep on it, let me see if there isn't some way it can be worked out"; once you are willing to dally with the devil and tamper with temptation, then the jig is up.

> Vice is a monster of so frightful mien,
> As to be hated needs but to be seen;
> Yet, seen too oft, familiar with her face,
> We first endure, then pity, then embrace.

The great Augustine told the story of every sin in these four words: a thought, a form, a fascination, a fall. Your only hope of victory lies in dealing decisively with the first; but once you allow the thought to linger in your mind, it acquires a form whose fascination proves irresistible and leads to a fall.

II

Balaam's first mistake was that he allowed himself to linger in the presence of evil. The second was that he decided he could do wrong and in some subtle way bring it within the rules of conscience.

When he came out the next morning after sleeping on it and thinking it over, he announced that the Lord had told him to "Rise, go with them; but only what I bid you, that shall you do." Here you have a picture of why your first thoughts on moral questions are best. Because when you allow yourself a second thought, human nature is such that it practices a subtle self-deception and persuades you that what is wrong can somehow be right.

The contemporary name for this trick of the mind is rationalization, and it means finding a reason for doing the thing you want to do, even when something in you tells you it is wrong. Here is a psychiatrist in New York, Smiley Blanton, who counsels hundreds of people in the course of a year, and he says that "This is the great narcotic that people use to anesthetize their consciences and to justify yielding to temptation. An embezzler," he goes on, "tells himself that he is just 'borrowing' the money and will surely put it back. An unfaithful husband assures himself that what his wife does not know won't hurt her. In a thousand daily temptations, from padding the expense account to exceeding a speed limit, the rationalizer's attitude is, 'Everybody is doing it, why shouldn't I?' "

When you stop to think about it, you can find the explanation exactly at this point as to why people go along with Balaam in giving in to temptation. For example, the papers have been full of the illegal sale of auto liability insurance. Certain companies have given kickbacks to their salesmen who were willing to falsify the driving records of their clients in order to overcome the delay providing coverage. When the judge asked one man why he was willing to engage in such wrong practice, he answered that he thought he was performing a public service in helping people to get insurance. His mind had come up with a reason which justified a practice which his conscience must have condemned. So it is that one of the men convicted in the basketball scandals told the court it was right for him to accept a bribe because that was the only means he had for securing funds for the support of his wife and child. So it is also that a girl will justify premarital affairs with men on the ground that a majority of the girls her age do the same thing. And so it is too that many a man will fudge on his income tax form. He will tell himself that government waste in tax money is so large that he is just preventing some of that waste by withholding a portion of his own tax.

Balaam was a past master at rationalization. He thought he

could do what was wrong and somehow bring it within the rules of his conscience. But he should have known better because nothing can be right and wrong at the same time; and if it was wrong the first time to accept the king's offer, a second offer with larger rewards did not make it right. "Complete self-honesty," says Dr. Blanton, "is never easy. But if you can remember, in making a moral choice, that the temptation to rationalization is the most subtle temptation of all, you will be more likely to make the right decision."

III

So far then we have two counts against Balaam. First, he made the mistake of hanging round too long in the presence of temptation; and second, he tried to pull a little hocus-pocus which would please himself without displeasing God. Then, a third thing happened: In seeking to face in two directions at the same time, he blinded himself to the law of retribution which says that you can't do wrong without paying for it.

The historian who wrote this story had a marvelous insight into human nature and a sense of humor. Look at the way he makes this point. Once our man has made up his mind that he can juggle moral values so to be able to do wrong and somehow make it right, he begins the trip with the princes of Moab. Just then the strangest sort of things began to happen. First, this animal which had served him well for years refused to follow the road. She turned aside into the field, and Balaam had to whip her over the head to get her back. Then a little farther on, with the obstinacy which anyone who has ever worked with mules knows well, she thrust herself against the wall and crushed Balaam's foot and tried to rub him off; and again Balaam had to use his riding whip. A little farther on the ass fell down and rolled over and rubbed him in the dirt, and once again he used his whip.

Then the story says that "the Lord opened the mouth of the ass," and she spoke to Balaam." And what the animal said was this: "You poor fool, can't you see you are riding for a fall? Don't you know that you can't fly in the face of the moral law of God and get away with it? Don't you know that the way of the transgressor is hard and that whatsoever a man sows that shall he also reap?" God was doing his best to tell Balaam that he was on the wrong track, and he wouldn't listen. "Then the Lord opened the eyes of Balaam, and he saw the angel of the Lord standing in the way, with a drawn sword in his hand." He was headed straight for destruction and didn't know it.

The story uses a bit of Oriental imagery, but the meaning is plain. Here is a dumb beast whose moral insight is twenty/ twenty vision compared with the blindness of a man who is headed in the wrong direction. Right is right and wrong is wrong, and it is never right to do wrong, and no man can do wrong without paying for it. Many a man whose intellectual sense is high enough to make him a Phi Beta Kappa is yet inferior in his moral sense to this humble donkey. As Mark Twain puts it, "Man is the only animal that blushes, or that needs to."

When you take this fact out of the life of Balaam and turn it round, you can make it pay dividends. What it says is this: Whenever you come face to face with temptation, look before you leap. Take the long look down the far future and see that every line of action has not only a place where it begins, but also a place where it ends. Whenever you pick up one end of a stick you pick up the other also. And the man has not yet been born who is smart enough to put one over on the

33

moral order. When you eat salt herring, not even the grace of God can keep you from getting thirsty. Punishment is tied to sin like the burnt spot to the blaze. "God is not mocked for whatever a man sows, that will he also reap." What that means is that you cannot sow wild oats and reap Quaker oats. Sometimes you can put one over on the income tax people, but no man yet ever failed to pay his "outcome" tax.

Since that is the case, it is just plain common sense, is it not, to look ahead and take into account the law of consequences? In just about every case I can think of where temptation is concerned the ultimate disadvantages far outweigh the momentary satisfactions. Is the pleasure of social drinking worth the price, when one of every sixteen modern drinkers becomes a confirmed alcoholic, with all the misery that entails? Is the game of chance worth the candle, when gambling is not so much a way of getting something for nothing as of getting nothing for something? Is the moment of pleasure in sexual adventure worth the cost of a possible pre-marital pregnancy? Is the advantage gained by cheating in school commensurate with the sentence of expulsion? Ask those men who are now behind bars for their part in the basketball fixes; my guess is they would tell you they wish to goodness they had had the good sense to look ahead and foresee the consequences of their deal with the devil.

Balaam's donkey belongs to the horse family, and she showed mighty good horse sense, and any man lacks good sense who lets this dumb beast beat him in an intelligence test.

IV

Having tampered with temptation to the point of rationalizing his conduct and having blinded himself to the law of retribution, this man fails ultimately to gain the rewards of his wrongdoing. When the Lord opened Balaam's eyes, Balaam saw his mistake and confessed his stupidity: "I have sinned," he said, "for I did not know that thou did stand in the road against me." And in a later chapter we learn that Balaam was slain with the sword when the Israelites won a further victory over their enemies.

There is no need to labor the point, except for the sake of the record to note that it always happens thus. "The wages of sin is death"—and that is not true because the Good Book says so, but the Good Book says so because it is true.

As we bid farewell to Balaam, we would like to close on a more hopeful note; and such a fact is close at hand. In our dealings with the devil we have an ally unknown to Balaam. We have a friend who met his devil in the wilderness of temptation and who came off with flags flying. He did not tamper with evil for one moment. With absolute decisiveness he said, "Get thee behind me, Satan." And the better you know him, the more surely you will find the promise of the apostle Paul: "God . . . will not let you be tempted beyond your strength, but with the temptation will also provide the way of escape."

So might it be!

MICAH: ON HAVING YOUR RELIGION STOLEN

In the book of Judges we read that in the hill country of northern Palestine, there lived the man Micah who once had his religion stolen. He built a little shrine, with images and an altar, and persuaded a wandering priest to serve as chaplain. Then Micah said to himself, "Now I know that the Lord will prosper me, because I have a Levite as priest."

Not long after, when Micah was away from home, a group of strangers came along. They belonged to the tribe of Dan. Their territory down south was too crowded, and they were looking for more living space. They went on to capture a city called Laish and changed its name to Dan, and it gives rise to the expression you have heard so often, "from Dan to Beersheba," meaning the length and breadth of the land. This story explains the presence of the tribe of Dan in the far north.

Some of their fellows had been along that way before, spying out of the possibilities, and had seen the well-equipped chapel in the house of Micah. The planning commission of this new community knew that every good town ought to provide a church, and they looked with longing eyes upon Micah's neat arrangement.

But they did more than look, they lifted the images and furnishings and made off with them. When the priest objected, they quieted him by pointing out how much better off he would be to serve an entire tribe instead of a single family; so he took the call as the voice of God and went along with them.

Then Micah returned to a sad homecoming, for his chapel, the joy of his heart and the pride of his life, was no more. In hot anger he pursued the thieves, who laughed at his helplessness against their superior force. "What ails you that you come?" they asked. And he said, "You take away my gods which I made, and the priest, and go away, and what have I felt?" It is the picture of a man who lost his religion by having it stolen.

Anyone with an ounce of imagination can find in this ancient story a contemporary counterpart. Some kinds of religion are not burglar-proof; and we look at Micah to see why it is that sometimes you lose your religion by having it stolen.

I

The first thing which the story suggests is that Micah's was a neglected religion. When the marauders came and made their deal with the priest, Micah was nowhere around. He had left his gods tucked away safely at home and was otherwise engaged. A religion that is neglected is easily stolen.

Some years ago at Yale there was an intelligent and attractive instructor named Horace Bushnell. During a season of religious emphasis on the campus all of the faculty except Bushnell and all of the students except those who followed him were deeply touched by the movement. The fact that unconsciously his aloofness was influencing his little band brought him up short and made him take inventory. He said he had been reared in a Christian home and had never intended to become an unbeliever; but on the campus he simply had other things to do, and it was by sheer neglect that his faith had been stolen. He reminds me of the man who said he never purposely discarded his faith; he simply put it on the shelf, and when he went back to look for it, it was gone.

Neglect is a thief which can rob you of almost anything worthwhile. As a businessman, you need not commit forgery to lose your business; just neglect it long enough, and it will be stolen. As a student, you need not cheat on examination to be suspended from college; all you need do is neglect your work to the place that you will lack sufficient quality points, and the administration will do the rest. You need not wrong your friends to lose their friendship; all you need do is neglect them long enough, and you will find you have lost them. As a husband, you need not be unfaithful to your wife to lose your marriage; just forget your home for business and sport long enough, and you will find that the thief of neglect has come along and stolen your marriage.

And what is true in the fields of business, college life, friendship, and marriage holds good also in religion. Like Micah, you may have a perfect setup for the needs of your spiritual nature. You have a Bible at home, a prayer habit which you learned as a child, and a church on the corner where services are held every Sunday. But if you let that Bible remain unopened on the shelf, if you fail to keep your friendship with God in constant repair through daily prayer, if you find something else to do when people are meeting for worship on Sunday morning—then you will find that the thieves of neglect have stolen your god and carried him away.

Last summer as I sat one morning in Trinity Church in Boston, I thought of something I had read about the building. It seems that it rests on land that was made by filling in the bay, and in that part of the city the water is only a few feet below the sidewalk. The church building rests on 4,500 wooden piles. So long as the wood is kept under the water, it does not decay; but once the air gets to the wood, that is the end of it. So Trinity Church in Boston has wells in the cellar, and every week the Committee in Charge of Water Levels has to check to see that the water is high enough to protect the pilings. It is not necessary to ram the walls with bulldozers to destroy the building; just neglect to pump the water to the proper level, and destruction would be complete.

In like manner your life rests upon a foundation of religious faith. There are certain pumps called the means of grace which keep the water at the proper level; but if the Committee on Water Level goes to sleep, or is otherwise occupied, the thief of neglect will come and steal away the foundation. You must "keep yourselves," says the Bible, "in the love of God."

II

Furthermore, the religion of Micah was not only neglected, but it was man-made. He took two hundred pieces of silver which his mother gave him and turned the pieces over to a smith who melted the silver and made it into a molten and graven image and set it up in his chapel; and then he hired a priest he would have all for his own. Then when the thieves made off with his image and his priest, and he followed them and protested, and when they asked him what was eating on him, he said to them: "You take away my gods *which I made*." Micah's religion was a man-made religion, and a man-made religion is never burglar-proof.

It has often happened that a student who grew up in a home where religious faith was part of the environment has seen it stolen away during the years of college. One mother told me that her daughter, after taking a certain course in a university, was absolutely sure there is no God. Let me say in behalf of our forces of administration and faculty that I have never known a professor who made it his business purposely to rob anybody of his faith and who would rejoice in such a result.

There are two reasons why the student sometimes finds himself robbed of his religion. The first is that it just happens that about the time a young person goes to college is also the time when he begins to think for himself. It is all a part of his growing up. The age of doubt is a phase which every young person goes through. He cannot help it if his mind begins to ask questions and to develop a certain amount of intellectual curiosity. He has brought with him from home a faith which was inherited; but an inherited faith is always secondhand, and it will never do him any good in a time of real need unless it becomes firsthand.

And a second reason a college student sometimes finds his religion stolen is that the inherited faith which he brings with him consists of man-made theories which will not stand up in the face of truth. The business of his professor is to help him to know the truth; and if he has been loaded down by his home or his church school with man-made propositions which will not bear the light of truth, then he will find it less than burglar-proof.

For example, here is a man who said he had never been inside a church since he was a student; and when he was asked why, he told this story. He had been taught, he said, that the Bible said the world was made in seven days. In a course in geology he had learned something of the long periods of time which it took to form the earth, and there seemed to be a contradiction. He went to see his minister, and his minister told him he would just have to believe what the Bible said. Either the minister did not know, or did not take the trouble to tell him, that the Hebrew word *Yom* translated "day" in the book of Genesis does not necessarily mean a span of twenty-four hours, but can mean a period of time of indeterminate length. Therefore there is no contradiction between the Book of God and the textbook of geology. It was simply a man-made theory which had robbed a man of his religion.

Or take prayer. Some of us have inherited man-made theories of this part of religious life. We have grown up thinking of prayer as a way of getting something from God: a substitute for hard work, or a rabbit's foot against bad luck, or a letter to some celestial Santa Claus. But if a student lets the daily assignments go by the board and on the night before the final examination asks God for a passing grade and doesn't get it, that is not the fault of prayer or the professor. That is the fault of man-made theories which do not hold water. For prayer is something else: It is the communication between the mind of man and the mind of God. One night Jesus prayed, and what he got for it was a cross.

Or take the man-made theories of divine providence. You grow up singing "God Will Take Care of You." Then some calamity hits you broadside, and you want to give God his walking papers. But the Bible never says that everything happens for the best or that God is a private bodyguard who will keep you from trouble. What it says is that "in everything God works for good with those who love him." One day during the Second World War a man went to his minister and demanded to know: "Where was God when my son was killed?" And the minister replied: "Right where he was when his own Son was killed."

When Micah had created his gods and hired his priest, he said: "Now I know that the Lord will prosper me." The idea that religion is something which guarantees prosperity is a man-made theory and is always subject to being stolen.

Here then is a task for parents and church school teachers: Give our boys and girls a faith which can stand the light of truth, so that when they are led into a larger truth, their religion will be burglar-proof.

III

Finally, Micah's religion was stolen because it was not only neglected and man-made, but also because it was completely external to him. It consisted entirely of a chapel, some images, and a priest. It had never become part of his experience.

A friend told me once that when he was growing up, his father offered him a choice of two things: a farm or an education. He said he chose the education on the basis of the fact that he might lose the farm but that no one could ever take away from him the meaning of an education. You see, you can steal anything a man *has*; yet you cannot steal anything that a man *is*. And it is when your religion crosses the threshold of something that you *have* and becomes something that you *are*—when belief becomes trust, and explanation is transformed into experience, and faith becomes fellowship—it is then that you have a burglar-proof religion.

Once when Phillips Brooks was serving as chaplain of Harvard University, a student came to his office and said, with an anxious air: "Dr. Brooks, I would like to talk over some of my doubts; but I don't want to disturb your faith." And this great Christian sat back in his chair and laughed uncontrolably. When I read that the other day, I thought again of being at Trinity Church last summer. When the service was over, I walked round to the side entrance to see once again that famous statue of Phillips Brooks. After he had served for years as rector of Trinity, the people had his likeness carved in stone. There he stands in his pulpit; and right behind him, so close that a hand is on his shoulder, is the Christ. The two were so completely one that to talk of disturbing a faith like that is a laughing matter.

As long as God and Christ and prayer and the Bible are merely parts of the paraphernalia of religion which you have inherited along with the family jewels and are now interred all together in the strongbox at the bank, then some thief might break in and steal them. But if you can say with Mr. Moody: "I believe the Bible is inspired because it inspires me"; if prayer is not pious phrases which you parrot while your mind is a thousand miles away, but rather an altar stair to the throne room of the Eternal; if Christ is not simply the Carpenter of Nazareth who picnicked on the shores of Galilee two thousand years ago, but a friend who knows all about you and likes you just the same; if God is not simply that spirit that is "Infinite, eternal, and unchangeable, in his being, wisdom, power, holiness, justice, goodness, and truth," but is the shepherd who restores your soul and prepares a table before you and makes your cup to overflow—then there is not a thief in all the underworld that can steal your religion from you.

E. Stanley Jones put it down in the first book he ever wrote. When he was called to the ministry, he had a vague notion that he was expected to be God's lawyer and argue his case; when he told his minister of his call, the man surprised and frightened him by asking him to preach a sermon in his home church on Sunday night.

Dr. Jones said he prepared himself thoroughly because he wanted to argue his case well. There was a large crowd of his friends present. He says he had not gone more than a half-dozen sentences when he used a word he had never used before or since—the word was "indifferentism." When he used that word, he saw a college girl put down her head and smile. That so upset him that when he came back to the thread of his discourse, it was gone. He said it seemed an age while he stood there rubbing his hands and waiting for something to come. Finally he had to tell the audience that he had forgotten his sermon, and so started down the steps leading from the pulpit in shame and confusion.

"As I was about to leave," he writes, "a Voice seemed to say to me: "Haven't I done anything for you?" "Yes," I replied, "you have done everything for me." "Well," answered the Voice, "Couldn't you tell that?" And so instead of going to his seat, he came around in front of the pulpit and said: "Friends, I see I cannot preach, but I love Jesus Christ. You know what my life was in the community—that of a wild and reckless youth—and you know what it is now. You know he has made a new life for me, and though I cannot preach, I am determined to love and serve him."

If you happen to know E. Stanley Jones even slightly, you know there is nothing in the world that could steal his faith. In like manner, I covet for you a religion that is burglar-proof.

DANIEL: A STUDY IN CHARACTER EDUCATION

There are two methods which you can use to educate yourself. You can pour into your mind a set of facts and figures and formulas so that your mind is well informed; or you can fix upon a certain capacity in the mind, like the ability to reason, and cultivate it. The word "educate" itself favors the latter. It comes from a Latin word which means to bring out, and this kind of education is that process by which a person is enabled to develop, enlarge, and give expression to the powers that are within him.

Thomas Edison suggests the value of the second type of education. When he was a boy, he went to school; and his teacher tried to pour a number of things into his mind. Unfortunately they ran off like water from a duck's back. She thought he was stupid and dismissed him from school, sending his mother word that she couldn't do anything with him because his brain was "addled." But the world knows the rest of the story: how his mother discovered his aptitude for experiment and invention, and how she sought to draw out from him his own powers. That is the best way to educate the mind—and also the best way to educate the man.

When you begin to look at the stuff that is human nature in a boy or a girl, you will find that it is a mixture. On the one hand, there are certain things you do not wish to develop. There is the fact of original sin, which means that each of us was born with a built-in tendency to rebel against God. Here is a little boy who one day, all day long, had given his mother more than the usual amount of trouble. In exasperation she exclaimed to him, "Tommy, *how* can you be so bad?" And Tommy said simply, "Easy, Mama, easy." Human nature is such that without half trying, we can be less than our best selves.

Yet, in addition to original sin, there is the fact of original goodness, which reminds us that we all are made in the image of God and in addition to the tendency toward evil, we have a potential for goodness. When Jesus described the change that came in the life of the prodigal son, he put it like this: "And when he came to himself." The implication is that in turning his back on his father he was not himself; he was something other than himself. But his real self, his true self, was one which recognized his oneness with his father and which desired to become a true son. The followers of Jesus repeat this truth in the New Testament; one of them named John puts it like this: "Now are we the sons of God, and it doth not yet appear what we shall be" (I John 3:2 KJV).

So what we are saying is this: If you want to train this boy or that girl in the good life, then fix upon the potential in his human nature and cultivate it: Bring it to the surface, draw it out, educate it. As a child of God, he has a right to think thus highly of himself. When I read the story of Daniel, I find there are several ways in which this truth helped to make a man of him.

I

For one thing, it taught him how to tell the ~~different~~ *difference* between what is right and what is wrong. You remember the story. The king of Babylon had conquered the land of Palestine. He had his private secretary bring some of the choice young men to Babylon to serve in the king's palace, and one of these young noblemen was Daniel. By order of the king they were to eat the royal food and drink the royal wine; but Daniel resolved that he would not defile himself with the king's rich food or with the wine that he drank. When he protested, the king's secretary told him he might appear in poorer condition than the others, and the king would be angry and fire the secretary. So Daniel made him this proposition: "Set up a ten-day test and let me and my friends eat vegetables and drink water. Then let our appearance and the appearance of the youths who eat the king's rich food be observed by you, and according to what you see, deal with your servants." So the test was made, and at the end of ten days it was seen that Daniel and his friends were in better condition than the others.

When you take that story and put it in the midst of contemporary American life, it fairly shines with meaning for the young person today who finds it hard to tell the difference between what is right and what is wrong. Like Daniel, we live in a strange new world which in many ways is foreign to our upbringing. A generation ago the young person was not bothered by many of the decisions which trouble him today because there was general agreement on questions of right and wrong. When the boy scout is lost in the woods, he can take out his compass and get his directions. So it was that the compass of custom provided guidance. But today customs have changed—drinking customs, sex standards, gambling practices —and the young person is at a loss because often the church will say one thing, and his parents another, and his friends another, and the books he reads and the movies he sees something else altogether.

When Daniel found himself in that new world where customs were different from his own, he said to himself: "There is in my life something too fine to be misused, too sacred to be desecrated." And he resolved that he would not defile himself. Anything which made him a better man and which made him better fitted for his job was right, but anything which robbed him of such an opportunity was wrong.

Here, it seems to me, is a guide for the young person to follow. Even if you consider the church outdated and your parents old fogies, this is no arbitrary straitjacket. As you consider the drinking question, the sex question, the cheating question, the gambling question, remember that you are a child of God. Anything that defiles that image is wrong; but anything which makes you a better athlete, a better student, a better driver, or which better equips you for your future role as parent and breadwinner, is right.

II

Walk through a second door and notice that Daniel's high opinion of himself as a child of God not only helped him to tell the difference between right and wrong; more than that, it armed him with the courage to do the right.

Because Daniel was able to interpret the king's dream, he found favor at court and was appointed to a high position in the government; but it is human nature for people to envy persons more highly favored, and so his political enemies began to plot his downfall. They set out to dig up some dirt on him and smear his name and cause a scandal that would bring him down. But there were no skeletons in his closet. "He was faithful," says the story; "no error or fault was found in him."

Foiled in their attempt to find anything morally wrong with the man, his enemies turned to his religion. They knew that he worshiped a different God; so they went to the king and persuaded him to issue a decree stating that, upon penalty of being thrown to the lions, no citizen for thirty days was to pray to any god but the king. You know what happened. Daniel had the courage to obey his conscience and found himself in the den with the beasts, but he came out safe; and somebody has said that the reason the lions could not eat him was that he was all backbone.

When I try to put my finger on the secret of this man's courage, I remember a story which I heard some years ago. Dean Athearn of Boston was speaking to our seminary student body. He said that in his home there was a tradition of longstanding that no member of his family ever used tobacco. From his earliest recollections his mother and father and his old maid aunt had pounded into him the fact that no Athearn ever used tobacco in any form. Then one day, when he was a boy, the members of his gang decided that everybody would take a chew. One boy went to the store and bought the plug, and it was passed around. One by one each cut off his piece. When Athearn's turn came, he balked. No, he didn't care for a chew. Didn't he? Well, he would take it and like it. They piled on him and pinned his shoulders to the dust. He said it seemed to him that all the members of his family for generations back gathered around and shouted with one voice, "Be an Athearn!" The biggest bully in the crowd demanded that he open his mouth. "No," he answered. And as the fellow tried to force the tobacco between his teeth, there came the shout of many voices again: "Be an Athearn! Be an Athearn! Be an Athearn!" And he said that with the help of his family tradition, he remained an Athearn.

When you get your hand on a high opinion of yourself as a child of God, you will discover that consciousness of oneness with other children of God will give you backbone. You feel that your own kind are backing you up and you cannot let them down. It is a case of *noblesse oblige;* noble birth calls for noble action, and the very tradition itself gives the power to act nobly. It is the moral lever which the author of the letter to the Hebrews put into the hands of his people when they faced a difficult task. He reminded them of their forefathers, noble children of God like Gideon, Barak, Samson, Jephthah, David, Samuel, who through faith subdued kingdoms and wrought righteousness, and then he said to them: "Therefore since we are surrounded by so great a cloud of witness, let us run worthily the race that is set before us." I am sure that as Daniel thought of these noble sires of his race and remembered his oneness with these children of God, he found the courage that he needed.

They tell us that when the *Titanic* struck its iceberg and it was certain that the ship would go down, the captain called his men to the bridge. "Men," he said, "we are facing a crisis. We are facing a crisis in which lives will be lost. We are facing a crisis in which heroism will be needed. You are subjects of Great Britain. You know the history of our great nation on the high seas. You know the noble tradition which her sons have maintained. You belong to the long line of His Majesty's noblemen. I remind you of that tradition and I say to you, Be British!"

Young men and women, you and I live in a time of crisis, of crisis in character. The sober voices of wise men are telling us that the moral climate of America is on the downgrade. It is a time that demands heroism. You are children of God. You know the history of the heroes of faith. You belong to that long line of the Lord's noblemen. Remind yourself of that high tradition; and in the hour of your crisis, say to yourself, "Be a child of God!"

III

Move on now and notice a third fact. Daniel's high opinion of himself helped him to tell the difference between right and wrong, and it gave him the courage to obey his conscience. But I notice also that this was true: He was careful to cultivate daily that relationship which told him who he was.

His enemies at court, you remember, laid the trap for him. They persuaded the king to issue an order that any man who prayed to any god other than the king would get the lion's den. "Now, O King," they said, "sign the document, so that it cannot be changed, according to the law of the Medes and Persians, which cannot be revoked." The king did so. Then the story goes like this: When Daniel knew that the document had been signed, he went to his house where he had windows in his upper chamber toward Jerusalem; and he got down on his knees and prayed and gave thanks to his God, as he had done previously.

When the crisis came, he did not go to pieces. When the emergency arose, he did not feel at a loss. He had a working relationship with God, and he had built up a backlog of reserve across the years. The point of the story is that his religion was not foxhole faith, called in to get him out of a tight spot; when he went home that day, he prayed just as he had been praying all his life. He was able to get his hands on God because he had never lost touch with God. A family tradition will die if it is not kept alive by cultivation; and a child of God will lose his high opinion of himself if he does not keep in repair his sense of oneness with his Father.

Some of you adults are parents, and some are teachers in a church school. Whatever you do, give your boys and girls a working relationship with God. No matter what else you teach them, see that they make friends with God and that they keep that friendship in daily repair. See to it that not one of them leaves your class or your home before he has built into his life the habit of daily prayer. Someone along the line, either a parent in the home or a teacher in the synagogue, did it for Daniel; and there came a day when it stood him in good stead.

There is a famous painting, "Head of Christ," by the contemporary artist Warner Sallman. More than one million copies of it have been published and distributed throughout the world since it was printed in 1924; and I do not wonder, for it is a work of art. Not long ago in Los Angeles a robber rang the doorbell to an apartment. When a lady opened the door, he put his gun in her face and told her: "This is a holdup. Give me your money and jewelry." Just then he looked up and saw behind the woman a large picture on the wall. It was a copy of Sallman's "Head of Christ." For a moment he seemed to freeze, and slowly he lowered his gun. "I can't do it, lady," he said, "not in front of that picture." Then he hurried down the stairs.

For years on top of years, since the time of Daniel, that sort of thing has been happening. A daily look into the face of God has been calling men and women back to themselves, their better selves, their real selves, as children of God.

And whenever a teacher in the church school or a parent in the home does that for a boy or a girl, then we are getting somewhere in this business of education for life.

JOB: A MAN WITH A PROBLEM

One of my favorite authors and lecturers is a man named J. S. Whale of Cambridge. Some years ago he delivered three addresses on the radio in England; and even though his subject was a theological one, within two weeks' time he received five hundred letters from people who were total strangers to him. The only explanation is that his theme struck home with them.

In December of 1958 a play opened on Broadway with only two letters for a title, *J. B.* In spite of the fact that the newspapers were on strike and there wasn't a single printed notice of it anywhere; in spite of the fact that it was written in verse and on a Biblical theme; in spite of the fact that it had none of the elements that many times make a play a success—things like comedy and romance and music and dancing and vulgarity— every performance was sold out for weeks.

The reason for the widespread interest in the play and in the lectures was the same, for the theme of both was human suffering. *J. B.* is short for Job, and Job is the book in the Bible which treats this theme. It is written in the form of a dramatic poem, and now we look to see what it has to say to us.

I

We can get into our subject by noting first of all that Job was a man with a problem, and his problem was created by suffering.

When first you meet Job, he is sitting pretty, as we say. He has a good character, great wealth, and a large family. There are ten children, seven sons and three daughters; his sheep and camels and oxen are numbered in the thousands; and his life is perfect and upright. He is the greatest of all the people of the East.

Then the scene shifts, and we find ourselves in the court of heaven. God speaks to man's adversary, called Satan, and says to him, "Have you considered my servant Job, that there is none like him in the earth?" Satan is ready with the satanic suggestion that Job is good because goodness is profitable—that if only his blessings were taken away, he would curse God. So the Lord turned Job over to Satan and told him to go to work on him.

Then, without Job's knowing that he had become a test case, things began to happen. The hammer blows of adversity started to fall in dramatic rapidity. A messenger came to announce that an Arab tribe had come and carried away all his cattle. While the messenger was speaking, another came to say that a storm had destroyed all his sheep and goats. While he was still speaking, another came to announce that a tribe of Chaldeans had carried off his camels. And while that one was still speaking, another brought the news that all his children were gathered for a banquet when a hurricane destroyed the house and all were killed.

On top of all this, Job's health broke: He was afflicted with boils from the top of his head to the soles of his feet. His only source of help left to him was his wife, but even she failed to understand. When she heard him give expression to his faith in words which are still used everywhere, "The Lord gave, the Lord hath taken away; blessed be the name of the Lord," that seemed too much for her and she said to him, "Why don't you curse God and die now, and get it over with!"

There you have the classic picture in all the world's literature of the problem of human suffering. If ever there was a man who had a right to ask why, that man was Job. "If God is good and powerful enough to be in control here, why does he permit good people like myself to suffer these losses, while all the time there are men who pay him no mind and yet enjoy good health and great prosperity?"

This is the kind of thing you bump into every day when you deal with people. Here is a child born with a brain injury who must live out the rest of his days as an invalid. Why? Here is a small boy who steps off a curb and is hit by a car and knocked down and killed. Why? Here is a good woman married to a fiend who makes life a living hell for her. Why? And here is a wife married to a man she adores, and then a virus comes along and carries him off. Why? If God loves us, as the Bible says he does, and is all-powerful, as the Bible says he is, why then do people who deserve a hand with kings and queens in it have to take all the low cards in the deck? One of the best women I ever knew lived in our home from as far back as I can remember. When she died, her diary was sent to me as a keepsake. For twenty-two years she lived as a widow; and I noticed that on the day her husband died by his own hand, she had written: "My God, my God, Why?"

For some of us this problem has been the greatest stumbling block to faith. How can you be honest and say you believe in God who permits war and cancer and rattlesnakes and hurrican Hazel? Sometimes it makes you want to shake your fist in his face when you see with what cruel pleasure he appears to pull the strings in this puppet show. There was a time when I knew what the man meant when he said, "Your god is my devil," and when I sympathized with the members of that primitive tribe that believed that while God was good, he had a half-witted brother who was always interfering with his plans. So deep was the torment of spirit created by this problem, that I remember the words of this book which spoke most truly to my mind were those in which Job wished he had never been born: "Let the day perish wherein I was born," he said, and "Why was I not as . . . infants that never see the light?" Job was not a man given to melancholia; and it was only out of deep anguish that he and others have won through to faith in the goodness of God.

II

The first thing the book gives us is a man with a problem, and the second is the inadequate answers provided by the best thinkers of his day.

The main section of the poem deals with a series of conversations between Job and his friends. They have the strange names of Eliphaz, Bildad, and Zophar. When they learned of the trouble which had befallen their friend, they went to see him. His boils had so marred his appearance that they did not recognize him, and they raised up their voices and wept. Then "they sat down with him on the ground seven days and seven nights, and no one spoke a word to him, for they saw that his suffering was very great."

The friends began by showing their good sense. Sometimes when you go into a home where trouble has come, the best thing you can do for your friend is to take him by the hand and let your eyes speak in silent sympathy. But that silence did not last for long. It was broken by Job who "opened his mouth and cursed" the day he was born. That took the lid off, and for the next twenty-five chapters you have three cycles of debate in which Job speaks first and is answered by his friends.

To be forced to endure adversity is bad enough, but often the worst part of it is mental. If you have an explanation of it, you can take it; but if it lacks meaning, if you cannot understand the way of it, this compounds the anguish. And that was Job's problem. He was an upright man who had trusted God, and yet look what happened. He simply could not explain his predicament in the light of his faith; so his friends proceed to enlighten him with the wisdom of the ages. It is easy for them to talk because they did not have the boils, and they had two stock answers.

"Look, Job," they said, "everybody knows that suffering is always caused by sin. That's the way it always has been and always will be. Of course you claim to be an upright man, but maybe you're holding something back; maybe you are leading a double life. Honest confession is good for the soul; come clean with us, my friend, and the problem will vanish." But

Job was adamant, and he stood firm upon the rock of his up-rightness.

You see what is meant by "Job's comforters." The only help they had to give him was to tell him he had brought the whole thing on himself. And this is a doctrine which dies hard; for even in the time of our Lord his enemies argued that he could not be the Son of God for the reason that he suffered, and suffering was due to sin and sin alone.

There are two things to be said about this idea: First of all, there is some truth in it. Sin does cause suffering. This is a moral universe, and never has anybody yet been able to break the law of God without somebody's having to pay. "Whatever you sow, that shall you also reap."

And yet there is this other truth: While sin always causes suffering, there is some suffering which is not due to sin. Jesus stood up for that fact. One day they brought him a man born blind, and his men wanted to know if his blindness came from the man's sin or his parents! Jesus answered, "Neither did this man sin nor his parents." No, Job's comforters are wrong. It will not solve Job's problem to say that his suffering is due to his sin.

In addition to the three friends already named, there was a fourth, a younger fellow named *Elihu*. All the while the debate was in progress he was standing by listening and looking on, and finally he could hold his peace no longer. "I beg your pardon, gentlemen," he said. "I know I ought not to open my mouth in this distinguished company, but I must have my say. I have a view of this thing too, and it is this: All suffering is due not to sin, for some of it is given for discipline. It is the fire in which gold is refined. It is the anvil on which the good life is fashioned into shape."

And of course there is some truth there, but it failed to speak to the need of Job. The one thing of which he was certain was his own uprightness, and it did not make sense that he should suffer the loss of his property and his children and his health just to make him a better man.

The friends of Job had done for him the best they knew. They told him that either he would have to hold on to his faith in the justice of God and deny his own uprightness, or he would have to hold on to his integrity and deny the justice of God. It is to the everlasting credit of Job that he did neither. There was a third alternative, and that brings us to the final section of the book.

III

In this final section God himself speaks directly to Job. The first time you read it, you have the feeling that what he says has nothing whatsoever to do with the man's problem; but the time came when Job got the point, and so will you.

"Then the Lord answered Job out of the whirlwind: . . . Where were you when I laid the foundation of the earth? . . . Have you entered into the spring of the sea, or walked in the recesses of the deep? . . . Where is the way to the dwelling of light, and where is the place of darkness? . . . Can you bind the chains of the Pleiades, or loose the cords of Orion? . . . I will question you, and you declare to me. Will you even put me in the wrong? Will you condemn me that you may be justified? Have you an arm like God, and can you thunder with a voice like his?"

As the Lord speaks, Job begins to get the point. Here is a God who made the world and who governs it by his gracious providence; and in the face of that great goodness Job has no right to deny that goodness on the basis of his own individual trouble. Comforted by such mystery, he realizes there is so much he does not know that he becomes willing to trust where he cannot understand, and he says: "Behold, I am of small account; what shall I answer thee? I lay my hand on my mouth."

There are three comments in closing. First of all, Job tells us that on the basis of intellect alone you can never find an answer to this problem. The pieces of this jigsaw puzzle simply do not fit together. You can beat your brains out trying to find a pigeonhole into which you can file your questions, but there is no neat formula into which you can fit all the facts. And so the time comes when you have to walk by faith and not by sight, when you have to say: "Though I cannot prove it, I believe in an ultimate decency of things."

Second: The encounter between Job and the Lord in the whirlwind provides some help in being willing to walk by faith. What this man came to see was that his knowledge of the world and of life was so limited that he had no right to pass judgment upon the ways of God. One man put it like this: "An insect crawling up a column of the Parthenon, making his way painfully through one of the pores in the stone, is as well qualified to judge the architecture of that magnificent building as we are to pass judgment upon the infinite plans of Almighty God." When you turn that truth around, what it means is this: A little more knowledge would change the picture of things entirely. For example, if only Job had known what you and I know, that in the courts of heaven he had become a test case, he would have been spared the anguish of his soul. As when one for which you are tempted to blame, and then with further of your friends does something you cannot understand and knowledge you say, "If I had only known," so it is that fuller knowledge and further experience often throw light upon the mystery of divine providence. And so, like Job, you become willing to trust where you cannot understand.

3. Finally, you and I stand on higher ground and have a better view of the heart of things than did this man from the land of Uz. Since the days of Job, God has spoken again—this time, not in the whirlwind but in the life of his Son—and we have the word of him whose name is love itself that "he that has seen me has seen the Father." I shall never forget that night, in the long ago, when I sat where Job sat, hurling my Why's in the face of God, and my friend said to me, "You believe Christ is good, do you not?" "Oh, yes," I said, "a blind man can see that." "Well," he replied, "don't you know that when you look at Christ, you are looking at God?"

It was in that moment that the light broke, and I was able to say with Job: "I have heard of thee by the hearing of the ear; but now my eye sees thee." And from that day forward forever my faith has been that of Robert Louis Stevenson: "I believe in an ultimate decency of things; aye, and if I awoke in hell, would still believe it."

So may it be!

ELIJAH: THE MAN WHO HAD THE BLUES

Many times you have heard people talk about being "under the weather." What they mean usually is that they are not feeling up to par physically, that there is some slight indisposition of health which has them in its grip momentarily. Being "under the weather" often gives you "the blues," that condition of the spirit which is as inelegant as the expression.

And one thing you can say about it is that in most people it is natural and can be expected. Just as the mercury rises and falls according to the temperatures of the weather, just as the surface of the earth is not level but rises at some points into mountains and falls away at others into valleys, just as the tides ebb and flow—so there are ups and downs in the weather and topography of the spirit. No one can expect to live always in the hills of thrills. It is only that sometimes moods change and the road winds down into the valley.

For example, take a man like Elijah. When you think of him, you think of a man who was as strong as iron; but anyone who is familiar with his life knows that there came a time when he had the blues. The text tells us that he "came and sat down under a broom tree; and he asked that he might die, saying, "It is enough; now, O Lord, take away my life.' "

You have felt that way too sometimes; and while you would like to know the cure, you wonder what it has to do with religion and by what right it is made the subject for a sermon. The answer is that the blues is just a name for low spirits, and anything which concerns your spirits concerns your faith. God knew what to do for Elijah to put him back on his feet; and when you read between the lines in this story, you will find there a set of truths which have meaning for you.

I

The first thing God did for Elijah was to tell him to look out for his physical well-being. The prophet had been through a severe physical and emotional experience, and his resources were at a low ebb.

You remember the situation. When the Israelites moved into Palestine, they found there a native religion known as the worship of the Baals. Baal worship was a nature religion, whose object was to persuade the Almighty to grant production of crops and reproduction in animals; and its emphasis upon the sex motif went the length of providing temple prostitutes for licentious rites. For many years there was a running battle between the pagan religion and the true religion, and it came to a climax during the lifetime of Elijah. He gathered the 450 priests of Baal on Mount Carmel and challenged them to a test. The test was to see which God, Jehovah or Baal, could send fire to burn the wood under a sacrifice. "You call on the name of your god," the prophet said to the priests, "and I will call on the name of the Lord; and the God who answers by fire, he is God." The priests of Baal tried and tried, but nothing happened; and then Elijah called on the name of the Lord, and the fire fell and the sacrifice was consumed. And having won the test, he seized the 450 priests and put them to death.

Now Ahab was king, and his wife was Jezebel. She happened to be a worshiper of the Baals; and when she heard what had happened, she was hopping mad. She sent a messenger to Elijah and told him, "So may the gods do to me, and more also, if I do not make your life as the life of one of them by this time tomorrow." Then Elijah was afraid, "and he arose and went for his life, and came to Beersheba." Then he went a day's journey into the wilderness and "came and sat down under a broom tree; and he asked that he might die, saying, 'It is enough; now, O Lord, take away my life.' "

Just put yourself in his place, and see how you would feel. Suppose you had gone through that nerve-racking test on Mount Carmel: one man against 450, with all the tension of waiting for the result. Then no sooner was that over, when you get word that the queen is on your trail with the purpose of putting you to death. You don't stop to think of getting anything to eat, and you set off to put as many miles as possible between yourself and your pursuer. Is there any wonder that this man was utterly exhausted—physically, emotionally, nervously exhausted?

The trouble with him was that he was tired and hungry.

After Elijah had slept, God, like the good physician he is, sent an angel who said to him, "Arise and eat." When he awoke, he found food and drink by his side. After he had eaten, he slept again; and the angel of the Lord came again and said to him, "Arise and eat, else the journey will be too great for you." The first thing God did for the man who had the blues was to look after his physical well-being.

The laws of health are the laws of God; and one of the most useful bits of God's truth you can get your hands on is this: You are compounded of body, mind, and spirit. These parts of your being are so closely tied together that the condition of one vitally affects the condition of the others. If the vitality of your physical being is at a low ebb, it is nothing to be wondered at that you are depressed in mind and spirit.

The Englishman F. W. Robertson—Robertson of Brighton, as he is known—preached sermons that are still read as models by preachers after more than one hundred years. In one of his letters he says that he could never trust his feelings on any subject before Wednesday of any week, because the work of Sunday left him so nervously depleted, and his physical condition colored his mental outlook.

Louis Evans says that the parts of our being are so closely related that they "catch each other's diseases." So take a cue from Elijah. When your husband mopes around the house, with the corners of his mouth set at twenty minutes after eight, and colors the whole atmosphere with indigo, give him a good lunch and send him out for a game of golf. The food and exercise will work wonders. And then, when you need it yourself, have the good sense to make the same diagnosis and take the same prescription.

II

That was the first thing God did for Elijah: He taught him to look out for his physical well-being. The second was this: He suggested that Elijah change his pattern of thinking.

The prophet had developed the bad habit of always looking on the dark side. Here was the king of Israel who had gone up to Tyre and had married a foreign queen, and she was the stronger personality of the two and had wound him round her little finger and kept him under her thumb. More than that, she was a devotee of this pagan religion and had given the blessing of the royal house to the priests of Baal; and many of the people, not wishing to risk the disfavor of the queen, had deserted the worship of the true God. Elijah could think of nothing else. Listen to him: "O Lord," he says, "I feel sorry for you. The people have broken your covenant, and thrown down your altars, and slain your priests by the sword; and I am the only one left."

And what did God do? He told Elijah to take his eyes off the dark spots in the picture and to form the habit of thinking about the plus instead of the minus. The royal house is in the hands of pagans, and that is bad. The true faith is suffering from the meddling of this idolatrous queen, and that is bad too. But look at the assets, Elijah. You are left to me, and you have shown yourself a stout ally in times past; as long as I have you, I have a powerful leader, do I not? And not only do I have you, but I have others as well. There are yet seven thousand left in Israel who have not bowed the knee to Baal.

And that number was symbolic, as is the number seven usually in the Bible. It adds the number four which means completeness, to the divine number three, to make the perfect number seven. What God was saying to Elijah was that there were yet resources sufficient to turn the tide of paganism and save the nation for the true God, and that the time had come for him to stop thinking so much about the difficulties and begin to look at what might be counted upon to yield dividends.

There is a useful truth here: Sometimes the cause of our low spirits is not so much physical as mental. We think about the wrong things. We develop a habit of thought which majors on the minus, and there is no one so fortunately circumstanced who cannot become a pessimist of the first order if he wishes to think only of his hard luck. You can take a little thing as small as a dime and hold it so close to your eye that it shuts out all light; and you can take your tough breaks and let them monopolize your thinking to the point of feeling so sorry for yourself that you are ready to throw in the sponge.

According to one historical account of Thanksgiving, things did not get much better after the first year of hardship for the Pilgrims; and a meeting was called to authorize a day of fasting and prayer in search of divine favor. But a plain farmer got up right in the middle of the meeting and said he thought the Lord was tired of hearing their complaints and that even though their outward lot was not the most prosperous, still they had found the freedom which they had come seeking. He proposed that instead of a time of fasting and prayer they should designate a day for giving thanks.

According to this account, the custom of an annual Thanksgiving came from the insight of a man who had the good sense to accentuate the positive and minimize the negative; and that is a part of the cure which God worked for Elijah. If you wish to do so, you can always work yourself up a good case of the blues by counting your complaints. But, if, first thing on waking every morning, you try to think of at least ten good things you are grateful for at that moment, then your facial clock will move from eight-twenty to ten-ten.

Wallace Hamilton has a story about a man who had lived on the same old farm all his life, who grew tired of it and wanted a change. Nothing about the place suited him, and at last he made up his mind he would sell it and buy another more to his liking. He listed the farm with a real estate broker, who at once prepared a sales advertisement for the newspaper; but before turning in the copy, he read over to the man the flattering description of the property which he had prepared. He talked of the farm's advantages: its ideal location, its up-to-date equipment, its fertile acres, its well-bred livestock. "Wait a minute," said the farmer, "read that again, and take it slow." So the salesman reread the description. "Changed my mind," said the farmer. "I'm not going to sell. All my life I've been looking for a place like that."

There is an old song that some of us used to sing in Sunday school which has a refrain like this: "Count your many blessings. Name them one by one, and it will surprise you what the Lord has done." That is the second thing the prophet learned.

III

Having brought Elijah's physical condition up to par and having given the right direction to his mind, God does a third thing for him: He gives him something to do. "What are you doing here, Elijah?" He wasn't doing anything, except lying flat on his back feeling sorry for himself. And God gave him something to do. "Go . . . to the wilderness of Damascus," he said, "and anoint Hazael to be king over Syria; and Jehu . . . you shall anoint to be king over Israel; and Elisha the son of

Shaphat . . . you shall anoint to be prophet in your place." God gave Elijah something to do, and it made a new man of him.

You will notice that your pessimists are always the men and women who sit on the sidelines in their comfortable armchairs and write books about how fast the world is going to the dogs— like Schopenhauer, George Eliot, and Bernard Shaw. But let them leave the sidelines and get in the game, and you have a William Booth with his Salvation Army, and a Jane Addams with her Hull House, and a Wilfred Grenfell with his mission on Labrador. I have read somewhere that during World War I the only problem of morale among the soldiers was with those who had been moved from the front, back to rest positions. When they became inactive, they grew despondent; but once they were moved up again to the front lines and got into the thick of things, their spirits rose, and the problem of morale was licked. That is what happened to Elijah. "Get up and get busy," God said to him; and once he went back to the firing line, you hear no more from him about the blues.

Here is a truth which will work just as well now in our twentieth century as in the eighth century B.C., and what it says is this: If you get blue because you think your world is going to the dogs, then take hold of some part of it and see that it doesn't happen. If it be the problem of war which bothers you, then get in the game on the side of peace; line up with some group who works for world government based on law. If it is the ineffectiveness of your church which bothers you, get in the game: Go down there on Sunday mornings, and you will find plenty of young Elishas waiting to be taught. If you are concerned about the disintegration of the family, get hold of a conviction concerning the permanence of marriage, and put a stop to this pagan propaganda that if a husband and wife do not have a feeling of affection any longer, that is reason enough for separating. If you deplore the ravages of alcoholism, make up your mind that you know at least one person who is willing to practice voluntary abstinence. If you are concerned about the breakdown of moral standards among young people, you can be sure that there is one parent in your town who knows where his sons and daughters are and what they are doing.

The Chinese have a proverb for it. They say: "It's better to light a candle than to curse the darkness." And the very act of lighting will drive away the darkness.

Here then is God's prescription which worked for his prophet; you can take it and interpret its meaning for yourself.

JONAH: MAN OF ADVENTURE

Probably you have never thought of the prophet Jonah as a particularly romantic figure, but have you looked up the meaning of the word "romance" recently in the dictionary? Most people would no doubt define it as the story of the love life of a man with a maid, and yet the dictionary says nothing about love at all. We learn that "romance is the character of that which appears strange and fascinating and adventurous and mysterious."

So Robert Louis Stevenson defines all of life as romance: "An affair of cavalry," he calls it, "to be dashingly used and cheerfully hazarded." And the late Justice Oliver Wendell Holmes wrote to a friend, and the friend took a sentence from that letter and framed it and keeps it over his desk in Washington: "Life," he said, "is romantic business; it is painting a picture, not doing a sum. But you have to make the romance, and it comes to the question how much fire you have in you."

The life of Jonah was filled with adventure; and we can pick out three factors common to our own life which can redeem existence from its staleness and restore the quality of that which is romantic.

I

For one thing, the life of Jonah was an adventure in which he had constantly to deal with the unexpected and the uncontrollable, and to show what he had in him by what he made out of them.

The story begins with a call to the ministry: "Arise," said the command, "go to Nineveh, that great city, and cry against it; for their wickedness has come up before me." Nineveh was the capital of Assyria and Jonah was a Jew, and the Jews and the Assyrians were sworn enemies. When Jonah accepted the call to the ministry, the last thing he expected, I am sure, was to be sent to Nineveh.

The first thing he did was to rebel against his duty, and he took off in the opposite direction. He went down to the seaport of Joppa and found a ship headed for the port of Tarshish in Spain, and paid the fare and got on board. Not long after, a great wind blew up a storm; and it looked as if the ship would break in two; so the sailors began throwing the cargo overboard to lighten the weight. Then they decided to match each other to see who the "jonah" was; and, sure enough, it turned out to be the prophet. They asked him what they might do with him to avert the danger caused by his presence, and he told them to throw him overboard. "So they took up Jonah and threw him into the sea; and the sea ceased from its raging."

Then it was that a great fish swallowed up Jonah, and he was in the belly of the fish three days and three nights. After Jonah had prayed, the Lord spoke to the fish; and it deposited Jonah upon the dry land. Then the word of the Lord came to Jonah a second time, saying, "Arise, go to Nineveh, that great city, and proclaim to it the message that I tell you." So Jonah arose and went to Nineveh.

When you think of romance as adventure into the unexpected, Jonah is your man *par excellence;* and yet when you stop to think about it, his life has little on yours and mine. For example, while writing this, a letter came to me with an invitation to speak for a high school graduation. That started me thinking about commencements and reminded me that one of the features is always the class prophecy. The prophet looks into his crystal ball and peers into the future and predicts what will happen in the lives of his classmates. He lets his imagination run riot and gives free reign to his fancy. And yet, if you will check the facts by the forecasts twenty-five years later, you will always find that truth is stranger than fiction. The presence of the unexpected and the uncontrollable makes hash out of his predictions. Some members have caught the tide at its flood and have gone on to fortune, while others have had to face an unwelcome duty, as did Jonah, and have found themselves thrown overboard in a storm.

Some few of us are like that son of a smalltown Presbyterian minister down in Georgia who went through high school and then on to Davidson College and Oxford University later to become head of the State Department of the strongest government in the world. The romance of Dean Rusk reads like a book. And yet most of us are like that boy who also grew up down south and for whom the unexpected was the undesired;

like a bolt out of the blue he was called into the ministry, and that was the last thing in the world he wanted. And like Jonah, he did his best to run away from it.

In a way known only to yourself, it may be that for you the unexpected is also the undesired: the denial of the dream of your life, a demotion in your job, the death of one who is the mainstay of your life, a physical handicap like deafness or blindness, the failure of your children to live up to your expectations. What then?

Remember Joseph. Here was a farmer boy who was doing his best to do his duty; and then before you know it, he was kidnapped by his brothers and sold into slavery. Down in Egypt his boss's wife had eyes for him; but when he refused to play her game, she lied about him. He was forthwith thrown into jail; and then almost before you know it, the wheel of fortune began to turn, and he found himself sitting behind the desk as prime minister of the empire. There was a whole bushel full of events of the unexpected and the unwanted in the life of this man; yet because he refused to grow bitter against the fate which played havoc with him, because he had a will with a won't tied to it, and because he believed in the good purpose of God for his life and kept himself ready to fit in with that purpose, his career was a romance unmatched in the pages of fiction.

What life does to you depends upon what life finds in you. The most important things are not always what happen to you but how you take what happens to you. And, according to the apostle Paul, *all things* can be made to work for good to those who love God and are lined up with his will. "Life is romantic business; . . . but you have to make the romance, and it comes to the question how much fire you have in you."

II

Move on and notice, in the second place, that life is romantic business because it deals so constantly with people, and people are never fixed quantities. They tend rather to become what you see in them and call forth from them.

You remember that Jonah was sent to Nineveh because of the evil of the city: "Arise," said God, "go to Nineveh . . . and cry against it; for their wickedness has come up before me." When finally the prophet reached the place, following his detour in the belly of the fish, he began to proclaim his message of doom: "Yet forty days," he said, "and Nineveh shall be overthrown." Then the people fasted and put on sackcloth. When this news reached the king, he left his throne and removed his robe and put on sackcloth and sat in ashes and sent out a proclamation: "By the decree of the king," he said, "let everyone turn from his evil way and from the violence which is in his hands." And, do you know, they did so! So much so that "when God saw what they did, how they turned from their evil way, God repented of the evil which he said he would do to them; and he did not do it."

That is also part of the romance of life: It deals so constantly with people, and people are never fixed quantities; they tend to respond to what we see in them and call forth from them.

Take marriage, for example. It is here that people live in the closest companionship. Marriage is romantic business, but sometimes you have to make the romance. For example, a friend of ours in another city was on a bus and overheard two women talking. The daughter of one had been married not long before, and the other asked how she was getting along. "Just fine," said the mother; "I've never seen her happier in her life. But there's just one thing wrong." "What's that?" asked the friend; and this is the answer that came back. "She just can't stand her husband." There's not much to be said in a case like that, but the other was equal to the occasion: "Well," she said, "when you're married, there's always something, ain't it?"

Grace Sloan Overton has a story about a husband who had grown irritable, and his wife was "scared" lest the great happiness of their marriage had passed. She decided not to say a word about his irritability, which came from a loss of faith in himself, but rather to find ways to talk about his ability. "It worked," she said, "and Bill and I are off to new levels!" And who can tell: It may be at this very moment that someone will make up his mind that, like the people of Nineveh, he will "turn from his evil way" and respond to the love of his mate and reward the fidelity which has gone far beyond the line of duty.

Or take parenthood. You mothers love your children, but you fail to see the romance in fixing bottles and washing dishes and mending clothes and sweeping floors and settling quarrels. And yet there is hardly anything more fascinating and adventurous than the unfolding of a human life; and the challenge to those responsible to bring out the best that is there and to start that little life on its way to a healthy, happy, and wholesome enjoyment of experience is enough to redeem the monotony of the daily grind.

And what shall we say of the teacher, the doctor, the lawyer, the office manager, and the personnel director? We all deal with people, and people are never fixed quantities; they tend to become what you see in them and call forth from them. Remember what one young woman wrote to a friend: "I want to thank you for what I am when I'm with you."

Once when Paul returned to Jerusalem, he fell into the hands of the council and was mobbed. "Away with such a fellow from the earth," they said. "For he ought not to live." His life was actually in danger, but Paul was always ready for romance, and he saw here an opportunity for adventure in human nature. He knew that his accusers, the Pharisees and Sadducees, had different ideas about the resurrection. Immediately he identified himself with the former and asked them if they were going to condemn him for preaching what they themselves believed. "Then a great clamor arose; and some of the scribes of the Pharisees' party stood up and contended, 'We find nothing wrong in this man. What if a spirit or an angel spoke to him?' " In the twinkling of an eye Paul had made friends out of his enemies.

Does that say something to you? Most of us have people who do not like us; try as hard as we will to live on friendly terms with others, there are always some who harbor hostile feelings— and of course the natural temptation is to return the compliment. The only real way to get rid of an enemy is to turn him into a friend, and the game can be wonderfully fascinating. Pick out something good in the person you do not like. Whenever you think of him, think of that about him; praise him to other people; do him a favor; and above all, when you are saying your prayers, see him in the presence of Christ as he might become under the touch of the master Maker of men. The romance in human nature is endlessly rewarding.

III

Finally, Jonah found life romantic business not only in events and in people, but because it runs on out to the point where it bumps into God.

The problem which Jonah had with God was a peculiar one. When God ordered him to go to Nineveh and he started running in the opposite direction—when God sent the storm and the fish, and brought him back to his duty, he could understand that. But he could not understand why his God was interested in those foreign devils in Nineveh. The reason he ran away in the first place was the fear that they might repent, and God would bless them. When that happened, Jonah was mad at God. And he prayed to the Lord, saying, "That is why I made haste to flee to Tarshish; for I knew that thou art a gracious God and merciful, slow to anger, and abounding in steadfast love, and repentest of evil. Therefore now, O Lord, take my life from me, . . . for it is better for me to die than to live."

Herein lies the genius of the book: It is a rebuke to the narrow nationalism of the chosen people and a challenge to the larger outlook based upon the universal concern of God.

But for our purpose we are concerned only with the fact that God was a problem for Jonah. Whereas Jonah's problem was that God is too good for his own good, our problem is that God is not good enough for our good. Why, we say—why, if God is good, should the Communists gain one third of the world in less than fifty years? Why, if God is good, should things like cancer eat out the life of people I love? Why, if God is good, should I have to live with an alcoholic? Life is mystery—there is no doubt about that—and part of the romance comes from finding and following a clue that will see you through. And how do you do that?

Not by the prosaic method of the arithmetic table. You can never get your faith as you get the number four by adding two and two together. Some folks think life is good and enjoy it while others think it not good and are embittered by it. Here is Augustine who prays, "O God, thou dost love each one of us as though there were but one of us to love." And there is that man whose name I have forgotten but whose line I once followed: "I could never worship your God," he said, "because when I see the way things are in this world, I want you to know that your God is my devil." And yet both he and Augustine had the same evidence: With the same facts in hand, one man calls God good while another counts him demonic. No, life is "not doing a sum," as Mr. Holmes put it.

What is it then? It is an adventure, a romance, a betting of your life. As long as you live by the rule "seeing is believing," you will never find it. You can never prove it and then believe it; you have to believe it, and then you can prove it. You find it the same way Columbus discovered America—by stepping into your boat, and pushing off from shore, and sailing out, bag and baggage, into the mysterious unknown.

And to those who wait on the shore, wanting the assurance but wary of the risk, here is the word of one who has seen the dark and taken the plunge: "Come on in, my friend, the going is fine—because God is good!"

THE MAN WHO BROUGHT GOD DOWN TO EARTH

We always think of Christmas as coming on the twenty-fifth of December; but when you remember your history, you will recall that it has not always been thus. It did not happen until the year 336, and this is the way it happened: The Romans had a holiday that lasted for a week, beginning with the nineteenth of December. Originally it was a religious festival which brought men to their knees as they thought about the mystery of existence, but gradually its religious emphasis deteriorated. It faded into the background until it became a week of feasting, merrymaking, and rioting. It was called the Saturnalia in honor of Saturn, the Roman harvest god. Then, in the year 336, the Christians decided to celebrate the birth of the Son of God on this Roman holiday; and little by little the Christian festival replaced the pagan holiday.

There are persons of serious mind who are wondering if we are in the midst of the same sort of change in reverse. Just as Christians captured the Roman holiday and turned it into a religious festival, is it possible that pagan forces will capture Christmas and turn it into a winter carnival? The word "Christmas" is a combination of two words, *Christ's mass;* a mass is a religious service; and so Christmas is a religious service in honor of Christ. What makes Christmas is Christ; and if we are going to keep Christmas as we have known it, then we must keep Christ in Christmas. So we want to go back to the New Testament and see what it has to say about him.

I

The first thing it says is that he was a man, even as you and I. John puts it like this in the text: "The Word was made *flesh*" (John 1:14 KJV). The Gospel writer says further that he did not need anybody to tell him what human nature was like because he knew; he knew because he was a man.

That is the truth which stands out above all else at Christmastime. Christmas celebrates the birth of Christ, and this means, of course, that he was born. He did not descend from the sky full-grown, as Venus is said to have appeared out of the sea. His life began as your life and my life began: as a little seed within his mother's body. I know a child who lived in Virginia, whose mother spent the summers at her former home in North Carolina. When someone asked the little boy where he was born, he said he was born in North Carolina while his mother was "on vacation." It was something like that with Jesus. Mary and Joseph had left their home town of Nazareth to go to a town down south named Bethlehem to enroll in a census for purposes of taxation. "And while they were there, the time came for her to be delivered. And she gave birth to her first-born son and wrapped him in swaddling cloths, and laid him in a manger." Babies are being born every day in our hospitals, and the mechanics of birth have not changed in these two thousand years: He was born even as you and I were born.

And he had to grow up as we grew, through the regular stages of growth. There is only one incident preserved for us from his childhood, but it tells us that when he went back to Nazareth from Jerusalem, he was obedient unto his parents; and he "increased in wisdom and stature." I like to think he would be chosen "Boy of the Year" in Nazareth, but even then he was a normal boy—playing as other boys played, doing his chores around the house, fretting under his parents' discipline. I heard of an older woman from the mountains who told a friend she certainly was glad she had her children before the doctors discovered this newfangled disease called "adolescence." Well, Jesus was an adolescent, struggling over the hill when he was more than a child and not yet quite an adult.

The point is that his human nature was real. There are all sorts of false biographies which picture him as a wonder-working child. For example, one of them says that he was playing one day and another boy crossed him, and Jesus performed a miracle and struck him dead. But you find nothing like that in the Gospels. If he didn't like the boy next door, he had to get along with him just the same. When he went into his father's carpenter shop and picked up a hammer and missed the nail only to mash his finger, he saw stars too. When dinner was late, he felt hunger, even as you and I; when there was no time to rest, he grew tired, even as you and I; and when he was tempted, he felt desire, even as you and I.

One of the finest things Christmas could do for you is to

open your eyes to the fact that when you deal with Christ, you are dealing with a man who knows what human nature is like because he has lived life under the same conditions which you face.

For example, you probably have heard of Theodore Parker Ferris of Boston, minister of Trinity Church. Not long ago he told his people about being in a bookstore and finding a new edition of an old book and what it had meant to him. The book was *The Manhood of the Master* by Harry Emerson Fosdick. It was published in 1913, and many of you have read it, as I did years ago; and when Dr. Ferris saw it again, he said it reminded him of how it had helped him to know Jesus as a real person.

He had been brought up as a boy in the Episcopal Church with great reverence for Jesus as the Incarnate Lord. But in those years he never thought of Jesus as a real person, with real decisions to make, with real temptations to face, and real doubts to deal with. He never thought of him as a person who wept real tears, laughed real laughter, or went out camping on the hills to spend long nights with God. He says that in the church where he grew up as a boy there was a window over the chancel which pictured the ascension. There in the window was Jesus, with his hands outstretched in blessing, dressed all in white, rising upward in the sky; and down below were the disciples, looking up at him from the ground—puzzled and dumbfounded. That was his picture of Jesus.

"Then," he says, "I read *The Manhood of the Master*. One by one the twelve chapters describe some human quality of Jesus, like his joy and his magnanimity, his loyalty and his fearlessness. As I read, little by little the stained glass figure stepped right down out of the window in its blaze of glory and began to walk the streets of my town. Jesus, in other words, became a real person to me, and my interest in him as a person has never ceased."

In like manner, there is the Lord Christ in the window in front of you in many of your churches. Every Sunday you see him there, and it is so easy to leave him there, up in the air. If now we could somehow come to terms with the manhood of the master and remember that on that first Christmas night the "Word was made flesh," then perhaps he would come down out of the stained glass and walk our streets with us and rub shoulders with us and become a real factor in experience.

II

The first thing that Christmas says is that Jesus was a man, even as you and I, but it does not stop there; it goes on to say that this is the man who brought God down to earth. The text says, "the Word was made flesh." The Greek for Word is *logos*. It means the divine principle of reason in the universe: all that God thought and was and is. So when John says that "the Word was made flesh," what he means is that God became man. In this Christmas Christ we have the man who brought God down to earth.

This is what these lovely stories which cluster around the birth of Christ are trying to tell us: This man is more than man; he is the God-man. Before he was born, the angel Gabriel appeared to his mother Mary and said to her: "Hail, O favored one, the Lord is with you! . . . You will conceive in your womb and bear a son, and you shall call his name Jesus."

There is the story of the angels that sang when he was born and a bright star which appeared in the sky, as if the writer wanted to say: "This child is something special—even the heavenly beings sing for him, and the heavenly bodies shine for him."

There is the story of the shepherds who came to see him, as though people wanted to make it plain that while he was God, yet he was bringing God down to earth where common folks would hear him gladly and respond to him gratefully.

There was the story of the wise men from the East giving him the richest gifts they could find, as though men were trying to say that the leaders of thought recognized in him their teacher and that from henceforth men would find in him the truth which gives reality its meaning.

Finally, there is the story of the virgin birth, which you may or may not believe to be a fact. But whether you believe it or not, you can see what it is seeking to say: Here is a person who is unique because he bears a unique relation to the Father. He is a true man, but he is more than man; he is the man who brought God down to earth.

Every time you date a letter, you bear witness to the uniqueness of this God-man. You say that this is 1965, the year of our Lord. As a matter of fact, scholars tell us that this is in reality 1969 because calculating by the known dates of the rulers under whom these events transpired, Jesus was born about four years prior to the beginning of our era. But that is not the important thing about his birth. The important thing is that we determine the date of our birth by the calendar; but in the case of Jesus alone, the date of his birth determines the calendar. His is a uniqueness which splits history in two; and he is the only person ever to walk this earth of whom it can be said: He is what God means by "man," and he is what man means by "God."

86

I have a friend who likes to hear a symphony orchestra, and he lives in a city where he can attend a goodly number of performances. As he listens, he says, he looks at the conductor, and what he sees is his back. You can tell by watching him when the music is quiet and tender and when it is powerful and strong. But, he says, if ever you can get into a position where you can see the conductor's face, you see something different. All the warmth and human feeling which you miss when you are sitting behind the conductor radiate from that face, and this adds a new dimension to the whole picture.

That is something of the difference Christmas makes. Whenever you look at God in the world of nature without or in the law of conscience within, you are seeing only his back. You will never know the warmth of feeling he has for you until you see his face in the face of his Son. "The Word was made flesh and dwelt among us, and we beheld his glory . . . full of grace and truth" (John 1:14 KJV). I think the most important thing which ever happened in my life was to learn for the first time that the God who sits on the throne of the universe is like the Christ who proved himself a friend to man.

III

Move on now and notice a third fact: The closer you come to Jesus as a man, as a real human being, the more likely will you find in him the reality of God. "The Word was made flesh," says John; and because we saw in him a real man, we came to see he was more than man. We beheld his nature, that he was a unique Son of God.

Here, for example, is a man who lives in Danville, Kentucky. He says it was the week before Christmas and he was baby-sitting with the four older children while his wife took the baby to the doctor. He admitted that baby-sitting for him meant reading the paper while the kids messed up the house. Only that day he wasn't reading; he was fuming. On every page of the paper there were advertisements of things which he couldn't afford and nobody needed. What, he asked himself, did all the glitter and the rush have to do with the birth of Christ?

Then there was a knock on the door of a room where he had barricaded himself, and his daughter Nancy asked him if he wanted to see a play which she and the others were putting on. He didn't, but he had fatherly responsibilities and so followed her into the living room. Right away he knew it was a Christmas play, for at the foot of the piano stool was a lighted flashlight, wrapped in swaddling clothes, lying in a shoebox.

Six-year-old Rex came in wearing his father's bathrobe and carrying a mop handle; he sat on the stool and looked at the shoe box. Ten-year-old Nancy draped a sheet over her head, sat behind Rex, and said: "I'm Mary, and this boy is Joseph. Usually in this play Joseph stands up and Mary sits down. But Mary sitting down is taller than Joseph standing up, so we thought it looked better this way." Four-year-old Trudy came in with pillow cases over her arms. She spread them wide and said only, "I'm an angel." Then came eight-year-old Anne. He knew she must be a wise man; she moved like she was riding a camel because she had on her mother's high heels. She was bedecked with all the jewelry available and on a pillow she carried three items: undoubtedly gold, frankincense, and myrrh.

She undulated across the room, bowed to the flashlight, to Mary, to Joseph, to the angel, and then announced: "I am all three wise men. I bring precious gifts: gold, circumstance, and mud."

Gold, circumstance, and mud. That pretty well describes our condition, does it not? Enmeshed in a materialism, which all but chokes to death the breath of the spirit; victimized by circumstances which so often are far different from what we might wish; and with the mud of this human clay splattered all over the good intentions of our better selves. Gold, circumstance, and mud.

Yet in the hands of the Christmas Christ all three are transformed. As a real human being, he lived in a material world and gave his blessing to all gold put at the service of God. As a real human being, he accepted unwelcome circumstance and turned a cross into a crown. As a real human being, he met men and women who were nearly all mud and turned this mud into building material which fashioned more stately mansions for the soul. You simply cannot get away from the fact that the closer you come to Jesus as a man, as a human being, the more likely you will find in him the reality of God. And I have to confess with the song writer:

> I know not how that Bethlehem's Babe
> Could in the godhead be;
> I only know the manger child
> Has brought God's life to me.

So I bring you the man who brought God down to earth, and I trust that in every Christmastime he will come close to where you live.

THE ONE-TALENT MAN

There once was a businessman who took a trip; and before he left home, he called in three of his employees and gave them some of his property. A talent was a measure of money; and to one man he gave five talents, to another two, and to another one. The first two men went to work and invested the funds entrusted to them and doubled their money. When the owner returned, he called them in and commended them and gave them larger responsibility: "Well done, good and faithful servant; you have been faithful over a little, I will set you over much; enter into the joy of your master."

But the man with one talent went out, dug a hole in the ground, and buried his money; and when he made his excuses, the master let him have it. "You wicked and slothful servant. You ought to have invested my money with the bankers, and at my coming I should have received what was my own with interest. So take the talent from him. . . . And cast the worthless servant into the outer darkness."

When you read the story, you cannot escape the conviction that it was told mainly for this one-talent man. It is he who occupies the center of the stage, and of course the one-talent man is most of us. The five-talent men are few and far between. The two-talent men are a trifle more numerous; but most of us are one-talent people, and the failure of this man stands as a warning to us. There are peculiar dangers which face the one-talent man, and our business is to understand them and guard against them. As you read between the lines of the story and bring the situation down to the place where you have to live out your life, there are three truths which are suggested.

I

In the first place, success with God is doing the best you can with what you have. In the story there was a difference in endowment: One man had five, another two, and another one. And there was a difference in achievement: One man produced five and another two. Yet both men received the same word of commendation: "Well done, good and faithful servant." Each man did the best he could with what he had, and that is how to be successful with God.

So it is that sometimes failure stems from demanding too much of ourselves. For example, some twenty years ago I had a friend who was chaplain at the Military Academy at West Point. He was kind enough to invite me up one Sunday, and it was an experience I shall never forget. The chapel is an architectural gem, commanding the campus from its rocky promontory; the interior was made colorful by the flags of the states; and the lift which came from the voices of 2,200 men singing the hymns was inspiring. During the service the chaplain announced that the speaker was a Presbyterian and would be glad to meet any of the cadets who wished to talk with a minister of that persuasion. One boy walked into the study that afternoon with the stride of a soldier and gave every impression of being the master of his fate; but when he sat down and began to talk, it was a different story. "I'm in my first year here," he said, "but am most unhappy, and I'm thinking about leaving. I came to ask if you could help me make a decision."

After a conversation which lasted for an hour and a half, these facts came to light: His parents had planned West Point for him from the beginning; he had been sent to a prep school whose graduates always made good records at the academy and had stood at the top of the class there. But during the summer after graduating there had been a serious accident, and he had had to stay out a year. His accident had left him with a limp; his powers of concentration were impaired; and his grades, though good, were not at the top. The answer to his problem was apparent. He was expecting too much of himself. His work in reality was not inferior to his capacities which had now been impaired; and he would simply have to accept the fact that in the same student body which enrolled five-talent and two-talent men, he was now a one-talent man.

There is a word here for parents who have sons and daughters coming along in school. Anybody who has any connection with a college campus knows that every year there are students who break down and have to leave school and go home because somebody is expecting too much from them. With four-cylinder minds they are competing with students who have eight-cylinder minds, and the pressure is too much for them.

What would you think of a rose bush which looked across

the garden and saw a fig tree and said to itself, "I'm not as tall as the fig tree and am a failure." Or of a fig tree which looked over and saw a maple and said, "I've tried hard to grow as tall as that maple and cannot, so I'm a failure." Or of a maple which looked at the oak and said: "I've tried hard to throw my shadow down as far as the oak and cannot; therefore I am a failure." But the job of the rose bush is to be a rose bush and not a fig tree.

Somebody tells about a gravestone which bore this inscription: "She hath done what she couldn't." But God does not expect that. One thing that this story of the talents teaches is that success with God is doing the best you can with what you have.

For example, some years ago there was unveiled at one of our midwestern universities an unusual memorial. It was erected in honor of a graduate who was definitely a one-talent man. He never won a prize or an important election. He went out for football all four years but never made the varsity. He studied hard yet averaged only a B. But year after year he did his best; and later he lost his life in World War I. The French government awarded him the Croix de Guerre, and friends in this country honored him at his alma mater. On the tablet set up in his memory they carved this inscription: "He played four years on the scrubs, but he never quit." In the eyes of God and of his friends he did his best with what he had, and that spells success in any man's language.

II

When you come back to the one-talent man, you find that another cause of failure is fear. "I was afraid," he said, "and I went and hid your talent in the ground." One thing the story makes plain is that everybody is given some capacity; but for the person who fails because he demands too much of himself, there are a dozen who bury their talents in the soil of fear.

Some years ago there was a book widely read which bore the title *Wake Up and Live*. In it the author wrote that one night she came in sight of a truth which changed her life, and it was this: If you will face your task in the confidence that you can accomplish it, then picture yourself as succeeding rather than failing—you will more than likely achieve your goal. If you know anything about human nature, you will be aware immediately of how true this is. I have never forgotten the story with which she illustrated her thesis. She wrote that there was a dramatic group preparing to put on a play when the leading lady fell ill and her understudy was called in. The very thought of being thrust before the footlights gave her stage fright, and she was completely unnerved. The director knew she had the lines on the tip of her tongue, and had her hypnotized; once set free from the paralysis of fear, she gave an admirable performance.

As a boy I lived on a plantation, and I remember how the farmers used to put scarecrows in the fields. If the birds were getting too many watermelons, the farmer would plant a wooden frame in the ground and dress it up with ragged coat, trousers, and a battered old hat. It was harmless, of course, and yet it served to frighten away most of the marauders. Your fears are like scarecrows: When you take counsel of them, they will rob you of many feasts of achievement.

A long time ago I made two clippings in my reading, and now I find that they fit very well alongside each other. The first is the lettering on a poster which some of you men saw in the briefing rooms of American air bases in World War II. It said this: "By all the known laws which can be proved on paper or in the wind tunnel, the bumblebee cannot fly. The size of his wings in relation to his body, according to aeronautical and mathematical science, simply means that he cannot fly. It is an impossibility. But, of course, the bumblebee doesn't know about these rules, so he goes ahead and flies anyway."

The other statement comes from Margaret C. Banning the novelist. She remembers the story which Thomas á Kempis tells in his *Imitation of Christ* of a certain person who was so filled with fear that he could not bring himself to act. As he wavered back and forth in his uncertainty, he thought, "If I only knew such and such, then I should have the courage to persevere." And presently, wrote Thomas, he heard within himself this answer from God: "And if you did know—what would you do? Do now what you would do then—and you shall be very secure." And Mrs. Banning makes this comment: "These have proved useful words for me to live by. I've used them many times."

That was the trouble with our one-talent man. He was saying to himself what many of us say to ourselves, "If only I knew that I could succeed and win the approval of my master, then I should have the courage to persevere." But "I was afraid and went and buried your talent in the ground."

Sometimes I am asked, as no doubt you are, what is my favorite verse in the Bible. It happens that I have two, and one of them is Paul's ringing affirmation in Philippians 4:13: "I can do all things in him who strengthens me."

There are two reasons why I like this verse. First of all, as a one-talent man I was born with this fellow's fear. As a boy I grew up saying, in the face of any difficult assignment, "I can't—I just know I can't do it." It wasn't long before I learned that a person who says that is defeated before he starts. And then I met Paul, and I found him saying, not "I can't," but "I can." He approached every task with the confidence that he could accomplish it.

But his confidence was more than whistling in the dark. He did not pull it out of the air, as it were; but he found it in his faith: "I can do all things in him who strengthens me." I can because God can and will make me able. One day that truth came alive to me. God had given me a job to do which I felt I could not possibly accomplish; and after I had given him all the reasons why, he said simply: "All I ask is that you do your best, and I will do the rest." That was a long time ago; ever since we have been working on the same basis, and he has never let me down.

III

Come back now to the story, and you will find that it ends on a somber note: When the one-talent man failed to use his talent, he lost it. "So take the talent from him," said the master, "and give it to him who has the ten talents. For to every one who has will more be given; . . . but from him who has not, even what he has will be taken away."

In the parable the word talent stood for money, and sometimes our tendency is to interpret this principle so. He who has gets, we say, as when a man already wealthy is willed a legacy and becomes wealthier still. It does appear that the rich get richer and the poor get poorer. But the statement stands for something else, and when you give it its fullest expression, you get the point: To every one who has the will to make use of his ability will more ability be given; and from him who lacks the will to exercise his talent, it will be taken away. And when you think of it in terms of playing a game, or singing a song, or writing a poem, or making a speech, or performing an operation, or cultivating the presence of God—you will see how it is true as a law of life: Either you must use, or you will certainly lose.

I remember a story about Dwight L. Moody who was speaking before a large audience in one of his meetings. He was putting his very soul into it, as he always did. He was thinking more about the content of his message and its meaning for his hearers than about the precise literary form of it. There was a certain fastidious gentleman on the platform that night, and at the close of the service he went to Mr. Moody and said to him: "By the way, I noticed you made eleven mistakes in grammar in your sermon tonight." "Very likely," replied Mr. Moody. "I don't doubt it for a minute. My early education was faulty. I often wish I had received more schooling. But I am using all the grammar I know in the service of Christ—how is it with you?" By his faithfulness in the use of the talent he had, Mr. Moody became the world's leading evangelist of the nineteenth century. "To every one who has will more be given; . . . but from him who has not, even what he has will be taken away." And that goes not only for his talent but for the sense of a higher approval upon his life. "Cast the worthless servant into the outer darkness," said the master; "there men will weep and gnash their teeth." The two faithful workmen received a welcomed "Well done" from their lord, while the unfaithful servant was left with a torment of conscience in a black night of despair.

Some years ago a distinguished chaplain of the British Army, G. Studdert-Kennedy, said that he was no longer afraid of hell, the kind of hell which the older preachers used to make so much of. "But," he added, "I am horribly afraid that a day will come when someone will look me in the eye and say, 'Well, what did you make of it?' "

That is the kind of question which this story leaves in the mind. This talent of yours—to secure an education, to build a Christian home, to leave the world a little better than you found it—what did you make of it? What are you making of it?

As each of you seeks an answer for himself, let this word given to the one-talent man speak its truth to you: "For to every one who has will more be given, and he will have abundance; but from him who has not, even what he has will be taken away"—both here and hereafter.

THE ELDER BROTHER

The story in the fifteenth chapter of Luke concerns a
father who had two sons. The younger boy was the more
famous of the two. He was warm, impulsive, and attractive,
and took his turn in the far country. We call him the prodigal
son. But sometimes we are likely to forget that he had an older
brother. All the while the prodigal was wasting his substance
in riotous living, the elder son stayed at home and kept the
rules; but when the younger boy returned and was welcomed
with open arms by the father, the elder brother's conduct revealed a character which left much to be desired. We make him
our subject, and his life suggests the question: How good ought
a Christian to be?

When you read between the lines, you find that Jesus is not
simply telling a story about a father who had two sons. He is

giving us a picture of two kinds of religion in his day. The younger son represents the people whom he called the publicans and the sinners, while the elder brother stands for the Pharisees and the scribes. The Pharisees made a business out of being good. They took the law of Moses and worked it out into hundreds of rules, and they governed their lives by the rule book. They thought of themselves, and others thought of them too, as possessing goodness in the highest degree. And yet one day Jesus startled his men by saying to them: "Unless your righteousness exceeds that of the scribes and Pharisees, you will never enter the kingdom of heaven."

That is a word which comes close to home, because there is something of the Pharisee in all of us. When Frederick W. Krummacher was asked the identity of the elder brother, he replied: "I learned it only yesterday—myself." And yet Jesus says: "Unless your goodness overtops the righteousness of these strict observers of the law, unless your goodness is of a higher order than that of these people who are looked upon as possessing goodness in the highest degree, you will never get into the kingdom of heaven." What can he mean?

When you take the life of the elder brother and look at it in terms of the verses which follow the text, you will see that he means three things.

I

First, the goodness of the Christian must exceed that of the elder brother by being more inward. There is an unforgettable story of the Pharisee who stood up to pray. He rose to tell God what a fine fellow he was. He boasted of his goodness, and it is instructive to note the virtues which he catalogued. "God," he said, "I thank thee that I am not as other men are. I am a good man, and I can prove it. I fast twice a week and give tithes of all I get." For that man, goodness consisted in matters altogether outward, things like obeying certain rules. He went to church, and fasted, and put his pittance into the treasury. He could check off his rules one by one; and if he had a fair batting average, he could pat himself on the back and put himself down as not only a good fellow, but a very good fellow.

So it was with the elder brother. He had stayed dutifully at home and worked faithfully on his father's farm. Outwardly he had obeyed the rules, but inwardly his mind was filled with all kinds of devils. You will remember that when the prodigal came back home, his father gave a dinner party. He put a ring on the boy's finger, a new robe around his shoulders, killed the fatted calf, and all began to be merry. When the elder brother came in from the field and heard the music and the dancing, he called one of the servants and asked him what this meant. And when he learned that his brother had come back and that his father was celebrating the prodigal's return, "he was angry." His mind was filled with the devils of anger and self-pity.

And Jesus has a word for that. He says that the goodness of the Christian must go beyond the outward to the inward, beyond the external to the internal. "You have heard that it was said to the men of old, 'You shall not kill'; . . . But I say to you that every one who is angry with his brother shall be liable to judgment; . . . You have heard that it was said, 'You shall not commit adultery.' But I say to you that every one who looks at a woman lustfully [that is, an intentional looking for the purpose of stimulating and delighting in impure desire] has already committed adultery with her in his heart."

And of course he is right. Goodness which stops at conduct may outwardly appear beautiful, but inwardly it is full of dead men's bones. It is not real until it exceeds the outward obedience and includes control of thought and feeling and desire.

And the reason for this is not far to seek. Today the students of human nature are backing up the teachings of Jesus. They are telling us that "as a man thinks in his heart, so is he." They are telling us that if a man tries to stop short his goodness at conduct, giving free reign in his mind to thoughts of things he would like to do but dares not do, the day will come when the dikes of restraint will give away before the inward pressure, and the waters of evil will flood the landscape of his life.

Some years ago in England a famous philanthropist fell victim to a certain sex temptation and, to the utter amazement of his friends, was forced to leave the country. Everyone was astonished that such an impulse had any power with such a man; but when a friend went through his desk, he found the secret: In a cupboard underneath the desk were stashed a number of lewd magazines. Thoughts are *things*, and out of the mind and heart come the issues of life.

How good ought a Christian to be? Jesus lights a candle and takes us down into the dusty, private recesses of our inward being. He asks: What do you dream about? What do you think about when you are not thinking of anything in particular? What kind of books and movies do you see? Your conduct may be as blameless as a babe's and your words as correct as Emily Post's; but what of your thoughts, your imaginations? Unless your goodness goes beyond externals so that it includes your inward being, you will never enter the kingdom.

II

In the second place, the goodness of the Christian must exceed that of the elder brother by being more positive than negative.

You will remember that the prodigal returned and his father gave him a party, and the elder brother was angry and remained outside. His father went out to invite him in, and this is what he said: "These many years I served you, . . . I never disobeyed your command." His goodness was a negative thing, a painful avoidance of evil rather than a positive expression of kindness.

We have already seen that the conduct of the Pharisees was guided by a code which included hundreds of rules. It is significant to note that more of this number were negative than positive. Their rule book was heavily weighted on the negative side. Moses reduced the rules to ten, but eight of them were negative.

Jesus takes the "Thou Shalt Not's" of Moses and transforms them into the "Thou Shalt's" of the Great Commandment. Do you know that there was a rule like the Golden Rule which had been taught by other teachers before Jesus, but it was in the negative? It went like this: Whatever you wish that men would not do to you, do not to them. But Jesus takes this negative and turns it into a positive: "Whatever you wish that men would do to you, do so to them." And in so doing he adds another particular to the ways in which the goodness of the Christian must excel: It must be positive.

In the light of that fact look at the difference between the teaching of Jesus and that of his contemporaries on the subject of the sabbath. During his lifetime, that was a burning question. It was on this point that he clashed with the religious leaders of his day more than on any other. And the reason was this: It was their belief that when the law of Moses was perfectly obeyed, then God would send his Messiah, and in deliberately breaking that law Jesus was postponing the time.

The scribes and Pharisees had reared a structure of prohibitions around the sabbath which made it a burden. Their theme song about the sabbath was "Thou shalt not." A tailor was not allowed to go out at dusk on Friday with his needle because the sabbath began at six, and six o'clock might catch him carrying a burden, and that was against the law. For the same reason, the scribe could not go out with his pen behind his ear. A man was not allowed to wear shoes weighted with nails because that too would be carrying a burden. A woman might not look into the mirror on the sabbath because she might find a strand of hair out of place and want to replace it, and that would be work which was against the law. The rabbis were never quite able to decide whether a cripple would be allowed to wear his wooden leg on the sabbath. The crowning absurdity of their system of negative ethics came when Jesus healed a man on the sabbath, and they criticized him for breaking the law which forbade any sort of work. But Jesus set them back on their heels with this question: "Is it lawful on the sabbath to do good or to do harm; to save life or to destroy?"

Our problem of what to do on Sunday has largely been complicated by this negative approach. Although it was nearly fifty years ago, I can still remember the distaste of waking up in the morning and realizing that it was Sunday; and the reason I detested the day so much was largely because our teaching about it was negative. I wanted to go swimming, but I couldn't because it was Sunday. I wanted to play baseball, but I couldn't because it was Sunday. I wanted to go to the movies, but I couldn't because it was Sunday. Sunday was supposed to be different from other days; and the chief ways in which it was different had to do with things we were not allowed to do. The whole approach to the day was negative.

I think if someone had explained to me the reason it was supposed to be different and what the day was *for* instead of what it was *not* for, I would have had another attitude. Even as a boy I think I could have understood that in ancient times, when some men were slaves and were controlled by their masters, it was a real benefit for them to have a law which gave them one day a week for rest. And even though going to church is not a favorite pastime for a boy, I might have understood that it is right to have a time for worship. In addition to rest and worship, it is good to have a day when you can catch up on the things you want to do for other people, like visiting the sick. Over against the prohibitions of the Pharisees, Jesus stated the truth in positive form: "The sabbath is made for man"—for the benefit of his physical, social, and spiritual nature.

But of course the question of goodness is a much larger thing than the use of Sunday, and it is amazing how often we judge a Christian, not by what he does but by what he does not do. Here is an enlisted man who had recently joined a company, and his fellow soldiers were discussing him. "He doesn't drink, he doesn't gamble, he doesn't smoke," they said; and one man spoke up: "Then he must be a Christian."

Yet when you read the New Testament, you discover that in many cases the people who received the condemnation of Jesus were blamed not so much for what they did as for what they failed to do. There were the priest and the Levite, who simply "passed by on the other side"; and in the parable of the last judgment, there were those who wound up on the side of the goats. "Why?" they wondered, in wide-eyed surprise. "Because," says Jesus, "you let the hungry go unfed, and the naked unclothed, and the prisoner unvisited. Inasmuch as you did it not."

And so the second way in which the goodness of the Christian must excel is this: It must be positive. It consists not so much in a painful avoidance of evil as in following the master who "went about doing good."

III

That brings us to the third point of difference. The goodness of the Christian must excel in being more inward and more positive and, finally, by being more inclusive.

You will note that the elder brother failed at this place also. When the prodigal returned and the party was in full swing, "he was angry and refused to go in." Unlike his father who met the wayward son with open arms of forgiveness, this Pharisee wrapped his cloak of self-righteousness about him and sat outside in icy isolation.

The word Pharisee means literally one who separates himself, and the Pharisees were the separatist party among the Jews. Originally the impulse was a noble one, because its purpose was to save the Pharisees from being lost in the melting pot in which the Greeks sought to fuse all religion and all culture.

But in the days of Jesus this separatist tendency had become too narrow and restricted, and was like a wall which shut out everyone else. The command to love a neighbor, given by Moses, was always limited to another member of the same nation; and a son of Moses felt no obligation to anyone who was not a Jew. So the feeling which had always been implicit had become explicit in the traditions of the Pharisee, and Jesus quotes it thus: "You shall love your neighbor and hate your enemy."

Against this background of a narrow and restricted morality, our Lord says that the goodness of the Christian must go beyond that of the Pharisees and become more inclusive. That is the meaning of the story of the good Samaritan. When the lawyer asks, "Who is my neighbor," Jesus answers that your neighbor is anyone in need, regardless of nationality.

And then I'm sure our Lord would want us to bring the truth closer home and make it apply to those of our own kind. Perhaps this is the point at which our truth will touch us most truly. I remember that once our maid said, "I think I could get along all right if it wasn't for human relationships!" So say we all! It is so easy to get fouled up with other people. It may be right at home. It may be that there is bad blood between you and your brother, as it was in the story. It may be between husband and wife. It may be between you and your next door neighbor, or some friend who has fallen out with you. How will you deal with that situation so as to heal the hurt?

"Well," says Jesus, "you have heard that it was said, 'You shall love your neighbor and hate your enemy.' But I say to you, Love your enemies and pray for those who persecute you, so that you may be sons of your Father who is in heaven; for he makes his sun rise on the evil and the good, and sends his rain on the just and on the unjust." And in that spirit of inclusive goodness you can follow the strategy of the poet Edwin Markham:

He drew a circle that shut me out—
Heretic, rebel, a thing to flout.
But Love and I had the wit to win:
We drew a circle that took him in!

So we come back to the question with which we began: How good ought a Christian to be? In the light of the life of the elder brother the answer must be this: It will go beyond the goodness of the Pharisee by being more inward, more positive, and more inclusive.

ZACCHAEUS: THE MAN WHO WAS CHANGED

There are times in the experience of most of us when Zacchaeus is a good man to know about. Zacchaeus was the fellow who heard that Jesus was passing through town and wanted to see him. The other people wanted to see Jesus too, and the street was crowded. For reasons that will be apparent later, everybody took pleasure in elbowing this public enemy number one to the rear. Being too short to see over their heads, Zacchaeus ran on down the street and climbed into a low-limbed sycamore tree to await the procession. When Jesus came alongside, he noted the eager interest of this tree-sitter and invited himself home to dinner with him; and Zacchaeus was never the same again.

That is the reason why Zacchaeus is often a good man to know. In one of his plays, George Bernard Shaw makes Adam say to Eve, "I like you, but I do not like myself. . . . I want to be different." Another put his wish in these words: "O that a man would arise in me that the man I am might cease to be." Harry Emerson Fosdick knew human nature and understood well this dissatisfaction with the old self and the desire for a new self, and he gave one of his sermons this title: "No Man Need Stay the Way He Is."

There is a verse in one of Paul's letters to the Corinthians which underscores this fact, and it goes like this: "For if any man be in Christ, he is a new creature; old things are passed away; behold, all things are become new." Let Zacchaeus stand up beside those words, and you will see that he is a living example of their truth.

I

The first fact which stands out in the record is that his life was completely changed.

The story says that he was a tax collector, and that fact speaks volumes. At this time Palestine was subject to the Romans. Tax collectors thus were in the service of Rome, and therefore they were regarded as quislings. The system of collecting taxes lent itself to gross abuse. The custom was to farm out the jobs: The rulers assessed a district a certain figure, and then they sold the right to collect to the highest bidder. So long as he handed over the assessed figure at the end of the year, he was entitled to keep what he could collect over and above; and since there were no newspapers to tell the people what they owed, he was free to collect whatever the traffic would bear. He could stop a man on the road and make him unpack his bundles and charge him well-nigh what he liked. It is hard enough to pay taxes when there are laws which keep the revenue agents honest; but when you know you are being gouged, there is no wonder these men like Zaccheus were the most hated in the country. No wonder they were classed with robbers and murderers; no wonder they were barred from the synagogue. A writer of the time tells us that he once saw a monument to an honest tax collector. Such a man was so rare that he had a monument built to him. And Zacchaeus was a tax collector.

The story says moreover that he was rich. He lived in Jericho, a wealthy and important town. Jericho was in the Jordan Valley, commanding the approach to Jerusalem as well as the crossings of the river to the lands east of Jordan. She had a great palm forest and balsam groves, and the Romans carried her dates and balsam to world-wide trade and fame; all this combined to make Jericho an important center of taxation. No wonder Zacchaeus was a rich man; the nature of the business he was in, plus the franchise he held, made him a sure winner.

This man was wealthy, but he was not happy; and he said as much to Jesus who went home to dinner with him. "Lord," he said, "the half of my goods I give to the poor; and if I have defrauded anyone of anything, I restore it fourfold." Whenever you find a rich man who is willing to give away half of what he has to the poor, refusing to keep the other half for himself but using it beyond the demands of the law in making restitution, you've got a changed man. And that is exactly what Zacchaeus did; he showed by his deeds that his life had been changed.

When you look at this topic, you no doubt react with a question mark. You remember having heard always that human nature is the one thing that does not change, and you quote to yourself an old proverb which says that "you cannot make a silk purse out of a sow's ear." In that case you will be interested to know that it has been done. A few years ago a group of scientists, tired of hearing that statement of impossibility, literally took a sow's ear, decomposed it into its chemical constituents, made synthetic silk, and a silk purse. If things can be changed, so can people.

Do I have any right to say these things unless I know people whose lives have been changed? When I look around among my acquaintances, sure enough, there they are. There is the lad whom I knew years ago as having the fieriest temper of any boy you ever saw. Last summer I spent some time with him: He is a grown man now, but you have never seen a more patient or tender father in dealing with his sons. And there is that young theological student who, during his seminary days, was such a playboy that he left school to keep the professors from having to tell him that he could not graduate; but he came back two years later and joined our class and did graduate and for more than thirty years has proved to be one of our most effective ministers.

One day I was calling upon one of the older women in our congregation, and she told me of her days as a teacher in our Sunday school. She said there was a class of boys so bad and unmanageable that no teacher would have them. They had driven off several teachers, and finally the superintendent asked if she would take these boys and see what could be done with them. Just for fun, I asked the names of some of them and was interested to learn that many of them are now elders and deacons in our church. It was as I had supposed: Life can be changed.

have said to him: "Zacchaeus, it is the itching palm that got you into trouble. Now that you are a changed man, I am not going to tell you to give up making money. I want you to go on making all you can honestly make, but I want you to do so for a different purpose. Instead of making yourself rich, you can harness your acquisitive instinct to the kingdom of God; and when you are willing to make all you can and save all you can, then give all you can; and you may have a little less money, but you will have a lot more happiness." The selfishness which poisons the acquisitive urge will have passed away, but the same old instinct will become harnessed to a new goal.

So it is with other native drives. Take the pugnacious instinct. You say, "I'm a fighter and can't help it. I was born that way and nothing can be done about it, and it is always getting me into trouble. What about that?" Well, Paul was a fighter, too. When his big moment came, he was breathing out threats and slaughter against the Christians. When he was changed, he did not cease to be a fighter; for near the end of his career he summed it up like this, "I have fought a good fight." The change within him came not by doing away with the fighting instinct but by harnessing it to a new purpose. Get in the game on God's side against the devil, and there is plenty of room for all the fight that is in you.

Someone else speaks up to say: "One of my greatest concerns in life is sex; what can I do about that?" Follow Jesus' example. He worked creatively in the realm of mind and spirit. He was bringing into being a new race, and mothering and fathering the people of God. "O Jerusalem, Jerusalem, how often would I have gathered thy children unto me, as a hen does her brood." Paul, denied home and children, becomes spiritual father to a multitude; and many a single man or

II

So much for the fact; look now at the nature of the change, as described by Paul in II Corinthians. He does not say that a person can be changed beyond recognition. He is not promising the moon. In the nursery class in a certain church, there is a little boy whose major problem is to decide whether he will be a man or a woman when he grows up. Some day he will discover that his opportunities are not quite so extensive. So it is with the person whose life is changed: There are some characteristics that will remain constant.

"The old has passed away," says Paul; and yet it has not passed away. It—the old—is "become new." That sounds like double-talk, but it is not in the least. It is a biblical description of a psychological process which we know today as sublimation. Sublimation is that procedure by which the psychic energy of an instinct is transferred into a higher channel by being harnessed to a different goal. For example, the modern peach was used in ancient Persia as a source from which to get poison with which to tip arrows for fighting. But today it is a new creation; the poison has been eliminated, but the fundamental life of the tree remains. So Paul discovered that the poison of the old instincts can be eleminated, but the instincts themselves can become new by being directed to a new goal.

Take Zacchaeus, for example. The instinct which got him into trouble is one with which we ourselves are most familiar. It was the acquisitive instinct: the desire to get and to have and to hold. Zaccheaus was so eager to get rich that he was willing to be bracketed with robbers and murderers and to endure the hatred and scorn of his people. The story does not say so, of course, but there is every reason to believe that Jesus migh

11

woman has found real satisfaction in working with growing boys and girls and bringing to birth their hidden capacities.

Or someone else says: "The thing that makes life go for me is ambition. I have a burning desire to excel and to reach the top: as a student in my class, as a salesman with my company, as a public servant in politics. That wish gives me more drive than anything I know; but it is selfish and, being selfish, is wrong." Well, for the sake of all that is high and holy, hold on to your ambition; only get it set in the right direction. I remember once, when my own mind was mixed up about this apparent conflict between the desire to excel and the demand of Christ to be unselfish, how the light came. I went to pay a call on a minister, and on the wall of his study he had framed and hung this sentence: "Make the most of yourself for Christ's sake." I realized that here was the answer; the old instinct to get myself ahead had passed away, but it came back as something new because it was harnessed to a new purpose. When you shift your desire to excel from yourself to the kingdom of God, then you can step on the accelerator and give it full power ahead.

That is what Paul means by a changed life. Old things are passed away, in the sense of passing in—into new goals, new purposes, new endeavors. Before you are changed, you harness all your powers to serve yourself; and after you are changed, you are the same person with this difference: You are all-out for God.

III

So much for the fact of change and its nature. Move on and notice, in the third place, that this word from Paul provides the secret of the change. What it says is this: "If any one is in

Christ, he is a new creation." To be "in Christ" is to be subject to his control, under his influence, mastered by his spirit.

When you come back to our friend Zacchaeus, that is exactly what you find. When was it that this gouging tax collector became a heavy contributor to the "United Fund," a restorer of conscience money? It happened when he took a certain guest home to dinner. It was in the presence and under the influence of a man named Jesus.

There is nothing mysterious about this secret. It is the kind of thing which is going on about us every day—the influence of one personality upon another. You see it often in the case of a younger man who admires an older man in his profession; he is subject to the older man's power and influence, even to the point sometimes of copying his elder's mannerisms. At the seminary they told us about a former professor there who was greatly admired as a preacher by the students. This professor had a habit of raising one foot in an odd gesture in the pulpit; and so there was born a generation of foot-lifting preachers. The younger men were so subject to the influence and power of the older man that they were his unconscious imitators. That is something of what it means to be in Christ. It is to be subject to his power and molded by his influence. It is to keep him always there in your mind, so that as you look at him, you cannot help becoming like him.

Back in college days some of us belonged to a class in public speaking whose professor had the theory that a man learns to speak by speaking. One of his exercises therefore was to call upon the students to stand up, one at a time; and after a man was on his feet, the professor would assign a topic and tell him to talk on it for a few minutes. There is a story of a man in such a class who was given the topic "Zacchaeus." This particular man had joined the class because he suffered from stage fright and wanted to overcome that fear and learn to think on his feet. He knew that a talk ought to be organized in outline form with several points that would show progress in thought. He did some fast thinking, and this is what he came up with. "Gentlemen," he said, "my topic today is Zacchaeus, and I want to say three things about him. In the first place, Zacchaeus was a man—so am I. In the second place, Zacchaeus was up a tree—so am I. In the third place, Zacchaeus came down—so am I." And with that he sat down.

When you stop there, however, you miss the point of the story. Today I want you to add a fourth division to the man's talk, and it goes like this: When Zacchaeus came down, he took a guest home to dinner with him; and for him life was different from that day on.

Something like that could happen now. You are up a tree because you don't like yourself. You are sick and tired of yourself and don't want to live with yourself any longer. You want to be changed, to be different, to be a new person. Very well. Look at Zacchaeus, and see that Paul was right: If any man be in Christ—subject to his influence and under the control of his spirit—he is a new creation; old things are passed away. Behold, all things are become as new.

DOUBTING THOMAS

I remember the first time I heard the problem of religious doubt discussed by a professor of psychology of religion in theological seminary. One thing he said was that it was beginning to show itself at an earlier age than formerly. For his contempories it did not begin until a student reached graduate school. That was thirty-five years ago when he was speaking, but at that time it had begun to be a factor in the experience of the undergraduate. In this generation it has moved back still earlier, for they tell me that in our church it is the high school student who is troubled by intellectual difficulties.

When you take this problem back to the Bible, the first person you think of is a man named Thomas. Although he was one of the twelve apostles, he was a doubter; and he has given his name to his successors. We call him "Doubting Thomas." He gets his name from his refusal to believe in the resurrection of Jesus. "Unless I see in his hands the print of the nails," he said, "I will not believe." Like so many of our contemporaries, he demands demonstrable proof; and if that is lacking, he refuses to believe. The story goes on to say, however, that he overcame his unbelief, and we look at him to see how a man can move out of doubt into faith.

I

The first thing the story says is that Jesus did not rebuke his doubt. When your child refuses to believe on your own authority what you tell him is true in matters of faith, you sometimes blame him and make him feel uncomfortable; but that was not the way of Jesus with Thomas. Look at the story.

Jesus has been put to death, and his men have scattered. Early on Sunday morning the women go to the tomb to anoint the body and find it missing. They find Peter and John and give them the message, and these two men investigate for themselves and find it even so. They spread the word that their master is not dead but alive. The news brings them back together, but on that first meeting Thomas is missing. No doubt he was told also but just could not believe the good news. Eight days later they come back together again, and this time Thomas is with them. "We have seen the Lord," they tell him. But Thomas is still the doubter. "Unless I see in his hands the print of the nails, and place my finger in the mark of the nails, and place my hand in his side, I will not believe."

Just then the strangest thing happened. Jesus appeared and spoke to them the greeting which you still hear all over Palestine: "Shalom"—"Peace be unto you." Looking straight into the face of this man of doubt, Jesus said to him, "Put your finger here, and see my hands; and put out your hand, and place it in my side; do not be faithless, but believing." The point is that Jesus did not blame him for his unbelief. He met it with sympathy and understanding and evidence.

It will help you young people to understand yourselves, and you parents to understand your sons and daughters, if you will stop and consider that doubt is a normal experience in the development of a growing person. You realize, I am sure, that all of us must begin our lives on the basis of a borrowed foundation. During infancy and childhood we must be provided for by others. Our parents must furnish us with food, clothing, a home, books, spending money, and whatever else we need.

And what is true in the physical realm holds good also for the intellectual and the spiritual. Just as you are incapable of providing for your physical needs and must live as a parasite in childhood, so does your mental life begin its existence on the basis of a borrowed foundation. It is necessarily true that in our earlier years we live by faith—in the faith of someone else; before we develop a faculty for testing truth, we must accept it as it is passed on to us.

But then when the years of adolescence come on and the intellectual life begins to bud, we are not quite so willing to believe a proposition simply because our parents and the preacher say it is true. In other words, we begin thinking for ourselves. We turn from a secondhand rehearsal of the truth to seek a firsthand, original acquaintance with it. While thinking about this, I took down from my shelves a book titled *The Psychology of Adolescence* and found the author saying this: "A distinguished educator once said that it was as impossible for one person to think for another as it would be to digest for him. And since truth is made one's own only by being thought out for oneself, it follows that the process of thinking out the truth is quite essential, if the mind is to attain normal growth." What we are saying is that in the light of the laws of development, and in the light of Jesus' dealing with Thomas, doubt is to be accepted as normal and dealt with sympathetically.

Yet we must remember that, while not wrong, doubt does become so when you are content to rest in it. It is not intended to be a permanent state but a passing phase. It is a doorway, and you will get nowhere if you stand still in the door. Doubts are stop-over places, but they are never the true home of the soul. Jesus said to Thomas: "Do not be faithless, but believing." We move on then to see what further light we can get from Thomas.

II

When you read between the lines of the story, you will discover that Thomas kept an open mind to the truth by keeping in touch with his fellow believers and being ready for any light that might come.

Sometimes when a young person cannot honestly believe the teaching of the church, he will cut himself off from its influence and close his mind to its truth. But Thomas, in spite of his doubts, refused to do that. He met with the friends of Jesus in that Upper Room even though he could not accept their testimony. When Jesus did appear and offer proof, Thomas refused to persist in his prejudices and acknowledged the logic of the facts and cried, "My Lord and my God." If you refuse to read your Bible and say your prayers, and if you cut yourself off from the church because you do not share in its point of view, you will always be a doubting Thomas. But if, with an open mind, you continue to cultivate your spiritual life and maintain your attendance upon the services of the church, then you have a better chance of coming out where Thomas did.

But sometimes you will find a young person who, if he cannot believe, feels that honesty demands that he stop reading the Bible and saying his prayers and going to church. He does not wish to be a hypocrite, and so he says: "How can I read the Bible and say my prayers and worship in church, when I am not sure what I believe? At least I will be honest and not pretend to be something I am not." Thus he cuts himself off from the sources of help.

You are impressed by that logic because it appears to make sense. Suppose, then, that your son or your daughter says that kind of thing to you; how can you answer him? You might try this: Ask him if he would apply that kind of logic to mathematics. Suppose he failed to understand some theorem in geometry. It would not be an evidence of honesty to say: "I do not understand this principle, and I will not study the textbook any longer, because that would be hypocrisy." On that basis he would never learn anything and might as well stop going to school. But what he does is to keep an open mind and expose his brain to the truth in the textbook, and by and by he begins to understand and is able to believe. That was the method of Thomas; by that means he found his way out of doubt into faith.

Another phase of the open mind is a willingness to give your doubts time. If you will face them honestly, note them down and then put them aside; time will bring unexpected answers. I remember reading about a distinguished scholar who showed a friend a little notebook which he carried with him constantly. In it he had written certain questions which occurred in his reading. He jotted them down so that at some convenient time he might read up on them. He said it had often been his experience that a month or so later when he took out his little book and looked at his questions, many of them could be crossed off at once because they had been fully answered by some experience or some chance reading. It is not good sense to call time on questions of faith; you can remind yourself that better minds than yours believe the things you doubt, and perhaps light will come with time. I remember that during the days of graduate school a serious doubt concerning God nearly wrecked my faith. But there was a professor there whose intelligence I respected and who believed the thing I could not believe. I decided that for the time being I would put my faith in his faith and just wait; and in due time doubt faded, and faith grew strong.

It is a mark of a closed mind to doubt your beliefs and believe your doubts; but the open mind which is willing to believe its beliefs and doubt its doubts will most often lead to faith.

III

When you go back to Thomas, you discover that not only did he have an open mind which kept him in touch with the sources of faith, but he was willing to act in obedience to the principles which he believed to be right.

For example, Jesus had a friend named Lazarus who lived in Bethany, and one day he received a message from the man's sisters that his friend was sick; the implication was plain that they wanted to see him. For two days Jesus waited, thinking over the issues involved; and then he proposed to his disciples that they go with him. These men remembered that Jesus had been stoned on his last visit to that place, and they were sure that his enemies were just waiting for another chance at him.

They were puzzled that he should even consider returning. "Master," they said, "the Jews were trying to stone you there only the other day; surely you are not going back." Jesus replied that he must do his Father's work while there was time, regardless of the danger. Then Thomas, this man who could understand neither the wisdom nor the necessity of going, nevertheless said, "Let us also go, that we may die with him." This man had his doubts; but he knew it was right to be loyal to a friend, and he would go with him to the bitter end.

In *Alice Through the Looking Glass* the Queen says she is a hundred and one years, five months, and one day old. "I can't believe that," said Alice. "Can't you?" said the Queen. "Try again, draw a long breath and shut your eyes."

Too often this has been the attitude of a misguided church or a misguided parent. To one who is struggling to believe the faith, asking how it can be that a man born in a stable is the divine Son of God, the word has been: "Shut your eyes; stop asking questions; take a deep breath and try again." That attitude has sometimes been responsible for the idea that faith is "believing what you know is not true." But the Bible says, "Prove all things"; and its method of proof is suggested by Thomas.

For example, one day Jesus went up to the Temple in Jerusalem and taught the people. The Jewish authorities were amazed at his teaching, and they said, "How is it that this man has learning, when he has never been to school?" So Jesus answered them: "My teaching is not mine, but his who sent me; if any man is willing to do his will, he shall know whether the teaching is from God."

In other words, faith in God and things spiritual is not something you get through intellectual pursuit and going to school;

rather it comes through a *doing* of that much of the will of God which you believe to be true. More than a hundred years ago F. W. Robertson in England delivered a sermon on this text, and it is still remembered and quoted. He called it, "Obedience the Organ of Spiritual Knowledge." Your mind, he said, is the organ through which you can learn facts; but when it comes to faith, the means is something else. It is a life lived in obedience to what you believe to be true. If any man is willing to do God's will, that much of it of which he is sure, then he will know God's truth.

Do you see the difference between Robertson's method and that of the Queen in dealing with Alice? When you are faced with something in which you cannot believe, he does not say, "Close your eyes, take a deep breath, swallow hard, and try again." What he says is this: "Find something which you can believe. You would agree that it is right to do right. All right, if that is all you can believe, then begin there. Begin to live in obedience to what you believe to be right, and you will find your way into faith." I heard of a man who went through the Bible and marked all the things he could not believe. If that is your method, go back and erase those marks, and then under-score the things you can believe. It may not be much, but it will be something; and then begin to live on the basis of what you do believe. You will find that faith will grow, because "obedience is the organ of spiritual knowledge."

As we have noted earlier, Horace Bushnell, while a young instructor at Yale, did not mean to be an atheist and was astonished to find that he had lost nearly all conviction of God. It did not present a pleasing prospect, and it troubled him. Then one day, while walking the floor in his room, there suddenly came the question: "Is there, then, no truth that I do believe?

Yes, there is this one, now that I think of it: There is a distinction of right and wrong that I never doubted, and I see not how I can; I am even quite sure of it." Then he asked the question: "Have I ever taken the principle of right for my life? . . . No, I have not; consciously I have not. Then here is something for me to do! No matter what becomes of my questions, nothing ought to become of them if I cannot take a first principle so inevitably true and live in it. Here then, I will begin. If there is a God, as I rather hope there is, and very dimly believe, he is a right God. If I have lost him in wrong, perhaps I shall find him in right. Will he not help me, or perchance be discovered to me?"

Then he dropped to his knees, and there he prayed to the dim God, confessing the dimness for honesty's sake and asking for help that he might begin a right life. He decided that henceforth that was his one aim. His biographer says: "It is an awfully dark prayer in the look of it; but the truest and best that he can make; . . . and the prayer and the vow are so profoundly meant that his soul is borne up into God's help, as it were, by some unseen chariot, and permitted to see the opening of heaven even sooner than he opens his eyes. . . . After this, all troublesome doubt of God's reality is gone, for he has found him."

Horace Bushnell not only became a believer in God but a preacher of his gospel. After forty-seven years as minister of a church in Hartford, Connecticut, he said, "Better than I know any man in Hartford, I know Jesus Christ."

If any man is willing to do his will, he will know whether the teaching is from God. Horace Bushnell found it so, and Thomas found it so. They both came to the place where they could say, "My Lord and my God." And so will you!

SIMON MAGUS: ON HAVING GOD
ON A STRING

The first century was a time when pagan religion had fallen on evil days. The old gods had more or less played out, and there was a keen demand for teachers with a knowledge of the unseen who could open up the way to God. So it was that the entire Mediterranean world abounded with seers, astrologers, and miracle workers. Some of them no doubt were sincere, but the temptation to exploit the credulity of the people for profit was too strong for most. So it was with Simon Magus who lived in that part of Palestine known as Samaria. For a long time, says the story, he amazed the people with his magic.

The persecution which followed the stoning of Stephen forced many of the followers of Jesus to leave Jerusalem, and Philip found himself in Samaria. There he began to preach; and as the people believed, miracles happened. Many who were paralyzed were healed, and others were cleansed of evil spirits.

Simon began to open his eyes. Here was a power he did not know anything about, the power of the Holy Spirit. He decided it was something he could use in his business, and he set out to add it to his bag of tricks. And so the text reads: "Now when Simon saw that the Spirit was given through the laying on of the apostles' hands, he offered them money, saying, 'Give me also this power.' "

By this time Peter had come from Jerusalem to assist Philip in his work, and he is the one who answers Simon Magus. In the lesson as we read it, Peter said to him: "Your silver perish with you, because you thought you could obtain the gift of God with money." But the translators have toned down his language. When I read this story for the first time in J. B. Phillips' translation, I nearly jumped out of my seat; for what I read was this: "But Peter said to him, 'To hell with you and your money! How dare you think you could buy the gift of God?' And then Dr. Phillips adds this footnote: "These words are exactly what the Greek means. It is a pity that their meaning is obscured by modern slang usage."

This man Simon Magus came to be regarded by Christian tradition as the father of all heresy, and the story is that he appeared as the foremost opponent of Peter in a series of debates in various cities. One legend tells of his death on this wise: "Denounced by Peter at Rome, he seeks to rehabilitate himself by a superlative feat of magic and offers to fly. The experiment had fatal results."

So much for the story. Now see what it has to say to us.

I

Take first of all this man Simon and what he stands for. His very name tells us he was a magician, and magic is an attempt to manipulate forces other than our own to change the course of events for our own benefit. When brought into the field of religion, it is an endeavor to put God on the end of a string and make him jump to our tune. Since self-centeredness is such a real part of human nature, there is a temptation to add religion to our bag of tricks and turn God into a handyman.

Even a blind man can see this utilitarian aspect of religion as one of the signs of our times. One of the most magnificent statements in all religious literature comes from the Westminster Shorter Catechism, and it goes like this: "The chief end of man is to glorify God and enjoy him forever." But some say we have turned this truth around and have made it read: "God's chief end is to glorify man and support him forever." The most telling bit of satire I have seen in a long time came from the pulpit of a Washington church, whose minister delivered an imaginary religious commerical which went like this: "Try God, folks. He will clear away your troubles in a twinkling. Works for you while you sleep. Works for you all the time. Cures your worries instantly. Nothing for you to do and so inexpensive. Go to your corner church today, folks, and get God! G-O-D—easy to pronounce, easy for you to remember, easy in every way." But God is more than an aspirin tablet or a tranquilizer.

One day a little girl was talking with her parents at the breakfast table, and she wanted to know where God was. Her mother told her God was everywhere. "Is he in this house?" asked the little girl. "Yes, he's in this house." "Is he in this room?" "Yes, he's in this room." Her eyes fell on the dishes on the table, and she said, "Is he in this sugar dish?" "Yes," said her mother, "he is in that sugar dish." The little girl clamped the lid tight and said, "Now, I've got him." You know people who think that religion is a matter of having God in a jug and the stopper in their hands.

Take prayer, for example. When someone asked a little boy if he said his prayers every night, he answered, "No, sir; some nights I don't want anything." Such a childish notion is excusable in a child, but the trouble comes when he grows up and fails to put away childish things. I have known grown-up and otherwise intelligent people who will tell you that they prayed for something and God didn't give it to them, and they will never speak to him again if their lives depend upon it.

Or take Bible reading. Through the mails there came one day an offer of something called "Prescription for Peace of Mind." As far as I could tell, someone had typed certain verses on pieces of paper and rolled them up and inserted them, one at a time, in little capsules with the instruction: "Take one a day, with a little faith." But the Bible is more than a prescription for peace of mind; and when you make out of it nothing more than a crutch, you miss the main point.

Or think of the matter of joining the church. Sometimes, they tell me, certain people join certain churches for purposes of social prestige and business advancement. Evidently ministers are not immune from this subtle form of simony, for we were warned as seminary students never to think of a call to some church as a stepping stone to something better.

Many years ago a woman whose husband had suffered a heart attack came to talk about it, and this is what she said: "I can't understand why God would do this to my husband, when all of our lives we have been tithers." And it was all the more surprising because this particular woman was in other respects apparently a mature Christian.

There is a story of an American soldier in Korea who seemed

to be most unhappy about his entire situation. When one of his buddies asked him what the trouble was, he said this: "I think I'll go back home—I'm not getting anything out of this war." Every time you are tempted to run out on God because you are not getting anything out of your religion, you are facing the sin of Simon Magus. For religion at its best is friendship with God; and the first law of friendship is that we think of our friends not as means but as ends.

II

Yet Simon Magus is not the only character in our story; there was another man there in Samaria. His name was Philip, and when he preached, things began to happen. "For unclean spirits came out of many who were possessed, crying with a loud voice; and many who were paralyzed or lame were healed." Here is a clear case of people who got something out of their religion: Nervous disorders were cleared up, and organic diseases were healed. This sort of thing happened around him wherever Jesus went—so much so that some one remarks that the atmosphere of the Gospels is more like the odor of a hospital than the scent of a sanctuary.

It is a law of life that when the pendulum swings, it often over-swings; and that has happened in our generation. The reaction against the sin of Simon is so strong that we have succumbed to the heresy of Nathanael which asks: Can there any good thing come out of faith? The answer of Philip is, "There can, indeed. For the core of the good news of the gospel is salvation; and salvation is being set free from dangers menacing to life and the consequent placing of life in circumstances favorable to its highest development." And that goes for here and now, as well as for then and there. The same Catechism which tells us that "Man's chief end is to glorify God and enjoy him forever" does not hesitate to use the word "benefits" in connection with our faith. "The benefits," it says "which in this life do accompany or flow from justification, adoption, and sanctification are," and then it lists a number of good things, among them "peace of conscience."

The truth is, there is a twofold function which the Christian faith serves in the life of the believer. Charles W. Gilkey used to speak of it as refuge and challenge. H. H. Farmer calls it absolute demand and final succor. And wherever you look in the Bible, you find these two operations at work. The same God who said to Moses, "Come now, and I will send you to Pharaoh," also said, "Certainly I will go with you." The same Isaiah who heard the challenge, "Whom shall I send, and who will go for us," found it possible to say also: "He giveth power to the faint, and to him who has no might he increases strength." The same apostle who said, "Forgetting the things which are behind, and reaching forward to the things which are before, I press on," said also: "I can do all things through him who strengthens." And the same Lord who gave his people their marching orders, saying, "You shall be witnesses to me," did not fail to add this word: "You shall receive power." When you make out of faith nothing but a formula for finding peace of mind and when you turn prayer into a grab bag for gifts that will make you healthy, wealthy, and wise—you are cheating God. By the same token, when you fail to find in your faith a power which can turn cowardice into courage and weakness into strength, you are cheating yourself.

No one would ever accuse the reformers of trying to put God

on a string and make him jump to their tune. They remind you of what W. R. Maltby said. He said that Jesus promised three things to his followers: They would be absurdly happy, entirely without fear, and always in trouble. Whatever they thought of the first two, the reformers would certainly agree on the last. The experience of Martin Luther was one unending struggle and finds its epitome in his appearance before the Diet of Worms. The powers of state and church had summoned him to trial; they piled his writings on the floor in front of him and demanded that he recant. He looked the representatives of the emperor and the pope in the face, knowing that refusal could well cost him his life, and gave answer in words that still raise goose bumps: "My conscience taken captive by the word of God, I cannot and will not revoke anything, for it is neither safe nor right to act against one's conscience. God help me. Amen."

The life of Luther was one long effort to meet the challenge which the will of God placed upon him; but his faith was not all challenge. It possessed resources which provided refuge, and he put that fact into a song which put backbone into his people wherever they sang it: "A mighty fortress is our God, a bulwark never-failing; Our helper he amid the flood of mortal ills prevailing." And Luther's God still lives today.

Simon Magus stands as a warning. Prayer is not an Aladdin's lamp. Faith is not a magical hocus-pocus to provide health, wealth, and prosperity. God is not a bellboy who can be tipped to run our errands. He is the Lord Almighty, before whom we bow in adoration and humility.

But Philip stands as a warning too. When he preached his gospel, there was no magic about it, but there were miracles which followed. "Unclean spirits came out of many who were

133

possessed . . . ; and many who were paralyzed or lame were healed." Let us not sell our gospel short. Doctors' offices are filled today with people who are devil-ridden with inferiority complexes and anxiety neuroses, and who are eaten up with the unclean spirits of guilt. And when they find their way into a true minister's study, he will not fail to get them in saving touch with him who was known in the days of his flesh as the great physician.

III

What then is the difference between the magical religion of Simon Magus and the miracle religion of Philip? The answer comes from the third character in the story. It was Peter who made reply to the magician's request: "Your silver perish with you," he said "for your heart is not right before God. Repent therefore of this wickedness of yours, and pray to the Lord that, if possible, the intent of your heart be forgiven you." It is in the subtle, inner area of motive that the difference lies.

The motive of Simon Magus was selfish; he wanted to glorify Simon Magus; but the motive of Philip was not self-centered; he wanted to glorify God. And the difference is as wide as the world. If your purpose in being a Christian and reading the Bible and saying your prayers and going to church is to buy the favor of God to make you healthy or to make you happy or to make you prosperous, then your religion is nothing but magic; and you deserve the word of Peter to Simon. But if you seek God as an end in himself and find him, then his favor overflows in by-products which provide these benefits.

There is an old story of the witch of Alexandria who walked

the streets armed with a pitcher of water and a flaming torch, and who cried out as she went: "Would that I could quench hell with this water and burn heaven with this torch, so that men would love God for himself alone." When you do that, then you will hear this word which comes from him whose is the last word: "Seek first his kingdom . . . and all these things shall be yours as well."

TITUS: GETTING OUT OF THE ROUGH

My chapter title comes from the title of a book on my shelves. Years ago I knew a minister named John M. Vander Meulen, president of Louisville Presbyterian Theological Seminary. During my college days he visited our campus for a week, and I can still remember the music of his voice as he talked about the meaning of our faith. But he was not only a good preacher; he was an avid golfer, and he wrote a book in which he likened the game of golf to the game of life. He called it *Getting out of the Rough*. I like it because it is realistic. It suggests that happiness is never something that you find by wishing for it: It is something you have to create, and often your only chance at it comes from a situation when the ball rolls out of the fairway and comes to rest in the rough.

For example, when Queen Mother Elizabeth of England reached her fiftieth birthday, the famous photographer Cecil

Beaton took some pictures of her. In an extravagance of tact, the photographer sent her proofs so retouched that not a wrinkle showed. Her secretary returned them with a polite note which said in effect: "Her majesty feels that, having weathered fifty years of life on earth, she would not like her photograph to suggest that she has come through completely un-scathed." In the same way it is extremely unlikely that any one of us will come through a single year completely un-scathed, and it is part of wisdom to set our sights accordingly.

I

Our thought is suggested by a young man named Titus, and the first thing he learned is that the rough is one of the facts of life that has to be taken into account.

Titus has been made immortal for us because he once received a letter from the apostle Paul. As a disciple of his master he had been left on the island of Crete in the eastern Mediterranean, and Crete was not at all a desirable place for a Christian. The situation is summarized in one verse in this letter: "One of themselves," says Paul, "a prophet of their own, said, 'Cretans are always liars, evil beasts, idle gluttons.' This testimony is true." Such is Paul's summary of the situation in Crete and of the character of the inhabitants. But listen to him as he writes to Titus: "That is why I left you in Crete, that you might amend what was defective."

That seems a queer reason for leaving a man in Crete: that the Cretans are always liars, evil beasts, idle gluttons. It sounds like a good reason for getting out of Crete, but Paul was not a man to run from the challenge of a difficult situation. There is something profoundly characteristic of the man himself and of Christianity at its best in that attitude: Crete—a hard place;

the Cretans—a bad lot; "that is why I left you in Crete."

Harry Emerson Fosdick helps us put ourselves in Titus' place as he received this letter. He supposes that it might have been a letter that Paul wrote to Titus in answer to one received from him, and it could have gone like this: "Dear Paul:" he might have said, "This is an awful place. The inhabitants are hopeless; and the poor, struggling, Christian movement is only rags and tatters. I am remaining here until you say Go, but I can't get away fast enough. For pity's sake, don't make me stay here all winter. There isn't a decent chance. Obediently but unhappily yours, Titus." And then he got this letter: "Titus," said Paul, "You are right about the Cretans. They are liars, evil beasts, idle gluttons. There isn't anything too bad that you can say about them. Crete is in deep need. For this cause I left thee in Crete."

My guess is that it was in that moment that Titus grew up into real maturity. As a young man he had supposed that experience is all fairway without any rough; but when he received that letter, he got his eyes opened to the truth that the rough is one of the facts of life and you might as well take it for granted. I read the other day about an Irishman who took our truth and put it like this: "Life," he said, "is not all you want, but it's all you've got; so stick a geranium in your cap and be happy."

I remember reading also an article by Bobby Jones on playing golf shots out of sand traps. He pointed out how few players ever practice that part of the game—and when I think about it, I remember that in thirty-four years of playing golf, I have seen many men practicing their driving and their long and short irons, but I have never seen one golfer practicing the sand shots. Bobby Jones went on to suggest that inasmuch as the best players find their way into the bunkers at least once every round, the average player should realize the importance of able recovery work. And then there was a sentence which has stayed with me word for word. "From the beginning," wrote the incomparable Bobby, "he may as well be convinced that he can never learn how to stay out of difficult situations. He will have to learn how to get out." And we might as well be convinced that we can never learn to stay out of Crete. We shall have to learn to get out.

II

The first thing Titus learned was that life is largely a matter of making the best of a bad mess. Having arrived at that point, no doubt the next thing he learned was the importance of his attitude toward life because it is one of the elemental truths of experience that you can change any situation by changing your attitude toward it.

It is just human nature that the first reaction to any Crete is a negative one, and it manifests itself in two ways. You begin by resenting it and rebelling against it. It is not difficult to picture Titus talking to himself. "Why," he would say, "wanting to do honest work in the world, should I be shoved off to this out-of-the-way place called Crete. These people are evil, and I think I am justified in feeling a righteous indignation which will tell them so and leave them to stew in their own juice." You know the reaction: Why do I have to stay married to a man like the beast my husband is; why do I have to get sick and face so large a hospital bill; why do I have to work so hard to make ends meet?

Then no doubt Titus' rebellion gave way to self-pity. "If only I could have been sent to Rome or to Ephesus or to Corinth instead of to Crete. Is there anybody who has had to take it on the chin as I have?" And you know that feeling too: if only the professor didn't have it in for me; if only I could get the breaks other people seem to get; if only I had the ability that other fellow has!

But the evidence shows that Titus changed his negative attitude to a positive one. When he landed in Crete, hoping to find it a pleasant place, he was doomed to disappointment. He walked up and down Crete looking for some sort of happiness, but it was not to be found. Because the Cretans were a bad lot, first he said, "Why?" Then he said "If"; and then he got Paul's letter. That changed everything! "The Cretans leave much to be desired, but that is why I left you in Crete." And he got the point. He had been looking for ready-made happiness; now he learns that happiness is not something you find; it is something you create, and you might as well begin in Crete as anywhere else. The entire situation was changed by a change in his attitude toward it.

I imagine that there are a good many college students who feel that they have been in Crete ever since they entered college. Take a freshman, for example. In high school he sailed along through his courses and graduated at the top of his class, made the varsity team and was president of this or that, and grew accustomed to being "big man on campus." Now, however, he is in college or university, and things are different. Courses are hard. Valedictorians are a dime a dozen, and athletes have been recruited from up and down the land. And more than once he has thought of writing a letter which goes like this: "Dear Dad: This place is awful. The food is not worth eating; the upperclassmen treat you like a dog; and the professors assign work like they think theirs is the only course you have. I'll stick it out a while longer; but when I come home for the holidays, I want to talk to you about some other plans." Suppose then his father learns about Titus, and in his talk with his son he talks like Paul and says: "Son, you are right. College is tough, but that is the reason you are there; it is supposed to make a man of you." If that boy can get the idea and change his attitude, so that he no longer thinks of college as a base from which to plan weekend pleasure trips but as an opportunity to grow up into useful manhood, then the entire situation will be changed.

Or suppose your Crete is a marriage which makes life a living hell. You had supposed that the man of your dreams would make your days like a dream; but "cloud nine" lasted no longer than the honeymoon, and now your dream has turned into a nightmare. Instead of looking forward to any happiness, you have been thinking of escaping from your Crete by way of the divorce court. Resentment against your marriage and pity for yourself have been building up in you. But suppose you changed your attitude. Suppose you learned to say: Happiness is not something you find; it is something you create, and you might as well begin in Crete as anywhere else. Once you take in the fact that a lot of people are in the same boat with you and that God stands ready to help you and wants you to succeed, then a change in attitude can bring about a change in the situation.

A famous preacher of our day says that when he was a boy his mother sent him out to pick a quart of raspberries. He did not want to pick a quart of raspberries, and he dragged reluctant feet to the berry patch in rebellion against an evil world where a small boy who wants to do something else has to pick raspberries. Then a new idea came: It would be fun to pick two quarts of raspberries and surprise the family. "That changed everything," he says. "I had so interesting a time picking two quarts of raspberries, to the utter amazement of the family, although it happened half a century ago, I have never forgotten it." That is what Titus learned: you can change any situation by changing your attitude toward it.

III

There is a third thing you learn from Titus, and it is this: Once you have accepted Crete as one of the facts of life and have adopted an attitude toward it that is positive, it is possible to do something worthwhile with it.

For example, today in Crete they are excavating the foundation of stately churches from which, in those early days when the gospel went out in the crusade against the paganism of the Roman Empire, came teachers, preachers, and missionaries of the cross. Whose name, do you think, is on those churches? Titus! Whose shrines were built there? Titus'! And that, in the same place from which he could not get away soon enough! Crete made Titus a saint; and Titus made Crete a powerful center of Christian influence.

The first professional golf tournament I ever saw was in Tampa down in Florida. Walter Hagen, one of the fabled figures in the game, came up to the last hole needing a birdie to win. The eighteenth was a par five; he put his drive right down the middle, then pushed his second into a sand trap, twenty-five yards from the green. Those of us who watched didn't see how he could possibly get down in two, but it did not seem to bother the Haig. He reached into his bag for his wedge, stepped into the sand, took his swing, and the ball dropped dead to the pin. He walked up to it, tapped it in, and walked off with the tournament.

It was also in Tampa that I saw the drama of Titus re-enacted not only on the golf course but in closer parallel in a church. A large segment of the population is Latin, and the people live in what is called Ybor City. There was a small church there which had fallen on evil days, and the Home Mission board sent a young man to revive it. Within a week after he arrived he came to my study, and I have never seen a more depressed man in my life. He told me he knew the situation was bad, but it was far worse than he supposed. The building was in a bad state of repair; half the members could not be found; there were no deacons; there were only two elders, and one of them was a Communist! When he left my study, he had made up his mind to get out of his Crete as fast as he could.

I have never known what changed his mind. It could be that he had a letter from the secretary of the board like the one Titus received from Paul: "Dear Walter: You are right. Ybor City is a tough place, but that is the reason we sent you there." Anyway, Walter Passiglia went to work, and he is still working there; and in these thirty-one years he has seen the desert blossom as the rose. Long ago the numbers grew so that a large new building was constructed, and from that church young men have done into the ministry and young women into full-time church work, and Mr. Passiglia today is one of the first citizens of Tampa. Ybor City made Walter Passiglia a man, and Walter Passiglia made Ybor City a powerful center of Christian influence.

When you translate that sort of thing into personal experience, you find it going on all around you. I know a college freshman who told me he remembers the very night he changed his attitude toward his Crete: He decided he was going to make something out of it so that it could make something out

143

of him, and he went on to graduate at the head of his class. I know a married man who told me he has never forgotten the day he and his wife decided they were going to make something out of their Crete: Today their marriage has grown more meaningful with the years. And through his writings I am acquainted with a man named Paul who put it like this: "In any and all circumstances I have learned the secret of facing plenty and hunger, abundance and want. I can do all things in him who strengthens me."

A Whisper
in the Wind

A Whisper in the Wind

BOOK TWO
OF
THE DALTON SAGA

B. J. HOFF

ABBEY PRESS
St. Meinrad, Indiana 47577

COVER ILLUSTRATION: Douglas C. Klauba

Library of Congress Catalog Number
87-70529
ISBN 0-87029-200-5

For Jim,
For Mother,
For Dana and Jessie...
Bail ó Dhia ort

A Whisper in the Wind

Thunder on the mountain
 or a whisper in the wind—
Truth will speak
 until Its voice is heard.

B. J. Hoff

PROLOGUE

Washington, D.C., 1845

"It's absolutely imperative that Dalton never know of your association with us." The cold, thin voice belonged to a man of great influence and small conscience—a man with the power to make presidents, wreck careers, create laws, and destroy lives.

"I understand, sir." The reply came from a dark-haired young man with a dream, an ambition, and a secret.

"You know what's expected of you?"

"Yes, sir, I do. I'm to advise you of his movements and how our strategies appear to be affecting him. Should he vary his routine significantly or react in a way we haven't anticipated, I will inform you at once." He blinked his dark eyes rapidly as he recited the words by rote.

The older man nodded and lightly drummed his well-manicured fingertips on the shining surface of his desk. "Very well. Your research would seem to be thorough. It's perfectly obvious the only weapon we have is his wife. Threatening Dalton himself would be futile, a total waste of time."

"Yes, sir. He seems to be entirely without fear for himself. But he's absolutely besotted with the woman."

"A common enough affliction—and a definite weakness. All right; we'll begin immediately. His wife arrives tomorrow?"

"Yes. Midafternoon."

The man behind the enormous desk brushed a dot of

9

imaginary lint from the lapel of his exquisitely tailored suit and rose from his chair, a signal that he was about to dismiss his informant. "Dalton will be gone when she arrives?"

The younger man quickly stood. "That's all been taken care of, sir. He'll be in Baltimore. He's asked the church caretaker to meet his wife at the train station and drive her to the parsonage. She'll be alone in the house at least until evening."

"Excellent." He studied the narrow, swarthy face opposite him for a moment, his eyes frigid and unreadable. "Before you go, I want to be sure you're perfectly clear as to the importance of this . . . effort . . . to my people—and to your future."

The slender youth moistened his lips and swallowed hard. "Yes, sir."

The impeccably groomed middle-aged man walked around his desk. "Of course you are. Do your job well, and your . . . problem . . . will cease to exist. In addition, you will assure your success in the political arena. Fail," he paused meaningfully, "and you'll spend the rest of your life as a lackey—a disgraced lackey." He smiled, a brief, chilling slash. "I want you to know that I have the fullest confidence in you."

"Yes, sir. Thank you, sir." Certain he was dismissed, he hurried from the office.

The slight man with the aristocratic features walked with easy grace to his office window and looked out on the city. *My city,* he thought, lifting his chin arrogantly. *Washington. The very word is synonymous with power,* he thought, his eyes shining with a glint approximating lust. *This is where our manifest destiny is actually born—where it's designed and planned and charted.* He tightened his jaw. *And no abolitionist pulpit pounder is going to come in and start tearing down what I've worked for years to build!*

CHAPTER
ONE

The barrel-chested carriage driver with the thick walrus mustache lumbered down from his seat and helped his passenger out of the carriage.

"Here we are then, missus," he announced soberly, lifting her small valise from the back of the carriage. "Safe and sound at the parsonage, just as the pastor instructed." He tucked the valise under his arm and started briskly up the walk, stopping just long enough to open the iron gate for Kerry, who could barely keep up with his long-legged stride.

As she scurried along behind him, Kerry stared at his broad, perspiration-stained back with a prickle of irritation. She would have preferred a leisurely first look at her new home. Instead, she was forced to take in as much detail as possible while they hurried along.

Her peevish mood wasn't the fault of the taciturn driver, she silently chided herself. Perhaps it was the result of the oppressive August heat. Jess had been right; he'd warned her that Washington's muggy summer temperatures were drastically different from the brisk fresh air of West Point. In addition, the rough carriage ride from the railway station had taken its toll; Kerry was feeling definitely squeamish.

But then, her stomach had been somewhat undependable for several months now, she admitted to herself with a smile. Making an effort to smooth her rumpled skirt, she discreetly touched her rounded abdomen.

"Ah, my little love, just you be patient a bit longer now," she murmured. "We'll soon be having us a proper rest. And

11

best of all, your Da will be joining us before the night ends."

Unable to keep up with the driver any longer, Kerry deliberately stopped to catch her breath a few feet from the porch. She tilted her head back and gazed up at the giant oaks which stood like matched sentries guarding the house. The highest branches from one tree searched out branches from the other. Where they met, they entwined like giant tentacles and formed a massive arch that framed the house.

Kerry remembered the description they'd received a few weeks ago from one of the deacons. It made the parsonage sound impressively attractive. She supposed it was a grand enough dwelling, looking at it from the outside. It was far more elegant than the average parsonage, Jess had written in one of his first letters to her. There was even a brick carriage house off to the side. And hadn't Jess mentioned a pond and a caretaker's cottage in back? Why then did she find its stately appearance oddly intimidating, even sinister?

Startled by her own thoughts, she felt an icy rivulet of fear creep down her spine. *Sure and the heat is working on my brain,* she thought, glancing at the overcast sky. The driver had mentioned an approaching summer storm; now she could feel the stifling closeness in the air as the sky grew dark with low, threatening clouds.

Returning to her study of the parsonage, Kerry noticed that the old red bricks were in good condition, as were the black shutters framing the long, narrow windows. Perhaps it was only the untended shrubbery and randomly scattered enormous old trees that made the property appear neglected; for, in truth, the house itself seemed to have had good care.

She gave her flower-trimmed bonnet a gentle tug, allowing it to fall and hang idly about her neck by its ribbons while she removed her white silk gloves. A slight breeze stirred; she sighed with relief.

"I'll just unlock the house for you, missus, and then bring in the rest of your luggage," the man said, not meeting her gaze.

Murtagh Mackenzie was his name, he'd told her at the railway station, introducing himself as caretaker of both the church and the parsonage. That had been his only attempt at conversation, and even it was made with seeming reluctance.

Kerry offered him a weak smile, puffed her way up the

steps to the white-pillared porch, and followed him through the door. He set her valise in a corner of the large, paneled reception hall and shambled back outside to get the rest of her things from the carriage. While she waited for him to return, Kerry appraised the dark, formal hall.

Its parquet floor was clean and unmarred, and the rich walnut paneling had been rubbed to a satin sheen. For some reason, though, she found the room funereal.

A finely carved staircase flanked the reception area. She studied it with awed appreciation while Mackenzie brought in her luggage and carried it upstairs.

"Why, this place is a veritable mansion, it is!" she said aloud as her gaze followed the line of the intricately scrolled balusters upward. "Wait until Molly sees that stairway—and all this lovely wood!" For a moment she forgot her initial feelings of disenchantment, thinking instead of the way her housekeeper's eyes would bug when she walked into the reception hall.

When Mackenzie returned, he handed her a large ring of keys. "Will you be needing anything else for now, missus?"

"No, thank you, Mr. Mackenzie. Oh, but I must pay you, of course."

He shook his head vigorously. "No need for that, missus. The pastor has hired me for part-time work." He started out the door, pushed his cap onto his head, then turned. "Most folks just call me Mack or Mackenzie."

The large man nearly filled the doorway, and his stern face refused to soften even a trace. Still, Kerry believed she saw a glimpse of kindness in his dark gray eyes. She smiled warmly at him. "Then I shall be seeing you often—Mackenzie—if you're going to be working for us. I'm certainly obliged to you for meeting me in Jess's—the pastor's—absence."

"Good day for now, missus. And welcome to Washington, I'm sure." He lifted his cap and immediately set it back onto his balding head.

"Ah . . . Mackenzie?"

He half turned from outside the door. His spectacles slipped downward a notch over the wide bridge of his nose, and he pushed them up into place with his index finger.

"I'm Irish, too, you know."

"Yes, missus," he replied gravely.

Kerry decided she would make him smile before he left the house. "And our housekeeper, Molly Larkin—she'll be arriving in just a few days—she's from Ireland also. She appears to be quite fierce, but she's not at all. I'm sure the two of you will get along very well indeed."

He nodded, his expression never changing.

"Well," Kerry said uncertainly, "I suppose you need to be going then?"

"Aye, that I do. If you'd be needing any help before the pastor arrives this evening, my house is out back. I'll be working over at the church for a bit, but no more than an hour or two."

Pleased, for this was his lengthiest conversation since they'd met, Kerry smiled at him again. "Thank you, Mackenzie. It's a relief to know I can call on you."

Once more he lifted his cap and turned to go.

Finally alone, Kerry stood unmoving in the reception hall for a long moment. Then she began to walk slowly toward the parlor, her short, hesitant footsteps echoing about her.

Just inside the doorway she stopped, studying with some misgiving the darkly shadowed room. The parlor was austere to the point of being bleak.

She suddenly wished that Jess had chosen to stay here at the parsonage during the three weeks they'd been apart rather than at a hotel. *I'd not be having these creepy feelings,* she thought, *if the place had been more recently lived in—especially by my Jess.*

Kerry also wished, even more fervently, that he was here with her this very moment so she could lean into his tall, unflinching strength, instead of standing here uneasy and uncertain.

It had been a terrible disappointment, being met at the railway station by Mackenzie instead of by Jess. The burly Irishman had informed her, in as few words as possible, that Jess had been prevailed upon by the family of one of his parishioners to accompany them to a burial service in Baltimore.

Kerry had come close to tears but brightened quickly when she learned that Jess would be returning to Washington that evening. Mackenzie had given her a note from Jess,

14

filled with his regrets and assurances that he'd meet her at the parsonage that evening with *"far more eagerness than decency allows me to admit . . ."* How she longed for him to come sweeping through that massive front door and gather her into his strong, protective arms. He would dip his head down and whisper a soft, intimate greeting of love, just as he had each evening at their house at West Point.

With a firm shake of her head, Kerry dismissed her reverie and turned her attention to the parlor. Its paneled walls were a dark gray, well kept but depressing. Its widely planked floor was highly polished and protected only by a worn but still serviceable Aubusson. Each correctly placed piece of furniture looked stiff and uncomfortable and only intensified Kerry's initial impression of grim formality. With great resolve, she walked briskly across the room to open the dark velvet drapes, allowing the dim outside light to filter through the room.

A sudden, cold touch of warning caused her to whirl around from the window. "Jess?" She waited, listening, half-expecting to see someone else in the room. She knew she was being foolish, yet she felt gripped by dread. The thick copper curls at the back of her neck felt as if they were standing on end. "Is someone here?"

Her voice sounded ridiculously childlike, she thought. *And why not?* she scolded herself angrily. *I'm behaving like a wee wane!*

Swallowing with difficulty, Kerry made a brave attempt to submerge the fear battering at her stomach. She wondered anxiously if the babe she was carrying could sense her terror. For that very reason, she must get herself under control. She must not endanger the child, especially with superstitious nonsense.

She was uncomfortably reminded of Dr. Green's words when he'd put her to bed this last time, no more than a week before Jess had left for Washington to assume his pastorate: "I'm not trying to frighten you, Mrs. Dalton, and I'm certain there's no need to be overly concerned so long as you take care. However, this is the third time you've experienced these pains. I believe we must consider them to be warnings. From now on, you simply must refrain from even the slightest form of exertion. You'll have to spend most of your remaining four months in bed, I'm afraid. There's simply no help to be had for it."

The doctor had given Kerry his permission to travel to Washington only after realizing how depressed and anxious she was without Jess. She had pacified both the doctor and Molly by assuring them that she had written to Jess, that he would be meeting her at the station, and that she would go directly to bed and stay there for the duration. She had reasoned with Molly that she'd be no help at all in closing up the house at West Point and attending to the other last-minute details that had to be finalized before their move.

She smiled to herself now as she thought of Molly bustling around in furious fashion; the practical-minded housekeeper considered wasting time to be a most grievous sin. If Kerry knew Molly at all, she knew she'd be arriving in Washington within a day or two at the most.

Her thoughts returned to Jess, and her eyes danced with fond amusement as she imagined his surprise when he saw how round she'd grown in only three weeks. Wringing her hands together impatiently, she glowed with the thought that soon she could once more bury her head in the safe, warm haven of her husband's strong shoulder. They would talk about his new pastorate, the "weesy one," as Molly referred to their unborn child, and all that had happened since they'd been apart. Everything would be lovely.

For now, though, she must get on with her tour of the house. Afterwards, she would rest so she'd be fresh and clearheaded for the reunion with Jess.

Gathering her long skirts just above her ankles, Kerry left the parlor, stopping only once to glance behind her before making her way to the kitchen.

"Sure and I hope all the rooms aren't as cold and unfriendly as that parlor," she mumbled to herself.

The dining room, however, did nothing to reassure her. It was damp and drearily formal, with its enormous mahogany table and chairs and heavy, gray drapes. The large, elaborately carved fireplace gave the room its only semblance of warmth.

Shuddering with dismay, Kerry entered the kitchen expecting the worst. But the large, comfortable room evoked a long sigh of relief; it was far more welcoming and cheerful than she'd anticipated. In front of a wide, brightly curtained window, she was delighted to see a child's replica of the long pine table and chairs that occupied most of the center area of the room. All the furniture, including the massive corner cupboard, appeared to be plainly and sturdily constructed and well used.

Perhaps I'll just stay in here until Jess arrives, she thought to herself, knowing full well that her inquisitive nature would allow her to do no such thing. She decided to explore no further downstairs but to have a look at the second floor. After peering up the dark flight of steps leading off the kitchen, she immediately returned to the reception hall to use the front stairway.

By the time she reached the landing of the second floor, Kerry was breathless and had to stop to rest. After a moment, she moved slowly down the dim, narrow hall, stopping to open the first door on her left. When it revealed only a small linen closet, she went on. The next door opened onto what was obviously the master bedroom.

Sure and Molly will be calling this place the "house of shadows," she thought with a grim smile. She held onto the door frame for a moment to ease the shortness of breath that plagued her more and more often. Glancing around the room with a critical eye, she decided that the former occupants, devoted servants of the Lord though they might have been, must have also been of sour and dolorous natures. The room was as dark and intimidating as the parlor. An enormous bed with a towering headboard dominated the entire room; its wood was so dark as to be almost black. The dressing table was massive and looked like a museum piece. Only a big, sturdy-looking rocking chair close to the fireplace cheered her spirits. At least the room wasn't totally bereft of human comforts.

Ah, well, Jess always said that Molly could work her domestic magic with even the most miserable of dwellings. Certainly the gloomy parsonage would offer a challenge.

She suddenly felt a terrible longing for the staunch Irish housekeeper who had so readily and willingly taken Kerry under her wing that bright autumn day three years past when, as the reluctant ward of Jess Dalton, the Academy chaplain, she arrived at West Point. She had grown to love Molly as much as she thought she would have loved her own mother, had she ever known her.

Hesitantly, she walked the rest of the way into the bedroom. She knew her imagination must be playing tricks on her, but once more she was overwhelmed by an oppressive sense of something not quite right about the house. It felt especially strong in this room.

Kerry wondered if carrying a child would give a woman these peculiar sensations. But wouldn't Molly have told her so if that were the case? Sure and she'd appointed herself as Kerry's advisor in all other matters, even to sitting her down and giving her her bride's advice on the eve of her wedding day.

She thought then of Jess and smiled longingly—her dear, beloved Jess. He had been certain that the fourteen years' difference in their ages would prohibit her from loving him, when in truth she had loved him almost from the day she first arrived at West Point. He was a mountain of a man, both physically and in every other way. She missed him to the point of grief when they were apart. But he'd soon be gathering her into his embrace again, and all these silly fears would vanish.

So determined was she to banish as much of her uneasiness as possible, Kerry nearly managed to ignore the slightly swaying shadow beside the chest of drawers in the corner. When it moved again, she straightened her shoulders and thrust out her chin—though she could feel her lower lip trembling. Walking stiffly and determinedly in the direction of the subtle movement, she felt all the while the forbidding darkness closing in on her.

Jess had often said that fear was the hammer of Satan; well, she wouldn't be allowing Satan to pound at her with that or any other of his tools. She would face squarely on whatever was moving there in the corner.

Her resolve weakened somewhat when she saw the shadow weave ever so slightly to the right, then back to the left. *Reflections from the outside, no doubt.* Still, Kerry's mouth went dry and her breath caught in the tightness of her throat. She wiped her hands uncertainly on the skirt of her dress, wanting very much to bolt from the room and run from the house. But she kept walking.

In the silence of the room, she could hear the rapid pounding of her heart. The breath she struggled for was shaky, making her sudden explosion of laughter all the more startling when, with her hands clasped thankfully across her bosom, she met her terror face to face . . . or rather, face to form. There in the dark swayed a dress form, dimmed and brightened by ebbing shadows from a slightly open window.

Framing her face with her hands and weak with relief, she allowed herself the luxury of a feeble laugh at her own foolishness. "Ah, Kerry O'Neill Dalton, to think that you'll be having a child of your own one day soon, when if the truth be told, you're still a fanciful child yourself!"

Her feelings of foreboding now discharged, she whispered a brief, fervent prayer of thanks and started toward the rocking chair for a moment's rest. Smiling to herself as she glanced again at the dressmaker's form that had caused her panic, she stated merrily, "I'll not be telling my Jess what a silly lass his wife is. Sure and we wouldn't want him to be having second—"

Her words were cut off by an unexpected roar of thunder which at the same time muffled her blood-chilling scream of terror as two burly arms imprisoned her. A crashing blow to her head sent her reeling to the floor.

Unconscious, Kerry was blissfully unaware of the hulking shape that crouched over her. Her assailant tightly gagged her and tied her hands behind her back with a piece of rough rope. She had no knowledge of the cruel way her body was pushed and shoved into a bulky burlap sack and then carried clumsily down the stairs to a waiting carriage in the back of the house.

CHAPTER
TWO

Kerry awoke painfully to a darkness streaked with angry, frightening colors. She felt a sudden, hard jolt to her body, as if someone had kicked her down a flight of stairs. Weak and disoriented, she struggled to fight her way to consciousness.

The darkness engulfing her was more stifling than the gag that had been stuffed into her mouth to choke her screams of fear and rage. She gathered her wits enough to realize that she was trapped in some sort of covering. She couldn't move her hands, bound as they were behind her back. Worst of all was the way her body was bent, nearly doubled and crammed into an incredibly small space. She felt bruised and shaken, as if she'd been punched over and over again.

Tears of panic scalded her eyes and ran unchecked down her face, collecting in the rag that had been cruelly stuffed into her mouth and fastened tightly behind her head. She tried to scream for help, but the gag kept her from making a sound. She tried to pray but was too stricken with fear to do more than cry silently for the Lord to rescue her. She needed Jess, desperately needed his presence, his strength. She needed Molly, craved her indomitable spirit, her unshakable courage.

But there was no one, no one but an unseen, unknown captor. She was totally alone—alone in the darkness with her fears, her soundless prayer, and her unborn child.

Oh, Father, help me. Help my babe. Please, Lord, protect my babe.

A sudden thrill of relief surged through her when she felt something slide away from her head. Whatever she'd been trapped in was being removed. Large calloused hands pulled her free of what seemed to be a formless burlap bag. She was being rescued! Someone had found her!

But one glance at the face hovering inches from her own dispelled any hope she might have had for freedom. The man's head was large and oddly swollen. His wide-set eyes were pale and sullenly vacant of expression. His nose leaned to one side, giving the appearance of having been broken several times. Scar-layered skin stretched tightly over his blotched face, and he was completely bald. The man's misshapen skull had obviously been badly burned at some time in the past.

Kerry had seen more than her share of horrors among the destitute squatters in Ireland. More than once she'd tended the infants of starving, half-dead mothers, infants born with hideous deformities. She had prepared bloated, blackened bodies for burial when she was no more than a child herself, and she'd looked death in its ugly face all the way across the sea in the coffin ship that brought them to America. But never before had she seen a human being so miserably deformed. Had she not been so totally terrified of the man and her situation, she would have felt an instant wave of pity for him. As it was, she could only stare at him, wide-eyed with fear.

He said nothing, but continued to remove the burlap covering from around her. Kerry looked at him with a pleading stare, waiting for him to remove the gag from her mouth. But he left it in place. She felt a torrent of nausea crash against her; for an instant she was certain she would faint. When the man stretched out his enormous hand to touch her face, she recoiled as if he'd slapped her.

He cocked his head and stared stupidly at her. Finally, he removed the gag but immediately covered her mouth with his hand for another moment.

"Keep quiet," he ordered. He slowly removed his hand from her mouth as if testing her obedience.

"Wh—who are you?" Her voice was no more than a fragile thread of terror.

He gave her an angry, disapproving frown and shook his

head vigorously as he untied her hands. "I said don't talk."

His voice was thick and deep. The effort those few words seemed to require of him, plus the empty, fixed stare of his eyes, alerted Kerry that he was dimwitted at best. Even in the throes of panic, her protective instincts for herself and her unborn child asserted themselves; her quick mind began to spin with a number of possible escape routes.

Her captor sat on his haunches and watched her quietly for a moment, then hauled himself clumsily to his feet and took a few steps away from her.

Kerry glanced quickly and uneasily about her surroundings. Her mind was darting too erratically to assimilate everything, but she knew she was in a basement. It was cool, dark, and smelled of mildew, dust, and grime. The only light was a gray ribbon from a small, dirty window high on the wall against which her captor was leaning.

The floor was unbelievably filthy; she instinctively grimaced with distaste when she saw the grime clinging to her dress. Her gaze moved furtively to the rotting wooden steps that led straight up. She couldn't see to the top; it was too dark. Her heart pumped a bit faster as she considered her chances.

The hulking man propped against the dirty block wall seemed only half aware of her presence. A large rat had caught his attention. The frightened creature squirmed under the heel of the man's heavy, boot-clad foot, twisting and squealing in a futile attempt to break free. Kerry watched the despised rodent with horror, cringing at its plight, so similar to her own.

She took advantage of the brute's preoccupation by appraising her surroundings thoroughly, trying to ignore the frequent cramping in her abdomen. Again, her glance went to the stairs, then to the corner beneath them where a large shovel rested. She looked from the shovel to the man, who had now stooped down to study his prey more closely. Only a few feet lay between him and the shovel.

Kerry drew in a deep, steadying breath and turned a determined, fierce glare at the man. "I demand to know why you've brought me here! You've hurt me, you know!"

He lifted his head and stared at her with dull indifference. "For the chief. You be quiet."

"What chief? What do you want with me?" Kerry cried.

He scowled at her for a long moment, and she wondered if she should have held her silence. Then, as if he hadn't heard her, the man returned his attention to the rat.

Kerry chewed her lower lip, then decided she had nothing to lose. "Why don't you put it in the bucket if you want to play with it?"

He looked up at her, puzzled.

"The rat," she said, glancing down at the creature beneath his boot. "You're going to lose it if you don't put it in something. There's a bucket over there by the window."

He studied her for a long moment, then turned slowly to scan the wall behind him, keeping his one foot steady and heavy on the rat. Kerry knew she had to act quickly but felt an instant of paralyzing uncertainty. Feeling her heart stop, she drew in a deep gulp of air and dashed to the corner beneath the steps. She grabbed the shovel.

He heard her movement, but his awkward position threw him just enough off balance to make him clumsy. Before he could react, Kerry lunged straight at him with the shovel raised high above her head.

He roared and made a dive for her legs, but he was too big and too slow. Though stiff from her previous confinement and somewhat awkward with the child she carried, Kerry was small and fast—and desperate. She came at her captor like a wild animal and brought the shovel down on his head with all her strength. He fell, landing flat on his face. Kerry heard a sickening thud as his head hit the floor.

She hoisted her skirts, raced up the stairs, and yanked furiously at the chipped doorknob until the swollen door finally gave way. Taking no thought of her surroundings, Kerry ran through an empty pantry and an airless, foul-smelling kitchen. Ahead of her she spied a dirty white door with broken panes of glass. She nearly tripped in her haste to reach it, mumbling a prayer of thanks when she found it unlocked. Flinging it open, she bolted outside and fled down sagging wooden steps into a yard littered with garbage and debris.

She halted only long enough to look around in panic, trying to gain a sense of direction. After a moment, she took off running toward what appeared to be a road behind a dilapidated carriage house at the rear of the lot.

Screaming, she raced into a street thick with mud from an earlier rainstorm. Crazed with fear, Kerry stopped long enough to pull the shoes from her feet and fling them aside before resuming her flight.

She was vaguely aware of sagging frame buildings and the smell of decay. She almost ran into an abandoned cart, slipped, regained her balance, and went on. Hot tears of panic blinded her as she ran, and the brief, sharp cramps she'd experienced earlier intensified to fierce spasms that nearly stopped her getaway. But she continued to run, crying and screaming Jess's name. She ran as though death itself was chasing her until one huge crushing wave of pain brought her down, hurling her to her knees in the mud. A blanket of terrifying darkness began to drape itself around her. She cried for Jess once more, then surrendered to the yawning whirlpool of oblivion.

CHAPTER THREE

Jess was impatient. He wouldn't have stopped by his office at the church at all if Charles Payne, his secretary, hadn't accompanied him and the White family to Baltimore. Upon their return, Charles needed to stop by the office to get his carriage.

Jess had declined his secretary's offer to drop him at home. Thanks to his years of daily crossing the grounds at West Point, walking was as natural to him as breathing. He could cover the short distance from the church to the parsonage on Lafayette Square in only moments.

It was nearly dusk by the time he approached the parsonage. His heart began to thud heavily with anticipation. How he had missed his beloved Kerry. Only three weeks parted, but it felt more like three years. His days had been somber and meaningless without her smile; the nights had seemed endless.

If ever a man loved a woman to the point of desperation, he thought as he increased his already brisk stride, certainly his love for Kerry bordered on it. These past three weeks had taught him how utterly dismal and empty his life would be without her. His waking hours were filled with the memory of her dancing emerald eyes, the dimpled smile that could sparkle a generous dose of mischief as readily as affection, and a softly curling riot of copper hair that never failed to fascinate him. His dreams were filled with a love so passionately intense, yet so tenderly sweet, that he sometimes struggled with feelings of guilt.

He had promised his Lord and himself, when he'd first accepted the call to the ministry, that nothing would ever take precedence in his heart over his servanthood to Christ. While he believed with all his heart that his and Kerry's love was God-ordained, a priceless gift from their creator, the depth of his love for her occasionally frightened him. At those times, he would have to force himself to surrender even this, his heart's devotion to this small, fiery wisp of a girl, and ask his Lord to keep that love from becoming an obsession.

At this particular moment, attempts to bring his excitement under control were in vain. He was practically running by now, at the same time craning his neck for a glimpse of the stately brick parsonage which sat a sedate distance back from the street.

She should have arrived hours ago. Would she be fretful that he hadn't met her at the station as he'd promised? Ah, well, he'd rid her of her peevishness in short order. His smile transformed his care-lined face into a younger countenance. He was dusty and hot and rumpled. His curly mane of black and silver hair badly needed brushing; even his beard bore the evidence of a harried journey on a hot August day. But more than anything else, he was a man aglow as he raced those last few feet to the walkway of his house.

He stopped, puzzled, when he saw an unfamiliar buggy tied in front. Entering the gate, he saw that the front door was open, and Mackenzie was standing just outside it on the porch. He was turning his head this way and that as if watching for someone.

Jess glanced once more over his shoulder at the buggy, then back to the caretaker as he made quick work of the remaining few steps to the porch.

"Mack?" He nodded to the big, stern-faced Irishman. "What are you about so late in the day? Have you just arrived with my wife?" He peered hopefully inside the door.

Jess stared with surprise as the burly caretaker raised a large, calloused hand to block his entrance. The deep frown of concern on Mackenzie's face triggered a sudden sense of impending disaster.

"What is it, Mack?"

"Pastor, it's bad trouble you have, I fear," the big man muttered grimly.

"Trouble?" Jess suddenly found it difficult to breathe. "What kind of trouble? Kerry?"

Mackenzie heaved a sigh of regret. "She's been put to bed, sir. She's upstairs, and she'll be all right. But you've trouble all the same." Jess stared at him for a long moment, unwilling to discover what awaited him inside the house. He had a sudden, irrational desire to delay the encounter as long as possible, but a sharp stab of fear quickly overcame his hesitancy.

"Kerry—" He hurled himself through the door and took the stairs two and three at a time.

Adeline Corbett, his widowed neighbor, stood at the top of the staircase talking with a man Jess instantly recognized: George Marshall, a member of his congregation, a physician, and undoubtedly the owner of the buggy outside. They turned to Jess; he nearly stopped dead on the stairs when he saw the pained expressions on their faces.

Reaching the landing, he looked from one to the other with a growing sense of dread. "What is it? What's happened?"

Mrs. Corbett touched his arm uncertainly. Her usually flawless coiffure was in disarray, her clear blue eyes kind and concerned. "Mr. Dalton—"

By now, Jess was frantic beyond civility. "Where is she? What's wrong?"

"Pastor, please don't go in there just yet," the doctor said firmly, inclining his head toward the closed bedroom door. "Your wife has had a terrible experience, and there are a few things you need to know before you see her."

A wave of impatience washed over Jess, followed by raw fear. "What are you talking about? Is she ill?"

Dr. Marshall placed a strong, restraining hand on Jess's elbow. "Mr. Dalton, listen to me. Apparently your wife was— abducted. She's been injured. I've given her laudanum to make her more comfortable and to calm her."

"Abducted!" Jess wrested himself out of Dr. Marshall's grasp and moved toward the door of the bedroom, but the doctor stopped him again, this time with a sharp command.

"Pastor!" He immediately softened his tone when he saw the stricken look of disbelief on Jess's face. "Mrs. Dalton is all right. But I'm afraid . . ." His voice drifted off, and he shifted his gaze away from the intense emotion he saw in Jess's eyes.

"The baby?" Jess mumbled hoarsely.

Dr. Marshall shook his head. "I'm so sorry. I couldn't save the child."

"Our baby is—dead?" Jess repeated in a hoarse whisper.

Again the doctor nodded. "I tried everything I know, Pastor, believe me. But your wife was badly hurt. She appears to have been pushed or dropped from a considerable height, perhaps a flight of stairs."

He spoke hurriedly, tapping one wrist with a white envelope that he was holding in the other hand. "Somehow she got away. Apparently, she ran until she passed out. She must not have been all that far away because she got within a few houses of the parsonage. One of your neighbors saw her from a window and went to help. She said Mrs. Dalton was calling your name before she fainted. The lady who found her screamed for help, and Mackenzie heard her from his cottage. He carried your wife out of the street, then came for me."

Jess shook his head back and forth in stunned confusion. "Abducted? Who would do such a thing to her?" He turned anxious, hurting eye toward Mrs. Corbett. "Does Kerry—does my wife know about the baby?"

The silver-haired woman's eyes filled with tears. "Oh, Mr. Dalton, I'm so sorry. Yes, she knows."

"What she doesn't know yet," the doctor interrupted hesitantly, clearing his throat, "is just as bad, I'm afraid."

The big pastor towered over the small, sandy-haired doctor. Jess was a man accustomed to having people turn in the street and take a second look at him because of his uncommon stature and powerful physique. Yet, at this instant, he felt much like a small boy, a small frightened boy who knew he was about to hear something dreadful, something that would alter his entire life.

"Mr. Dalton," the doctor glanced uneasily at Adeline Corbett, who turned away and walked down the hall to give them privacy. He laid his hand on Jess's coat sleeve in a gesture of comfort. "Pastor, I'm terribly sorry, but Mrs. Dalton—well, there can be no other children. She was so badly injured . . ." He left his sentence unfinished.

Jess had known words could wound; he had felt their stab of agony more than once in his life. He had seen others reel beneath the assault of words that spoke of incurable illness, the passing of a loved one, or the destruction of something that had taken a lifetime to build. He knew the power of words to open or crush the heart.

Yet, all his years of experience as a minister, chaplain, and counselor hadn't prepared him for the pain that now slashed through his soul at the doctor's announcement. His grief wasn't only for himself; it was more for Kerry. With an aching heart, he knew what this would do to his beloved, the burden of sorrow it would place upon her spirit.

He swallowed once, then again with great difficulty. Meeting the doctor's gaze, he asked, "You're certain?"

George Marshall nodded sadly. "I'm sorry, Pastor, truly I am." He drew a deep breath, then said more firmly, "I wouldn't want to minimize your wife's condition. She's suffered major internal injuries and severe hemorrhaging. Actually, she should be hospitalized, but I'm reluctant to move her. Mrs. Corbett mentioned a housekeeper. Will she be available to help care for Mrs. Dalton?"

Jess rubbed the back of one hand over his eyes and tried to grab onto at least a thread of reason. His voice was tremulous and uncertain. "Molly—yes. She should be here within the next few days."

"Good. I'm sure Mrs. Corbett and some of the other women in the church will help until then." He hesitated for an instant, glancing down at the envelope in his hand. "Pastor, this was brought to the house no more than a few moments after I arrived to tend to your wife." He handed the envelope to Jess. "Mackenzie said a Negro child delivered it saying a gentleman had given it to him with the instruction that you were to read it right away."

Bewildered, Jess ripped open the message and began to read, stiffening with shock as he scanned the words. His chest tightened, and an excruciating pain assaulted his head. He felt the hot taste of nausea well up in his throat, and for an instant he nearly staggered. The note had been scrawled in large, childlike print: *You can have the woman back if you agree to take her and your abolitionist garbage and go back to the North where you belong. There's no room for you in this city. You'll be contacted in a few hours for your answer.*

He dangled the note from trembling fingers for a moment, then extended it to the doctor. He read it quickly, glowering with angry indignation.

"They wrote this not knowing she got away," he said tightly, glancing up at Jess. "As I said, it came only moments after I arrived."

Jess clenched his hands into rigid fists, fighting to put down the lashing waves of rage and fear roaring through him. Something deep inside him felt as if it were about to explode and shatter his sanity, but he knew he had to hold himself together for Kerry's sake.

He started to speak but the words choked in his throat. Putting out a hand to steady himself on the domed newel post of the stairway, he pulled in a deep breath and said in a ragged, pain-dulled voice, "Doctor, could you please— would you do just two things for me?"

"Anything I can, Pastor," the doctor answered quickly.

"Would you call the authorities and ask them to come? Then get a message to General Cummins for me. Ask him if he'll have Molly Larkin, my housekeeper, contacted at West Point. Tell her she's to leave there immediately. Kerry needs her."

"I'll see to it right away. And I'll return in a few hours to check on Mrs. Dalton."

Jess's mouth was now set in a hard, determined line. "Now, I've got to see my wife. Please!"

"Of course. But she may not be aware that you're with her, Pastor. If she does wake up, you mustn't let her become agitated again. She's already far too weak."

Jess nodded, taking an unsteady step toward the bedroom door. He hesitated and turned back to Dr. Marshall. "Doctor, the baby . . ."

The small, sad-faced doctor met his gaze with understanding. "A boy."

Jess looked away from him toward the wall, the stairway, then to Adeline Corbett. He nodded, a gesture of terrible, helpless grief. A son; he had had a son. "Where is he?"

"Everything has been taken care of, Pastor," the doctor replied gently. "We'll discuss arrangements later after you've had some time with your wife."

Jess turned away and walked to the closed door of the bedroom. He stopped for only an instant, drew in another long, unsteady breath, and lifted his shoulders. *Help me bear this, Father. Help me endure this for her—to be strong—for her.*

With only her pale oval face visible from beneath the lightweight blanket, Kerry looked like a child. Two unhealthy circles of red darkened her cheeks. Otherwise, she was white and drawn, her profile oddly serene. Her eyes were closed, and her breathing was shallow but even. A faint suggestion of pain hovered about her mouth.

The rocking chair he had bought especially for her sat near the bed, and Jess now moved it even closer. Not taking his eyes from Kerry's face, he quietly removed his black suit coat and laid it gently on the foot of the bed. He sank into the rocker and reached for her hand.

She stirred slightly but didn't awaken. He felt strangely relieved, as yet unwilling or unable to face her pain. What would he say to her? What *could* he say to her? How was he to tell her that the dream she had cherished since the early days of their engagement—and every day since—had been brutally destroyed by some unknown maniac?

I'm going to give you a house full of sons, my Jess, fine, strong sons to carry on the tradition of yourself and all the other Dalton men. We'll have us a hearth and home filled with big, curly headed sons who will idolize their father, as they should.

She had been so impressed—too impressed, he'd sometimes feared—with the generations of Dalton men who had spent their lives working to improve the lot of others, like his lawyer-father and politician-grandfather. She had promised him that together they would continue the line. He had teased her that he'd also like a little girl or two "with copper curls and shamrock eyes like their mother." His eyes burned with unshed tears when he remembered the way she had told him about their baby. She had been so impatient to begin their family. When two years passed without a child, she had begun to worry. More than once she had cried out her fears on his shoulder.

But then came the evening when he arrived at the house to find the dining room looking like something out of one of the currently popular romantic plays. The best silver and china gleamed on the lace-covered table, and the room was aglow with candlelight. Kerry wearing her deep green velvet evening gown—his favorite—looked mysterious and excited.

Her intention, she disclosed later in the evening, had been to say absolutely nothing until after dinner. But as soon as he walked into the dining room and lifted a questioning brow at the lavish table, she began to bounce from one foot to the other and wring her hands together, as she often did when she was excited. Her carefully designed strategy immediately crumbled, and she gave way to a peal of nervous laughter and a tumble of words announcing the expected event. She'd been upset with herself for hours afterward because she hadn't been able to carry off her original scenario.

Now, he leaned close to her, holding her hand and studying her slender fingers with great sadness. His eyes brimmed with tenderness and an unfathomable depth of love never seen by anyone except the young woman lying next to him.

For one bittersweet instant, he saw her again as she had appeared to him just three years past, a child-woman in a faded gingham dress and a worn black cloak. She had stepped reluctantly off the steamer at West Point, defensively clutching her small shabby valise to her side. She had been eighteen years old that bright autumn day when the defiant lift of her chin and sparkling emeralds in her eyes had gone straight to his heart and impaled him. His love had belonged to her from that moment on, though he had fought against it for months because of the vast age difference between them—and because he was, after all, supposed to be her guardian and protector.

Memories—such a wealth of memories flooded his heart as he brought her hand to his lips and held it there in a need to be as close to her as possible. His heart ached with silent words of self-recrimination and regret.

Ah, Kerry . . . mavourneen,* what have I brought you to? I've torn you away from the only real security of your life. We had so much—a home you'd grown to love, a happy life together—and I asked you to leave it all for—this?

He tried to pray and instantly felt the arid desolation of his soul. He had to force the words from his heart in an anguished whisper.

34

I thought you called me here, Lord. I was so sure it was your will and not my own. But is this what you have called me to, this monstrous, terrifying nightmare? Why . . . why would you allow this to happen to us—to this little girl who loves you so totally, so innocently? Have you brought us to this place only to break our hearts and wreck our lives? Why, Lord—why?

He shook his head in an attempt to throw off his questioning and doubt. Even now, in the midst of this unexpected sorrow, his faith and his love for his Lord had to be greater than doubt, larger than confusion.

Still, hadn't he already questioned the wisdom of leaving West Point? It had taken only days for him to discover that a strong element of hostile opposition to him was present within this new congregation. His reputation had preceded his arrival, largely because of the books and newspaper articles he'd written over the years dealing with the sin of slavery, the child labor problem, the degrading labor conditions in the factories, and the oppression and abuse of those thousands of immigrants now crowding the shores of the country.

He had discerned that for every person who wanted him here and agreed with his views on equality under God, there were three others who violently opposed him, as a minister and as a man. Many of these were politicians of great influence and power; the influential southern senator John Calhoun was one of them.

In spite of the obvious difficulties facing him, however, when he prayed for direction, his spirit sensed God's instruction to stay. But now? Kerry abducted, their child dead, and all hope of future children lost to them—and the threat of further violence implicit in the note. Would the abductors try again once they learned of her escape?

Suddenly Kerry stirred, moving her head from side to side on the pillow with a moan of protest as the fingers of her free hand fluttered lightly upon the blanket. Her eyes opened slowly, then blinked. For a moment, she stared into Jess's face with no recognition. But as he watched, he saw gradual, unwilling recollection dawn in her gaze, mirroring his own anguish and deepening to a bottomless despair.

"Jess, Oh, Jess . . ." She tried to raise herself to him, her arms reaching out to him, but he quickly restrained her, moving from the chair to the edge of the bed and gathering her gently into the circle of his arms.

He held her tenderly but securely. "Please, love, lie still. You must be very quiet for now," he murmured, pressing his lips softly against her temple.

But she wouldn't listen. She raised herself to rest her head in the hollow of his shoulder.

"No, love, don't." He felt her slender body begin to heave beneath his hands, and he thought his heart would shatter with the combined weight of their shared grief.

"Our babe—oh, Jess, our babe—"

His shirt was quickly wet with her tears, and the russet waves of her hair grew damp with his own. He groped for control, but her pain was more than he could bear.

"I know, I know, love, but you're all right, and how I thank the merciful Lord for that."

She sobbed even harder against him. "A son, Jess. I had a son for you . . . our son . . . and I never . . . even saw . . . his face."

He clung to her as though he could somehow infuse her with his own strength, unstable as it was at the moment. "Kerry, darling . . . don't . . . please. You'll hurt yourself."

". . . never drew a breath, Jess not even a breath . . ."

"Shh . . . I know, I know. But God needs little ones in his heaven, too, love, not just older souls."

". . . they wouldn't let me see him . . ."

"Yes, love, I know. But it's best that you didn't." He tried, tried with all his being not to give in to his own sorrow, but he simply couldn't control the knifing grief any longer. He wept with her, not knowing whether he was agonizing more for the loss of his son or the pain of his wife. They clung to each other and mourned together and attempted to draw strength from each other.

Finally, a long time later, Kerry was able to tell him what had happened. She described the man who had abducted her and conveyed as many details as she could remember about the house where she had been taken.

"If only I hadn't insisted on coming ahead without Molly," she sobbed. "If only I hadn't run, if I hadn't tried to get away. Perhaps our babe would have been all right, then . . ."

"Kerry—" Jess's voice was no more than a harsh whisper. "You must promise me that you'll never ever blame yourself for what happened! You did all you could—you tried to save our child—and yourself. The baby . . . the baby was most likely injured beyond help when you were . . . pushed down the stairs or whatever that monster did to you."

As if he suddenly realized he might be hurting her with his tight grasp, he relaxed his big hands and patted her reasuringly. "There's no explaining what happened today, love of my heart," he said softly. "Some things . . . we just aren't meant to understand . . . only accept."

He pushed a damp lock of hair behind her ear and kissed her forehead with infinite tenderness. "I've missed you so terribly, love."

Her voice caught on a choked sob. "Today was to have been such a happy time for us . . ."

"We'll still have our happy times, my darling," Jess attempted to soothe her. "We'll have to wait awhile for them, but we'll have them again, I promise you."

She pulled away from him enough to see his face and laid her hand gently upon his bearded cheek. "I'll have no happy times again, my Jess, until I give you a son."

Too late, he tried to stop the stricken look of dismay that glazed his face. He knew she had seen and, with the unerringly acute insight so much a part of her nature, Kerry immediately sensed his anguish.

Her eyes studied him relentlessly, and a terrible fear began to settle over her features. "Jess?" Her always husky voice darkened even more.

He could do nothing but stare at her with helpless pain.

A slow-dawning, reluctant awareness filled her gaze. "Oh, no . . ." she breathed.

His heart wrenched at the awful expression on her lovely, ravaged face. "Kerry . . . love . . ."

"No . . . please . . . nooo . . ." The chilling sound of desolation pouring from her was the ancient, grief-stricken keen of the Irish mourner.

Jess wrapped her tightly against him as though to absorb her pain into himself. "My love . . . my love . . . I'm so sorry. . . ."

"Barren . . . am I barren, Jess?" she cried against him.

"Please, no . . . not that . . . oh, please anything but that . . ."

All he could do was hold her against his aching heart. He had never felt so helpless in his life. There were no words; there was no comfort.

When Kerry finally realized he wasn't denying her protests, that her fear was an unbearable reality, she collapsed limply in his arms and gave way to a near irrational, helpless fit of weeping.

Jess continued to hold her and to make soft, soothing sounds of comfort as he tried to console her. But all the while, something dark that had been imprisoned deep inside him for the last hour banged angrily against his chest in hopeless fury, clamoring for release. A terrible, scalding rage threatened to cast aside the faith that had been a part of his life for as long as he could remember. Everything in his being cried out for revenge.

For years, he had believed himself to be a man of God, a servant. But at this moment of his life, he knew himself to be a man capable of blinding hatred. Someone should pay for what had been done to the shuddering, weeping girl in his arms. Someone must pay for destroying his beloved Kerry's dream, her hope . . . perhaps her very spirit.

CHAPTER FOUR

Kerry awoke feeling drugged and irritable. For the first time in days, the deep rose-colored bedroom drapes had been fully opened to flood the room with late-morning sunshine.

The room was stuffy, and her head pounded unmercifully as she attempted to accustom her eyes to the light. She half-rose from the pillows and squinted; someone was standing off to one side of the window.

Propping herself up on one elbow, she shielded her eyes with her hand. *"Molly!"* With a weak, relieved breath, she fell back against the pillows. "Oh, Molly—I'm so glad you're here." Her voice was no more than a broken whisper.

The tall, strapping housekeeper walked toward the bed. As usual, her silver braids were arranged in a perfect crown atop her head, and her sturdy, corseted body was encased in one of her immaculate white shirtwaists and a sensible brown skirt.

She came to stand beside the bed and folded her arms over her ample bosom. Gazing down at Kerry with unsmiling, maternal concern, she said lightly. "And so you've become a real slugabed, have you now?"

Kerry didn't answer, but simply looked up at the staunch Irish housekeeper with tear-clouded eyes. "When did you come, Molly?"

"Last night. I looked in on you as soon as I arrived, but you were sleeping too soundly to wake." She reached out and lay one plump hand gently on Kerry's forehead, smoothing a limp wisp of hair away from her face. "How are you feeling then, lass? You've had a bad time of it, I know."

Kerry turned her face away. "Oh, Molly . . . if only I hadn't been so determined to come ahead of you. If only I'd waited . . ."

Molly straightened and narrowed her eyes thoughtfully. "And didn't Dr. Green agree that you could come? You did what you thought best, lass, and you're not to be blaming yourself for things beyond your control."

Kerry turned to look at her, saying nothing for a long moment. When she finally spoke, her words were so soft Molly had to bend closer to hear. "I had a son, Molly . . . a little boy."

The housekeeper swallowed with difficulty, but her voice was steady. "Aye, lass, I know."

"I suppose Jess told you that—I can have no more children." Her eyes took on an unhealthy, burning glint. "I'm barren now."

Molly studied Kerry's face as she sat down on the bed beside her. "There's no denying you've been handed a sorrowful burden to carry, *alannah*.* But you'll not be bearing it alone, and that's God's truth. You have a husband who loves you more than anything and who needs you more than ten sons."

"No man needs a wife whose body is a desert," Kerry rasped bitterly.

Molly lifted her head a fraction, then said quietly, "Your body is for more than growing babes, Kerry Dalton. Above all else, you're to be a comfort and a haven for your husband."

"Jess deserves more than comfort. He's a man who should have children." Her eyes were smudged with dark shadows that only emphasized the glaring resentment of her gaze.

"And did he marry you, then, only for the sons you could give him?" Molly countered archly. "Faith, and I would have sworn it was because the lad is totally possessed with love for you!"

Kerry tossed impatiently in the bed. "You don't understand!"

"And don't I now?" Molly challenged, abruptly softening her tone before she continued. "Have you thought I never wanted babes of my own? It wasn't Patrick who was at fault for our childless union."

The housekeeper's words silenced Kerry. She looked into Molly's kindly face with surprise. "But you were only married a short time before your husband died."

"Long enough to want his child more than anything," Molly said matter-of-factly. "Long enough to pray my heart empty night after night that the Lord would open my womb."

Immediately contrite, Kerry bit her lower lip and reached out to touch the housekeeper gently on her forearm. "I'm sorry, Molly . . . I didn't know." She pushed herself up and rested heavily on both elbows. "Molly, tell me the truth. Does it still . . . cause you pain, that you have no children? There's such an awful hurting in my heart, Molly . . . I don't know how I'll ever live with it."

Molly glanced away for an instant. When she answered, her words came slowly and carefully. "Yes, lass, I know well the pain you're feeling. And I'll not be lying to you about it—there are times when the old hurting comes back to nag at my heart. It will haunt you now and again, too, no doubt."

She turned back to Kerry and looked directly into her eyes. "But you have a fine, wonderful man who loves you with all his being. That must be your consolation until our Lord sees fit to fill your life in other ways, to heal this hole in your heart. Don't you see, lass," the housekeeper's voice grew intense, "our Lord will not leave you empty of comfort forever."

Kerry wanted to believe her. She wanted desperately to believe that this pain now knifing her heart to shreds would eventually leave, that one morning soon she'd be able to face the day without cringing in the light of it. Yet, she couldn't help but wonder, as she turned her face away from Molly's compassionate gaze, if she would ever again feel anything but this agonizing, debilitating emptiness.

Molly rose from the bed. "I'll get some warm water so we can have us a bath now. Your hair is a fright, and your bed linen needs changing as well. Jess wanted to come in here early this morning already, but I told him he'd be waiting until I've had some time with you."

"Oh . . . don't let him see me like this, Molly! I must look terrible—I feel terrible."

"And hasn't the lad already seen you at your worst, now?" Molly said without gentling her words. "The widow woman next door—Mrs. Corbett, is it?—says he's barely left your side in three days going."

"Three days!" Kerry was stunned. "It's been . . . three days since . . ." The words died in her throat as she fell back onto the pillows.

"Aye, it has. The doctor has given you laudanum regularly, to ease things for you a bit. But our Jess has had to keep his wits about him, heartsore as he is, to help tend to you. Sure, and he's had to push his grief aside for a time. But now it's for you to do your duty as a wife and be strong for *him.* He should not have to bear this alone any longer."

Molly's blunt words caused a flush of guilt to warm Kerry's cheeks. She was right, of course. The child had been as much a loss for Jess as for her. And he had gone through the worst of it alone. "I know you're right, Molly, but . . ." She left her thought unfinished and turned to stare bleakly at the wall.

"Listen to me, lass—" Molly's stern, no-nonsense tone made Kerry turn and face her.

The housekeeper's dark eyes held a mixture of concern and understanding. "Our Jess would not be the first strong, honorable man to be weakened or even worse by the trouble of one he loves."

Her next words, uttered with a low, level passion, chilled Kerry. "I have strong feelings about what has happened to the two of you, and I'm asking you to think on some things, for Jess's sake even more than your own. There's evil at work here, if I'm not sadly mistaken—an evil that's trying to put a stop to our Jess's ministry and influence. This thing that was done to you," she paused and drew in a deep, worrying sigh, "was done *more* to *him,* if you take my meaning."

When Kerry moved to prop herself up against the pillows, Molly bent to help her, then sat down on the edge of the bed again before continuing. "Our Lord has placed a few brave men in this world who are so fiercely strong, so unshakable in their stand for right, that there is seemingly no way for the devil and his henchman to do them in."

She nodded to herself as if a thought had only now occurred to her. "Sure and Jess is such a man," she said softly.

In a stronger voice, she added, "What I'm thinking is that somebody has taken the measure of our Jess and knows his mettle, knows there is but one way to stop him."

The gaze she turned on Kerry was afire with anger and warning. "You're the way, lass. And it freezes my heart to think that someone else knows that. Jess's love for you is so great, so fierce—he draws strength and vigor and happiness from you, don't you see . ... it's a kind of weakness in a way, the only weakness in the man, to my eyes. What I fear," she stated darkly, "for you and for him, is that this . . . evil soul . . . is going to try to weaken—or even destroy—our Jess, using you as the weapon."

For a long, silent moment, Kerry stared at her with incredulous, frightened eyes. "If you should be right," she questioned in a tremulous voice, "what can I do, Molly?"

The housekeeper seemed to consider her reply with great care, but her gaze never wavered. "What you need to do, I should think, is to be very strong. A bit stronger than they think you are," she said with a nod of her head and a strange little smile that quickly sobered. "A bit stronger . . . a bit braver . . . and a bit smarter."

They stared at each other in silence for a long time. Finally, Kerry lifted her chin just a fraction and said levelly, "I believe I'm feeling up to my bath now, Molly, if you'll help me. And—don't let Jess come in yet, please. I have it in my mind to surprise him by looking . . . stronger today."

The housekeeper nodded her approval. "Fine, lass. We'll get you a pretty nightdress to put on after your bath—we'll fix your hair a bit, too. Then, while you and Jess visit, I'll make some stirabout for your breakfast. We must get some strengthening food into you quickly." She clucked her tongue and shook her head. "I've not seen you so poorly since you first stepped off the steamer at the Academy."

"I remember what you called me that day, Molly," Kerry said, smiling for the first time since Molly had entered the room.

"And what was that, lass?"

"You said I was no more than a whisper in the wind," Kerry replied, her gaze distant with the memory.

Molly opened her mouth and started to answer, then stopped, studying the small, lithe girl under the blanket. "And

I might just have been right, you know," she said thoughtfully. "Sure and it's a small thing, a wind's whisper, but it can't be stopped, don't you see? It can't be stopped at all."

She walked to the door, then turned back. With an evasive glance about the room, she cleared her throat and said awkwardly, "You're a fine lass, you know. And things will be all right for you and our Jess again, see if they're not." She then hurried out the door, closing it firmly behind her.

By the time Molly finished tending to her, Kerry was nearly faint with weakness. But she knew the effort had been worthwhile when Jess entered the room, stopping abruptly as an uncertain smile of relief broke across his face.

He looks exhausted, Kerry thought. A wave of tenderness for him flooded her, and she reached out to clutch his hand as he came quickly to her side. His eyes were deeply shadowed, and sharp lines of fatigue webbed across his face. She could tell he'd been raking his fingers through his unruly mane of hair, as he always did when he was worried or distraught. At the moment, he looked harried and slightly unkempt, but there was a definite glimmer of hope in his eyes as he took her hand, squeezed it gently, and bent to kiss her lightly on the forehead.

"You're looking infinitely better this morning, sweetheart." Kerry could hear the question in his voice.

"I'm feeling . . . much stronger, Jess. And so glad to know Molly is with us. Here," she patted the edge of the bed, "sit beside me."

He sank down gratefully onto the bed and studied her face. "It's so good to see you looking . . . more yourself, love," he said softly. "I've been so worried." His eyes drank in the clean lustre of her hair and the slight color to her cheeks. "Is it all right if I hold you?"

She opened her arms to him at once, and he immediately gathered her into a gentle, cautious embrace. "Oh, Kerry, beloved. How I've prayed that you'd be all right," he murmured into her hair. "I've been so frightened."

Kerry nestled her face against the soft white fabric of his shirt, allowing herself to draw comfort from his strength, as she had so many times in the past. "I don't want you to worry about me, Jess. I'll be all right, truly I will."

They remained that way for a long time, Jess holding her with extreme tenderness, smoothing her hair, rocking her gently back and forth as he would have a hurting child.

"I wish I could take you out of there and hold you properly—in our rocking chair," he said with a boyish smile.

Kerry glanced over at the massive rocker in front of the fireplace. "Is it our chair, then, Jess? I thought it was a part of the furnishings of the parsonage."

"No, I bought it for you," he explained, still smiling. "I thought since we were storing our furniture for now, it would be nice for you if you at least had a rocking chair of your own."

The gesture was so typical of him. Kerry felt her eyes mist. Always, his thoughts were of her. How to please her, how to make her happy, how to show his love for her. "Thank you, dearest. That gives me an incentive to get out of this bed as quickly as possible."

He gave her a small hug and smoothed her hair away from her forehead. "There are things we should talk about, if you're feeling well enough, love," he said quietly.

Kerry nodded. He released her gently from his embrace and helped her recline once more against the plump pillows, now smooth and fragrant with clean linen.

He told her of the note that had been received after her abduction and the futile investigation that had followed, revealing at the same time his belief that the abduction had been a way of striking at him. "The note leaves little doubt as to the motive behind the whole thing."

"There's no way of knowing who's responsible?"

He shook his head. "The authorities think they've found the house where you were taken. Your shoes were discovered near an abandoned area that's being considered for renewal; the street isn't too far from the Square, as a matter of fact. They searched a number of places, and there's one with a basement that fits your description. But that's all they know. Nothing else."

"And you think they did all this to . . . drive you away, to make you leave Washington?" Kerry questioned him anxiously, remembering Molly's earlier words of warning.

A spark of anger glinted in his eyes. "That's how it would seem, yes."

Kerry felt the familiar weakness wash over her again. "Oh, Jess, how could anyone hate so much? I don't understand."

He clasped her hands in his and looked at her anxiously. "I'm tiring you. We'll not talk about this any more this morning."

"No! We must talk about it," she protested, trying to sit up but quickly falling back, too fatigued to make another effort.

"Kerry . . . please." He brushed her cheek with the fingertips of one hand. "All we can do is let the authorities handle this for now. For the next few weeks you won't be strong enough to leave the house anyway. In the meantime, I intend to make absolutely certain that you're not alone in the house at any time. We have to be extremely careful until . . . I decide what's to be done."

"To be done? What do you mean?"

He clenched his hands together in a gesture of agitation and glanced away from her. "I can't possibly stay here if there's any chance at all that they may try something like this again."

"Jess! You cannot leave! You were so sure the Lord was leading you when you agreed to come here. You can't simply give up." Could it be happening already, what Molly had spoken of? Was his fear for her beginning to chip away at the strength of his faith? "I won't let you do that," she stated firmly, clasping his shoulders with both hands.

Despair tugged at her heart when she saw the uncertain, tormented expression in his gaze. "Kerry, they've already taken our son," he grated hoarsely. "And I might have lost you as well. Not for anything in the world will I stay here if you're in danger. We'll go back to the Academy—we'll live in the woods if we must. But I won't risk anything else happening to you."

"Oh, Jess," she said softly, only now coming to realize what an agony these past few days must have been for him. She drew his head down upon her breast and cradled him there, tenderly threading her fingers through his curly hair. "It will be all right, my treasure," she soothed. "You'll see. We're going to be all right."

He raised his head to look at her, and the depth of love and adoration in his gaze made her weak. "Yes, we will, love," he said softly. "As long as we're together, we'll be all right."

He stayed with her, holding her in his arms until she fell asleep. Even while she slept, he stayed, watching her, smiling softly at the way the copper waves of her hair tumbled stubbornly over her forehead. Occasionally, he would touch one finger lightly to her cheek or raise her hand to his lips and brush a tender kiss across her fingertips. Just before leaving her, he got to his knees beside the bed and prayed long and fervently from the depths of his aching, heavy soul.

. . . Father, heal her heart. She's trying to be so strong, so brave—for me. But I know her too well and love her too much not to see the pain that's consuming her. Oh Lord, I can't pretend to know your ways or understand your will. At this moment, I admit that to my limited, human mind, there appears to be no balm for the wound inflicted upon my beloved's spirit, no possible way to fill the emptiness she's been left with. But if I've learned nothing else in the years I've walked with you, I've learned that you delight in doing impossible things for your children.

So I ask you, Lord, in your time and in your will, to somehow give us a child. I'm pleading with you, Lord, not for myself—my beloved Kerry is enough for me; I don't need anything more than her love. But she so desperately wants a child, Lord. She wants that more than anything . . . and she has asked for so little in her life.

With you, there must be a way . . . oh, Father, in your love and in your mercy, make a way.

CHAPTER
FIVE

A month later, Kerry sat in her rocking chair by the long, narrow bedroom window. Her slender fingers played idly at the light quilt over her lap as she gazed out the window, staring mindlessly in the direction of the White House. The day was damp and gloomy, and her disposition equally dismal as she remembered other September afternoons, cool but bright and cheerful with West Point sunshine.

She was bored and restless—too unsettled to concentrate on anything. No one would yet allow her to lift a hand about the house. She didn't know who was worse, Molly or Jess, when it came to treating her like an invalid, though it was true enough that she didn't feel overly strong. Nor was she likely to, she thought with a touch of frustration, if they continued to coddle her so.

They weren't fooling her. Jess was especially transparent, insisting that she mustn't so much as poke her nose outside the bedroom. The truth was that both he and Molly felt more comfortable about her safety as long as she was cooped up inside the house. Even Molly—usually impatient with idleness—was doing her part to keep Kerry tucked safely under her wing.

She turned toward the door, brightening somewhat when she recognized Mackenzie's slow, heavy footsteps on the stairs. She smiled, knowing the caretaker would pause at the bedroom door, clear his throat gruffly, and ask if he could enter.

Anticipating him, she called out, "Come in, Mackenzie."

The door creaked on its hinges as the big, burly man pushed it open. He glanced inside before entering the room, then greeted her as he always did, with a small nod of his balding head and a polite, "missus." In one hand he clutched his cap, while the other hand appeared to be holding something inside his woolen vest. Behind wire-rimmed spectacles, his dark gray eyes darted around the room.

"Is the housekeeper about?" he asked shortly.

Kerry sighed. While Jess seemed amused by the feud between Mackenzie and Molly, she was bewildered and troubled by it. Not only did she love Molly as a mother, but she had grown especially fond of the taciturn caretaker. The kindness Kerry had detected in his eyes at their first meeting had revealed itself further over the passing weeks as a very definite trait of the big Irishman's nature, though he seemed to make a point of concealing it. From the beginning, he had taken Kerry as his own private charge, determined to assume sole responsibility for her well-being and comfort.

"I believe Molly is downstairs, Mackenzie. Wasn't she in the kitchen when you came in?"

He still didn't smile, but did relax his guarded look somewhat. "I came through the cellar door."

"Whatever for?"

"Didn't want to bring her wrath down on me. Here, missus—I found this poor mite wandering around my cottage. I thought perhaps you'd care to have him."

With a cry of surprise, Kerry watched as he gently removed from inside his coat a light gray tabby kitten with dark gray stripes. The kitten had four white-socked feet and appeared to be slightly cross-eyed.

The caretaker shyly offered the furry bundle to Kerry, who reached out for it with undisguised delight. "What a wonderful surprise, Mackenzie!" She raised the kitten in both hands and held it slightly away from her face for inspection. "Oh, the poor wee thing is no more than mere bones! And doesn't he have a funny little face!"

Two frightened green eyes stared out, accompanied by one loud and indignant meow. Kerry cuddled the kitten against her, crooning to it and smiling up at Mackenzie, who looked extremely pleased with her reaction.

"I can't thank you enough, Mackenzie! But you'll have to help me take care of him for a bit, I fear. The doctor still won't let me go downstairs."

With a brief shake of his head in agreement, the caretaker replied, "I'll fix him a basket right here in your room, missus. And I'll stop by every now and then to take him out for his little business."

Kerry gingerly set the kitten on his feet so she could watch him explore. He immediately became a different creature. Asserting his territorial rights, he inspected the room, padded around the bed, charged suddenly beneath it, then out from under it with a dive at Kerry's feet.

She burst into merry laughter for the first time in weeks, and Mackenzie's eyes glowed with silent pleasure as he watched her.

At that moment, Molly came charging through the open door, wearing a fierce frown and wiping her hands briskly on her apron.

"What is it, lass? I heard you cry out all the way—"

Her black eyes narrowed with suspicious disapproval when she saw Mackenzie. "And what might you be doin' up here, man? What have you done to upset the lass?"

Before the caretaker could utter one of his low, surly replies, the kitten, apparently startled by the housekeeper's unexpected entrance, hurled himself directly at Molly's feet, tackling her ankles with determined fervor.

Molly yelped in surprise and immediately began to hop up and down, first on one foot then the other, in an attempt to shake off her small attacker. Kerry covered her mouth with her hands as she desperately fought to control a burst of laughter. One glance at Mackenzie made it even more difficult to hold a straight face, for he was positively beaming at Molly's plight—the very first time Kerry had ever seen the solemn caretaker so much as crack a smile.

"Ochone!* Faith, and what have you let into this house, old man?" Still bristling with surprised indignation, Molly began to wildly flap her apron at the poor kitten, who scampered to safety under the bed, cowering there to peep out with cautious detachment.

"It's only a small kitten, Molly," Kerry said, hoping to ward off another shindy between the housekeeper and the caretaker. "Mackenzie found the poor thing wandering about outside and brought him in to me. Isn't he sweet looking?"

"*Sweet?*" Molly stared at her young mistress as though she thought Kerry had lost her wits. "He's a wild thing, a scavenger! Cats are deceitful creatures, every last one of them, sneaking about with their evil eyes—"

Mackenzie crossed his arms over his chest, still grinning wickedly. "The wee thing could use some food while I'm fixing it a basket; the missus wants to keep it close to her here in the bedroom."

The housekeeper planted her hands firmly on her ample hips and eyeballed the Irishman. "We will have no cat in this house! Shedding its fur and making a stink—"

"Molly—I want the kitten," Kerry declared firmly. "I've already chosen a name for him."

With his gaze still on Molly's face in an expression of spiteful satisfaction, Mackenzie asked, "And what will you be calling your new pet, missus?"

"Brian," Kerry said firmly. "His name is Brian Boru."

Molly drew in a sharp, horrified breath. "Boru?" she repeated in a scandalized tone. "You'd name this—animal—after our warrior king? A—cat named for the bravest, strongest king who ever drew breath upon the soil of Ireland?"

"Brian will grow into his name," Kerry said confidently, smiling to herself at Molly's shocked expression. "He will be a cat worthy of the title, I'm sure, won't you, Brian Boru?"

As though he knew he'd been granted a pardon, the kitten crept a few inches out from under the bed, then scurried the rest of the way from his hiding place to leap into Kerry's lap.

"Madness!" Molly snarled. "I'll not be cleaning up its messes, I'll tell you that right now! The both of you can blame yourselves for bringing this green-eyed goblin under our roof! And it's sorry you'll be for it, just see if you're not."

Having learned some years earlier that Molly's indignant explosions are quickly over and forgotten, Kerry turned an innocent gaze on the housekeeper. "Molly, there's some yarn in my basket there by the bureau. Would you give me a small ball of it, please?"

"Yarn?" With a suspicious arch of an eyebrow, Molly halted her rampage.

"Yes. Kittens love to play with yarn, you know."

Snorting with disgust, Molly hesitated, then marched stiffly over to the sewing basket and selected the tiniest ball of yarn she could find. Chin up and eyes flashing, she handed the yarn to Kerry with a withering glare.

The kitten immediately grabbed for it, tumbling off Kerry's lap and unraveling the yarn all across the bedroom floor. Kerry and Mackenzie laughed at its antics, while Molly sputtered to herself and tried to pick up the snarled yarn without tripping over it.

That was how Jess found them when he appeared at the bedroom door. "Kerry? Can you receive company? Ah, good—you're up."

With a puzzled but pleased smile, he walked into the room followed by two elegantly dressed ladies of extremely dignified appearance.

"Whatever is going on in here?" he said, crossing the room to kiss Kerry lightly on the forehead. "How good it is to hear you laugh again, sweetheart."

He straightened and turned to the ladies who had accompanied him into the room, and who now stood waiting a few feet inside the door. The taller of the two stared with incredulous disdain at the untidy room. She touched one hand to her perfect silver coiffure and lifted an expressive eyebrow at the other woman who was shorter, rounder, and appeared, Kerry thought, far less formidable.

"I've brought visitors, dear," Jess said, seemingly unconcerned by all the confusion in his bedroom. "Kerry, this is Mrs. Northcote." The tall, stately matron nodded to Kerry with a frosty smile. "And Mrs. Pence." Both women approached Kerry as they were introduced.

"Mrs. Northcote is president of the Ladies Benevolence Society at the church," he explained to Kerry with a smile and what she thought might have been a mischievous glint in his eye.

Somewhat intimidated by the tall, regal woman in the impeccable gray suit, Kerry smiled at her and her more kindly faced companion. "It's very nice to meet you, I'm sure," she said quickly, fervently wishing at least for Jess's sake, that she had been a bit more—composed for her first meeting with these obviously important ladies.

Mrs. Northcote stepped close enough to offer Kerry a book

and a small box of chocolates. "Mrs. Dalton, we thought you might enjoy a book of poetry . . ." She let her words fall off, marked by a definite question as she glanced from Kerry to Mackenzie, whose work clothing was anything but spotless and whose level stare held a suggestion of challenge.

Her contemptuous gaze moved to Molly. The red-faced housekeeper, in an effort to capture the roguish kitten, had instead managed to hopelessly entangle her feet in a maze of yarn. Growling furiously under her breath, Molly was making a futile attempt to escape her self-made trap. Finally, she turned a scalding, pointed look on Mackenzie, which he unabashedly ignored.

Mrs. Pence smiled nervously and coughed. "We're so sorry for your loss, Mrs. Dalton. We do hope you're feeling better."

Kerry returned her smile with an uncertain glance at Jess, who, rather than appearing perturbed by the scene, seemed mildly amused. As if he sensed her concern, he placed a steadying hand on her shoulder and gave it a light squeeze.

"I—yes, thank you," Kerry managed to say.

Mrs. Northcote glanced from Kerry to Mrs. Pence with a look that clearly said she saw no evidence of grief in the room. Looking down her long patrician nose, she appeared to sniff the air around her. "You have—a new pet, Mrs. Dalton?"

Kerry followed her gaze to the corner of the bedroom, where a disinterested Brian Boru was walking away, leaving behind him a rather substantial puddle.

"Oh, mercy," she mumbled softly.

Unbelievably, Jess chuckled. "Who's your new friend, Kerry?"

"Mackenzie brought him to me," she replied under her breath.

The caretaker grabbed a nearby newspaper and hurriedly began to clean up the puddle. As soon as he finished, he left the room carrying the small, disgraced offender in his arms.

"We'll have to teach him some manners, I think," said Jess easily. "But as long as he can make you look as well and happy as you do this afternoon, he has a home for himself."

He then favored the two women from the church with a dazzling smile. "Ladies," he continued equitably, "while my household isn't always quite so frenzied, I can't bring myself to apologize, not when I've found my wife looking more herself than she has for weeks. Perhaps you'll be generous enough to excuse our confusion this afternoon."

Oh, and isn't the man a charmer, Kerry thought with a touch of affectionate pride. Molly had said often enough that Jess could melt the heart of a stone, once he set his mind to it.

Apparently unaffected by his charm, though, Mrs. Northcote replied in a stiff, disapproving voice, "We understand perfectly, Pastor."

She turned her frosty gaze back to Kerry. "Do I understand that you're originally from Ireland, Mrs. Dalton?"

From behind her chair, Jess's hand once more tightened on Kerry's shoulder.

"Ah . . . yes. Yes, I am," Kerry replied. "As are Molly and Mackenzie."

"Of course. Isn't that nice for . . . all of you." The queenly matron then directed her attention to Jess. "Tell me, Pastor, are you of Celtic bloodlines also?"

Kerry turned to look up at Jess. Something flickered in his deep blue eyes, and Kerry was unable to tell whether it was amusement or irritation.

"Indeed I am, Mrs. Northcote, though I prefer to think of myself as simply an American. As Christians, we're every one of us brothers and sisters, are we not?"

Amusement, decided Kerry. He was definitely enjoying himself.

"Indeed." The formidable Mrs. Northcote curled her lips as if she had developed an offensive taste in her mouth. Turning briskly to Mrs. Pence, she announced, "Marian, we must be going now. We still have a delivery to make to the colored school, you know. Besides," she added dryly, "we mustn't tire Mrs. Dalton."

"The colored school?" Kerry repeated curiously.

"Why, yes, Mrs. Dalton. Your husband has initiated a new benevolence program for the church. We're providing a number of textbooks to assist one of the Negro schools in the city." Mrs. Northcote turned a smile on Jess which stopped short of her eyes.

Matching her smile with a far more genuine one of his own, Jess replied guilelessly, "And I'm extremely gratified that you ladies are giving the program your personal attention."

"Yes, well—" Mrs. Northcote flicked her gaze from Jess to Mrs. Pence. "You're certainly engaging our congregation in a number of—novel—programs, Pastor. Hopefully, these new ventures won't dilute our traditional ministries," she said pointedly.

With a final arrogant glance about the room, Lydia Northcote announced firmly, "Marian, we must go now. Mrs. Dalton, may we extend a welcome to our city as well as our sincere wishes for your recovery." She nodded to Jess and turned to go, stepping carefully around the trail of yarn that now led from Molly to the center of the room.

Jess escorted the ladies downstairs and out of the house but returned as soon as they were gone.

Once Molly disentangled herself enough to leave the room, Kerry looked up at Jess with a small grimace of apology. "Oh, Jess, I'm so sorry. I wouldn't embarrass you for the world. If only I'd known they were coming—"

He laughed at her discomfort, then carefully scooped her up into his arms, taking her place in the chair as he pulled her onto his lap. "Mrs. Dalton," he said softly, smiling into her eyes, "you could never embarrass me. Believe me, love, the ladies will recover nicely."

"I wonder," Kerry muttered worriedly. "They most likely think you married a brainless bumpkin."

"I married," he said firmly, "the most beautiful jewel of Ireland and the most wonderful girl in the world." He kissed her soundly on her pouting mouth, then traced the curve of her cheek with one finger. "How are you, love?" he asked softly. "How are you feeling?"

"Better. Truly, I am," she quickly insisted when she saw his skeptical look. "The doctor says I can go up and down stairs in a few more days and begin taking short walks as well."

Jess immediately knitted his heavy dark brows together in a worried frown. "Promise me you'll go very slowly, love. You must be careful."

"I will," she agreed. "But—oh, Jess, I simply must find something to do. I can't bear sitting around here, staring out the window any longer."

He hugged her closer and coaxed her head onto his shoulder. "Are you that unhappy, love?"

"If our child had lived—" She stopped for a moment unable to go on.

Jess tightened his embrace. "I know. Oh, Kerry—I want so much to be . . . enough for you. But I understand how you feel, dear, really I do."

She tipped her head up to look into his face. "Jess, you are enough for me. You make my life wonderfully full. It's just that . . . now that I know there will be no children for us, I need to find a way to fill the hours—something to give my life some . . . purpose. Molly will never allow me to do very much around the house—you know how she is. I simply have to find a way to keep busy."

"But you do understand that you can't leave the house by yourself yet, don't you, Kerry? Even when you're stronger, we have to get some answers about the . . . abduction before we can feel that you're safe again."

She pulled back from him and looked into his eyes. "Jess, it's been a month now. And there have been no other incidents, nor do we know any more than we did at the beginning. You can't keep me locked inside this house forever, you know."

"I don't intend to. But I also don't intend to take any chances with your safety. None," he emphasized firmly.

Hearing the stubborn resistance in his tone, Kerry uttered a resigned sigh and said, "Let's talk about something else for now. Tell me about this new project of yours, the Negro school Mrs. Northcote mentioned. I didn't realize there were schools for black children here in Washington."

"It's uncommon, that's true," he admitted, "but Washington has quite a large free Negro population, and they're doing their best to keep some schools going. I've been trying to get the city churches interested in providing textbooks, desks, and other necessary supplies."

"And?"

He cushioned her head in the hollow of his shoulder and rocked back and forth. "I've managed to get a great deal of solid support from some of them. But for those willing to help, there are many more who think I'm quite mad."

"What about teachers? How do they get teachers?"

"It's difficult," he said with a deep sigh. "There's one, though, who's particularly good at what she does. A young black woman from the north—Cely Johnson. She worked for a wealthy family who owned a gigantic industrial complex in Massachusetts. They became aware of her intelligence and saw to it that she got an education. Then they funded her first year here in Washington to work with the children at one of the schools. She's done a phenomenal job, but she needs help desperately."

Kerry's mind began churning out all kinds of bizarre thoughts. She was quiet for a time, thinking about the brave black woman and the job she had undertaken by herself.

"Are you tired, love?" Suddenly aware of her silence, Jess stopped the rocking motion of the chair and tipped her chin upward to study her face with concern. "Do you need to lie down?"

"Oh—no, no, Jess. I'm fine. I was just . . . thinking."

His gaze bathed her with affection as he pressed his lips gently against her temple. "And what are you thinking about, little missus?" he asked, borrowing Mackenzie's pet address for her.

"Jess . . . why couldn't I help . . . when I'm well again?"

"Help?" he repeated blankly.

"Couldn't I be of some use—to Cely Johnson, for example?"

Surprised, Jess drew back from her and searched her eyes. "You mean at the school?"

She nodded vigorously. "Listen to me, please—don't say no until you hear me out." Her words tumbled out in an excited rush as she tried to convince him. "You've tutored me for years, Jess, and haven't you said that I've learned quickly and well?"

He nodded his agreement.

"Well, don't you see? I could share with these children all you've taught me. What good is all my learning if I keep it to myself?"

When he started to protest, she hushed him with a finger over his lips. "No, now, wait—please. You said this Cely Johnson is trying to manage alone? That's a terrible burden, surely. I could be a real help to her, couldn't I? Do you know her, Jess?"

"I've met her, yes, but—"

"Then you could introduce us. I could be a kind of assistant to her perhaps. Oh, Jess, don't you understand? If I can't have children of our own, at least I could help someone else's!"

She framed his bearded face between her hands and gazed into his eyes intently. "Don't you see, Jess? It would give me a purpose—something important to do. I know I couldn't be a real teacher, but surely I could be of some value as a helper."

He searched her beloved face for a long moment. "The school is in a rough part of the city, Kerry—"

She pursed her lips thoughtfully. Finally, her eyes brightened. "Perhaps Mackenzie would be willing to take me back and forth in the carriage?"

Jess gently combed her hair with the fingers of one hand. "I believe Mackenzie would take you to China and back if you asked. The poor man cherishes every hair on your head." He smiled softly at her. "But I'm not sure—"

"Oh, please, Jess!" she pleaded, dropping her hands to his shoulders. "Won't you at least talk to her, to Cely Johnson, about me—once I'm strong enough to be of some use to her?"

"I suppose we could . . . think about it," he said reluctantly. At her quick smile, he added firmly, "But not for some weeks yet. You'll have to be patient."

"Oh, I will, Jess! I promise I will."

He drew her face to his and kissed her with great tenderness. "I wonder," he finally murmured against a soft wave of her hair, "if I'll ever be able to deny you anything?"

She hugged him in reply, feeling the first glimmer of anticipation she'd known since the day their child had been lost to them. "Just don't deny me this," she said softly, more to herself than to him.

CHAPTER
SIX

The first week of November brought a series of new experiences to Kerry, not all of them pleasant.

On Wednesday evening of that week she attended her first meeting of the Ladies Benevolence Society. Mrs. Northcote, as aloof and dignified as Kerry remembered, favored her with no more than a cursory glance and, later, a somewhat restrained introduction to the other women of the group. The round, nervous Mrs. Pence made an attempt to be cordial, but only when her domineering friend wasn't watching.

Many of the women made Kerry feel decidedly uncomfortable, even unwelcome. She couldn't shake the feeling that she had already been measured and found sadly lacking. Only the warmhearted Adeline Corbett and a few of her friends gave Kerry a genuinely enthusiastic welcome.

Before the evening was hardly under way, Kerry fervently began to wish for its end. She longed for the comfort of Jess's strong arms, and she felt a distinct need for the benefit of his wisdom and experience to help her deal with this unexpected rejection. But when she returned home later that night, she decided to say nothing. He looked tired and seemed unusually preoccupied; obviously, the man already had more than enough on his mind without her adding an extra measure of worry.

Two days later, Mackenzie drove her to the Negro children's school on the far edge of town for her first meeting with Cely Johnson, the teacher. Her hopes were high; dozens of ideas about how she might help with the children had been scurrying through her mind for days. At first, however, it appeared as though this experience would be no more successful than her evening with the Ladies Society.

Although Jess had arranged for Kerry to meet with Cely Johnson, when the day arrived he was unable to accompany her. Instead, he had been called to the bedside of a mortally ill wife and mother.

By the time Kerry arrived at the small, white frame schoolhouse, which had a forlorn and abandoned appearance in its setting on the isolated riverbank, she was feeling very young and extremely unsure of herself. In an attempt to disguise her uncertainty, she gave Mackenzie a bright smile as he helped her from the carriage. She fluffed her skirts and patted her hair in a reassuring gesture, then asked him to come back for her later.

A mob of boisterous black children played in front of the schoolhouse. Kerry started to slowly thread her way through them. The noise broke and quickly shattered in total silence as she followed the dirt pathway through their midst to the entrance of the building. Meeting their curious stares with a hesitant smile that was returned by only one or two of the very smallest children, she ascended the sagging wooden steps.

When she reached the weather-beaten porch, she came to an abrupt halt. Framed in the doorway stood one of the most strikingly beautiful women Kerry had ever seen. The young black woman blocking her entrance was at least a head taller than Kerry and as slender and graceful in appearance as a gazelle. Her face looked to have been struck in bronze, and her dark, severely short hairstyle emphasized her flawless features. A ruthless intelligence, as well as a definite glint of hostility, stared out at Kerry from large almond-shaped eyes.

Kerry immediately sensed the black woman's antagonism. Even so, the teacher apparently felt it necessary to express her opinion. Within seconds, Kerry was uncomfortably aware of the fact that, to Cely Johnson, she was just one more white do-gooder who couldn't possibly be of any conceivable value to her or the children.

The teacher was brutally frank. "This isn't your typical little church school, Mrs. Dalton," she said brusquely after they introduced themselves to each other. "I'm not just in the business of teaching these children how to read and do sums." Her voice was hard. "I spend more time putting ointment on dirty, cut feet that don't have any shoes or digging up food for hungry mouths who haven't eaten for two days than I do teaching. I also delouse heads, patch worn-out pants, and occasionally handwash soiled underwear."

She stopped for a moment, twisting her wide, perfectly molded mouth into a grim line. "I have my hands full just trying to keep these children healthy enough to be here. And when winter comes, it will be harder than ever."

After a tired sigh, her voice softened a little as she continued. "Look, Mrs. Dalton, I know about your loss, and I'm really sorry for you and the preacher. He's a good man, and I'm sure you're a fine lady. But you're not going to find your standard, cute little pickaninnies here. These children are often dirty, almost always hungry, and justifiably angry. At their best, they'll probably offend your delicate sensitivities. At their worst, if you should happen to end up caring about them, they'll keep you awake nights with worry and an aching heart. Do yourself and me a favor: go back to the parsonage and help pack goodwill baskets."

Kerry stood unmoving. Feeling her temper spark and flare, she was unwilling to look away from the tall woman's commanding, level gaze. At the same time, she was reluctant to accept any further humiliation. A long moment of silence hovered between them before she trusted herself to speak.

Burying her hands inside her cloak so her clenched fists couldn't be seen and lifting her chin, she replied with tightly controlled anger, "My husband told me you're a wonderful teacher, Miss Johnson. He neglected to warn me that you're also very rude."

She saw the black woman bristle but gave her no quarter. "Obviously, my reason for wanting to work with you was severely flawed. I was under the impression, you see, that your first concern was the children, not your own insufferable independence. Would you tell me then, Miss Johnson"—Kerry's tone sharpened even as her brogue thickened—"have I failed to meet your sterling standards because I'm Irish or because I'm white?"

Her question hung between them, suspended on a thin wire

of tension. Hurt and disappointed, Kerry refused to retreat from the hard, studying glare of Cely Johnson, though she fervently wished she hadn't been so quick to dismiss Mackenzie.

She knew she should say nothing more. She was angry, terribly angry—and hadn't Jess reminded her more than once that her temper was often her worst enemy. For days, though, she had thought of nothing but this new venture; she had prayed about it, planned for it, gone over it dozens of times in her mind. Now, to have it end before it even got started was more than she was willing to accept.

Kerry was almost startled to hear herself speaking again, her voice dark and husky with emotion. "You think I'm a stranger to poverty, do you?" She uttered a small, brittle laugh. "Let me tell you, miss, that I could most likely teach you more about poverty and dirty, starving little children than you'd ever be wanting to know."

The teacher's delicately arched eyebrows lifted with surprise, and her expression gradually softened as Kerry continued her tirade. "Can I more easily impress you, Miss Johnson, if I tell you how I found our neighbors and closest friends dead, along with their two children? Destroyed by fever and half-eaten by their own dogs, they were. Or perhaps I could better curry your favor by telling you how, as a child, I used my Da's gun to shoot rats off the corpses of my childhood playmate and her Mum until we could get them decently buried." Kerry knew she must stop. Too many horrors lay just below the surface of her memories—some of which she could never bear to face again.

Suddenly, she felt extremely tired. She no longer cared about her pride, her dignity, or what Cely Johnson thought of her. She no longer cared about much of anything except getting out of there and going home. Without another word, she turned her back on the teacher and started down the steps.

A firm grasp on her shoulder caused her to stop. "Mrs. Dalton—"

Kerry turned and waited, her gaze steady and expressionless as the young black woman silently searched her eyes. Finally, with a slight twitch at one corner of her mouth, Cely drawled, "Why didn't you just tell me you were Irish to begin with?" She then smiled a full, dazzling smile as she pressed

Kerry's shoulder gently and turned her around toward the schoolhouse door.

"I sure hope you know some good stories—the Irish are supposed to be great with stories, aren't they? The kids say I'm a terrible storyteller."

Cely stopped long enough to pick up a small bell from the windowsill; she shook it vigorously. "You'd best brace yourself, Mrs. Dalton. Recess is over!"

Kerry did everything wrong that first day. Anxious to impress Cely, she tried too hard and accomplished very little. But she quickly learned, with relief, that the teacher seemed to possess unlimited patience. Obviously, she intended to give Kerry all the time and guidance she might need. And by the end of the day, Kerry was convinced that poor Cely would undoubtedly find it necessary to draw on every precious scrap of that golden patience.

CHAPTER
SEVEN

Following the Sunday morning service, Kerry stood beside Jess in the narthex of the church saying good-bye to the departing worshipers. In spite of the heartening affirmation she'd received from Cely Johnson at the end of her first day at the school, this morning had brought a renewed plague of old, familiar doubts and feelings of insecurity.

She was grateful for the encouraging words and friendly smiles offered by a number of church members as they left the building. Perhaps Jess was right in maintaining that most of the people had accepted her. Indeed, many had been extremely kind to both of them since their arrival.

But Kerry was certain there were many who openly resented her. Jess continued to insist that the hostility of these few had nothing to do with her personally, that the real problem lay in their opposition to his abolitionist ties and the emotionalism with which he conducted his ministry.

Kerry wasn't so sure. Most of the outright antagonism she sensed came from a number of ladies who made up the elite inner circle of Washington's society. This particular group, headed by Lydia Northcote, made no effort to disguise their disapproval of the pastor's wife.

Adeline Corbett, their kindhearted, sympathetic neighbor, now approached and greeted both Kerry and Jess with genuine warmth. Laughing at the attractive older woman's comment about Molly and the mischievous new kitten, Kerry flinched with surprise when she felt Jess's firm hand grip her shoulder. She turned quickly with a questioning look, only to encounter the impassive gaze of Senator Preston Forbrush.

The diminutive, silver-haired senator was an enigma to Kerry. Although he had called on the Daltons during the latter days of Kerry's recovery and had appeared genuinely concerned for her, he was, nevertheless, a known opponent of the abolition movement—and of Jess. Kerry had found him stiffly polite, almost courtly in his manner the day he visited. Afterward, she suggested to Jess that perhaps they had misjudged the southern senator.

Jess, however, had surprised her with his statement that Forbrush was one of the most powerful and feared men in Washington. "That fine, courtly gentleman," he had stated in a tone lightly edged with distaste, "is said to have the power of life and death over most of the political careers in the country. From what I've heard, even a disagreement with him can be disastrous. He has the unsavory reputation of never forgetting a wrong and never letting go of a grudge."

A few days after the senator's visit, Jess came home one evening and glumly reported on a remark that Forbrush had supposedly made to several members of the church financial committee about Jess being nothing more than a "young hothead who uses his pulpit as a soapbox."

Kerry had distrusted the politician ever since, and now felt acutely uncomfortable in his presence. It took only a moment, however, for her to realize that the reason for Jess's steadying grasp on her shoulder—and the present focus of his attention—wasn't Senator Forbrush, but rather the tall young man standing beside him. Slender and handsomely attired in a perfectly tailored dark suit, the man turned to meet Kerry's astonished stare with a look of amused contempt. He flicked his cold hazel eyes over her with disdain.

"How good to see you again . . . Mrs. Dalton . . . ma'am." His easy drawl was thick with undisguised sarcasm.

Lowell Martin. Kerry felt herself flush, and for a moment she was sure she was going to be ill. Her throat constricted, her hands began to tremble uncontrollably, and a thin line of clammy perspiration dotted her upper lip. She was aware that Jess had draped a protective arm around her, and she reached up to cover his hand with her own, seeking even more support.

The man standing in front of her and measuring her reaction with interested scorn had been an upperclassman at West Point when Kerry arrived there as the chaplain's ward. Under the guise of escorting Kerry home one fall afternoon, he proceeded to verbally humiliate her. When his advances rapidly grew more brutal, only the intervention of a young plebe, Tom Jackson, saved Kerry from a physical assault.

Jess saw to Martin's dismissal from the Academy that very afternoon, and Kerry assumed she would never see the man again. Unbelievably, he now stood before her, looking completely at ease as he studied her with a disturbing, impudent glint in his eyes.

She was dimly aware that Jess had mumbled a grudging "Martin," and knew instantly that he had been shaken as badly as she by the unexpected meeting. Martin, however, made no effort to end the encounter, but simply smiled at both of them, allowing his insolent gaze to linger overly long on Kerry.

"What a pleasant surprise," he said smoothly, still raking Kerry with his bold, insinuating stare, "to find the two of you married. Certainly yours was a storybook romance, wasn't it? The chaplain and his ward—ah, and now the happy ending."

The look he turned on Jess was dark with a malignant undercurrent. "Naturally, Mr. Dalton, I'm delighted to see you again," he said in a tone heavy with sarcasm. "I always held you in such . . . high regard at the Academy." He glanced slyly at Senator Forbrush. "I'm so glad the senator invited me to attend services with him this morning," he continued. "I have the privilege, you see, of being Senator Forbrush's new aide. So . . . we'll be seeing much of each other in the future, Mr. Dalton." He nodded to Kerry. "*Mrs.* Dalton. Certainly, I'll look forward to seeing *you* again."

With disbelief, Kerry watched Martin hold the dark-paneled door open for the senator; he then followed Forbrush outside.

Jess bent his head to study Kerry with concern. "Are you all right, dear?" he asked softly, giving her hand a gentle squeeze before glancing quickly at Charles Payne, his secretary, who was next in the line of departing parishioners.

Unable to speak, Kerry nodded and continued to grasp his arm in a desperate vise.

"I think Molly's out on the portico," Jess said. "Shall I take you to her so you can get some air?"

"Yes—I mean, you shouldn't leave. There are still people in the line . . . I can go alone."

"Are you sure you're all right, love?" He studied her face with an anxious frown.

Kerry nodded. She wasn't all right, of course. An overpowering surge of nausea threatened to bring her to her knees. *She had to get out of here, but she mustn't make a scene . . . must not embarrass Jess.* Dropping her hand from his arm, she darted a weak smile at Charles. Then, as the dark-haired young man moved to shake hands with Jess, Kerry quickly turned and made her way on trembling legs to get her cloak and go outside.

On the portico, she stood alone for a moment, glancing around uneasily at the few small groups huddled together making conversation as they prepared to leave the church. Finally, she spied Molly across the crowd and started toward her.

Too late, she realized that in order to reach the housekeeper she would have to pass between several small groups of chatting women, one of which included Lydia Northcote, Marian Pence, and two other fashionably gowned ladies from the "inner circle," as she'd come to think of the tightly knit society group.

They seemed completely unaware of her presence, but Kerry couldn't help but overhear their conversation as she walked by. Their words went directly to her heart with a knifing stab of pain.

". . . so common, isn't she? But what else could we expect? Another Irish immigrant, you know."

Kerry recognized Mrs. Northcote's distinct, imperious voice. Still smarting from the sick horror of the scene with Lowell Martin, she now felt a sudden, almost vicious urge to strike out at the self-assured, smug face of the society matron. Instead, she continued to make her way between the groups, determined not to hear another word.

But when Mrs. Pence murmured something about the Dalton lineage reportedly being "extremely noble," Kerry again slowed her pace.

"Well, there won't be a continuance of that . . . *noble* lineage, will there?" Lydia Northcote's haughty remark sounded much like a sneer. "I have been told," she said importantly, through a delicate grimace of distaste, "that she is now . . . *barren.*"

There were a few deep breaths of surprise, then Marian Pence asked timidly, "Wherever did you hear that, Lydia?"

Lydia Northcote was obviously unaccustomed to having her pronouncements questioned. She rebuked her companion with a withering glare, cleared her throat lightly, and continued. "I have my sources, Marian, as I'm sure you're aware. And I was told that the woman went running through the street like a savage—ran until she dropped, they say. Not only did she lose the child—" she lowered her voice meaningfully—"but I was told that she can have no others."

Kerry's gasp of stricken astonishment caused the cluster of women to turn in unison and gape at her.

Marian Pence colored fiercely and uttered a weak, "Lydia–"

Mrs. Northcote silently studied the dismayed Kerry without a hint of contrition softening her gaze. If she felt any remorse at all, she effectively concealed it by simply lifting one patrician brow before turning away with deliberate indifference.

Kerry desperately wanted to run but refused to let them see the devastating result of their cruelty. She knew she was dangerously close to total collapse, but she would contain herself at all costs. It would be abject humiliation for poor Jess if she were to make a spectacle of herself right here in front of the church building.

She stood, unmoving, staring at the cluster of women until the entire group silently turned away from her and walked off the portico. Drawing a deep, steadying breath, Kerry then resolutely fixed her attention on Molly, who was talking with Adeline Corbett, both of them obviously unaware of the scene that had just taken place.

When Kerry finally reached Molly's side, she grasped the housekeeper's stout forearm and said tightly, "Please, Molly, could we go to the carriage? I'm feeling a bit wobbly kneed, I'm afraid."

Molly looked from Kerry to Mrs. Corbett with concern but wasted no time in tucking Kerry's arm through hers and firmly guiding her to the carriage where Mackenzie stood waiting.

Jess appeared moments later, having changed out of his clerical robe and into a black greatcoat. Quickly getting in beside Kerry, he put an arm around her and pulled her close to him. "Mrs. Corbett said you're not feeling well. Is it because of Martin, dear?" he asked with concern. "Did he upset you that much?"

Leaning against him, Kerry hesitated. She wanted to tell him everything, but should she add even more to the burden he was already carrying? What good would come of it? What exactly could Jess do? Nothing, she realized with grim resignation. There was absolutely nothing Jess—or anyone else—could do. While it was true that he had a way of making things better once he put a hand to them, he was powerless to change what his wife was or where she had come from.

Her decision made, Kerry nodded a silent agreement to his question about Martin; she kept her silence about everything else.

That night, Jess walked into their bedroom and found Kerry sitting at her dressing table braiding her hair with fierce, determined movements. He stood just inside the door a moment, watching her, then walked over and placed his hands on her shoulders.

He silently studied her reflection in the oval mirror, then pulled up a chair behind her and sat down. His warm, fond gaze met hers in the mirror. "Let me do that, love. You're going to yank all your curls out," he teased.

Kerry gave the job over to him with a restless sigh.

"Do you know," he asked softly, smiling at her reflection in the mirror, "that the only time you ever braid your hair is when you're worried or upset?"

She looked surprised, then relaxed a little. "Da used to say that you must occupy anxious hands or they'll stir a pot of trouble."

He chuckled. "Dear one, it will take more than braids to keep those little hands of yours from doing a bit of stirring, I believe. Anyway," he declared abruptly, "you know I don't like your hair braided."

He gently separated the thickly coiled braid, touching his lips as he did so to one stubborn copper curl intent upon flopping over her ear. Picking up a hairbrush from the dressing table, he began to slowly brush her hair with sure, even strokes.

With dismay, he saw her chin tremble and her green eyes

72

mist with unshed tears. "Kerry, sweetheart, what's wrong? Are you still worried about Martin? I won't let him near you again, I promise you that."

She shook her head in protest, knowing she had no answer for him; the day had simply been too much. His dependable, loving gentleness had broken through the wall she'd erected earlier and threatened to crumble her well-intentioned defenses.

"I'm sorry, Jess . . . I don't know what's wrong with me tonight. I must be tired."

He returned the brush to the dressing table. Dropping both hands to her shoulders, he turned her around to face him. "Here, love," he prompted softly, gathering her closer and tucking her head against the hollow of his shoulder. "Are you sure there's nothing wrong?"

Again she shook her head, unwilling to meet his searching gaze. "Why is it, I wonder," she said dully, her voice muffled in the cool silk of his dressing gown, "that the more I want to please you, the more burden I seem to be to you?"

"Hush, now, love. That's simply not true," he reassured her in a soft but firm voice. Carefully, he scooped her up into his arms and carried her over to the rocking chair by the hearth where flames were gently lapping at the large, fragrant logs in the fireplace. He sat down and settled her comfortably on his lap. "My foolish, darling girl," he murmured against her temple as he began to rock slowly back and forth in the sturdy chair. "Don't you know by now that you are always infinitely pleasing to me? Why, all you have to do is draw a breath to make me happy."

"Oh, Jess, you always say the very thing to make me feel better, but more and more I see the ways I'm failing you, and it hurts me, knowing how much you deserve and how little I can give you."

Frowning with protest, Jess drew his face away from her. "Don't ever say that, dear love of my heart." He strengthened his protective embrace almost fiercely, holding Kerry so tightly that she almost lost her breath against his solid chest.

"You have never, ever failed me! Not once! And you never will. You could only fail me if you were to stop loving me."

"That could never be, my treasure," Kerry whispered against him.

She tipped her head to look up at him, then lifted her hands and placed them tenderly on either side of his face. Her words were a smothered promise as she gazed directly into his eyes. "I could no more stop loving you than I could stop the breath leaving my body, *cuisle mo chroid.*" *

She lost herself in the sweetness of his love-softened expression, the exquisite tenderness of his touch, the fervent reassurance of his kiss. When he raised his lips from hers, he searched her eyes, his gaze brimming with adoration and yearning.

"Kerry . . . are you well enough . . . can we love?" he murmured hoarsely.

In answer, she pulled his head down closer to her face and smiled into his love-filled eyes. She nodded almost shyly.

He then saw her expression abruptly sober with anxious regret. "Is it going to make a difference, Jess . . . that I can no longer give you a child?"

His eyes misted. She was like a small, wounded animal uncertain of her worth. He knew this question had been burning in her heart for weeks. There was such a heaviness in his chest he nearly cried out with the pain of it.

Somehow, he stilled his own aching heart and let all the intensity of his love shine out to her. He attempted to draw her troubled spirit into himself by the very force of his gaze. Then, lifting her in his arms, he rose carefully from the chair, his eyes never leaving her face. "Nothing," he promised in a husky whisper, "will ever make a difference in our love."

He cradled her closely against him and brushed one soft kiss of reassurance across her forehead before carrying her across the room.

CHAPTER
EIGHT

Kerry could hear the call of winter in the late November wind howling through the old oaks outside their bedroom window. The angry, moaning wail made her feel sad and alone even though Jess was sleeping soundly beside her. In a week, they would celebrate Thanksgiving. She admitted to herself that her increasing heaviness of heart was due, at least in part, to the approaching holidays.

For Jess's sake, she made every effort to be cheerful; most of the time, she succeeded. It was impossible, however, for her to forget that only a few months ago they had discussed this year's holiday season with great anticipation, certain it would be the most joyous ever for both of them.

Their baby was to have been born in December. They had hoped for a Christmas baby who might share the Savior's birthday. Now she was afraid the holidays would only bring pain in remembering all they had lost.

With a restless sigh, Kerry turned her face toward the window and stared woodenly at the faint trickle of moonlight filtering in through the drapes. She knew it was wrong to feel this way; her gloomy attitude most likely grieved the Lord. But, try as she would, she could not shake the oppressive feeling that a storm was gathering on the horizon of their future, a storm that would somehow shake the very foundation of their lives. Sometimes, she felt as if the death of their child had been only the beginning, a dreadful, heart-wounding prelude to an impending disaster.

With an involuntary shudder, she turned to study Jess's face, shadowed and barely visible in the faint glow of moonlight hovering about their bed. As always, his arms were wrapped around her in a snug, protective embrace. Lifting her hand to gently brush a springy wave of hair away from his forehead, Kerry smiled sadly as she pressed a tender kiss to his bearded cheek and then rested her head in the hollow of his shoulder.

Oh, Jess . . . asthore* . . . what does the future hold for us? What is this frightening city going to mean to our lives together, to our marriage?

Of late it seemed to Kerry that she was terribly ungrateful, no more than a spoiled child. Didn't she have more, far more, than most women ever dream of?

The powerful but gentle giant sleeping beside her was a true man of God, an unshakable tower of a man. Some of the most influential newspapermen and publishers in the North had referred to Jess in such glowing terms as "brilliant," "a man on fire," "a man who wields a pen of power and a pulpit of change." Hadn't Mr. Henry Ward Beecher himself gone so far as to call Jess a nineteenth century prophet?

And yet he loved her—had loved her, so he said, since she was no more than a slip of a girl in a gingham dress and a tattered shawl. He had given her a place in his life, in his home, and in his heart. He had taken her in, cared for her, protected her, educated her—and finally married her.

Oh, and didn't she love him, too? *I love him more than everything, Lord, you know that. Sometimes my heart feels about to burst with love for him, it does. Why, then, am I hurting so? Why can't I simply be satisfied with things as they are? Why can't I let go of the grief about the babe? And why does it squeeze my heart so that there are those who seem to count me as worthless, who look upon me as no more than "Irish riffraff?" Why should it matter what anyone else thinks, so long as my Jess loves me?*

He would be furious and terribly hurt if he were to know the extent of the rejection and insulting treatment she had suffered from Lydia Northcote and the others. And that was exactly why she had chosen to keep silent. Surely she could handle this alone, without running to him as she was used to doing with each and every petty problem.

Lately he'd been besieged with a mountain of cares and concerns, an increasing load of responsibilities and burdens; he seemed engulfed by the problems of others. In addition to the voluminous duties of his pastorate, a growing number of politicians now came seeking his counsel. Too, he had his writing. Jess was never without a book in progress, and Kerry's head still reeled at the way his prolific pen could pour out dozens of articles for newspapers while fashioning a sermon that would leave one shaken for days.

No, she had been right to remain silent about her own problems. After all, she was no stranger to disapproval and suspicion. Hadn't she encountered it often enough in the hostile streets of Buffalo where she and her Da had lived when they first came to America?

Even at West Point, she had experienced the pain of rejection. The contemptuous assault of Lowell Martin served as a reminder that there would always be those who viewed her, and "her kind," as less than acceptable.

For Jess's sake, she would handle this alone. It was all so insignificant, really, considering the far more important matters he encountered almost daily. This much, at least, she could spare him.

Kerry turned restlessly in his arms, trying not to wake him. Lately, her sleep had been fitful at best. Often, her thoughts and questioning emotions kept her awake for hours after they retired. Now that the wind had quieted, she felt a welcome blanket of drowsiness settle over her. Burrowing more closely against Jess's large, solid warmth, she finally slept.

In the small, dark cottage behind the parsonage, Mackenzie reluctantly opened his eyes and lay still for a few moments as he tried to figure out what had awakened him. Finally, he sat up, yawned, and slowly swung his feet over the side of the bed. Grumbling irritably, he scratched his head and waited, listening.

There it was; he had heard something. Sure and weren't the mares snorting and carrying on in the carriage house?

With a tired grunt, he hauled himself into a pair of trousers over his union suit, hiked up his suspenders, and put on his shoes. He went to the small window and peered out across the few feet separating him from the carriage house. A thin stream of moonlight zigzagged across the lawn, but he saw nothing.

Still, the horses were afret about something; he best look in on them. The youngest was a feisty one, easily put off her feed, but he'd see to her, just to be sure. The little missus favored her something fierce.

Almost as an afterthought, he went back to the bed and pulled a shillelagh from beneath it. Shrugging into his woolen work coat and hobbling stiffly out the back door of the bungalow, he crossed to the rear of the carriage house. He stopped once thinking he heard something at the front of the yard. Seeing nothing, he shuffled on toward the carriage house and entered through the back door.

Mib, the older gray, was reasonably placid, paying him little attention. The small black mare, however, was obviously nervous, her eyes wild and her ears pricked stiffly forward as the breath from her nostrils steamed the cold air in the stall.

"And what might be biting at you, you young she-devil?" he growled affectionately while stroking and soothing her with his large hand and droning voice.

In moments, he had gentled her enough that she consented to nuzzle a bit of sugar from the small supply he always kept in his pockets. "Well now, and are we ready to take another snooze? It's heavy these old peepers of mine are. You've already cost me a good—"

He stopped and whirled around at the sound of a nearby shout—a shout soon followed by another. He heard a thud and a sudden crackling. The mare went crazy, and even the sluggish gray began to whinny and toss her head in agitation.

Mackenzie glanced at the shillelagh in his hand then moved as fast as his arthritic legs would take him to the front entrance of the carriage house. From there, he could see his cottage no more than a few feet away.

The sight that greeted him chilled his blood and made his once-drowsy eyes widen with stunned alarm. He had the presence of mind to flatten himself against the wall by the doorway where he could look out without being seen.

His small bungalow was in flames. The blaze was already high enough to shed a bright halo of light about the cottage and above the rooftop. Framed in the glow of the fire, four hooded, dark-cloaked men sat on horseback and silently watched the cottage burn. In the shadowy light from the flames, Mackenzie could see that all four were armed with rifles.

He clutched the shillelagh tighter and glanced anxiously around the carriage house. In a sick rage, he realized he was helpless. The oaken cudgel in his hand would be useless against the armed men.

Smoke began to burn his eyes and lungs as he stood unmoving, watching the little house he'd become extremely fond of over the years burn to the ground.

Lord, Lord, don't let the family wake, he prayed silently. *Keep them safe inside, for now at least!*

He expelled a deep breath of relief when he saw the four men abruptly turn their horses, at the instruction of the rider in the middle, and go thundering off into the night. He then ran as fast as he could toward the main house, shouting as he raced across the yard. "Fire! There's a fire!"

He stopped at the back porch steps and bent to pick up a rock. Hoisting a metal bucket from beside the porch, he started banging wildly and yelling at the top of his lungs.

Molly was the first out the back door, screaming as she charged off the porch, her unsecured braids tossing to and fro, her brown bathrobe flapping as she ran. She stopped a few feet away from the porch and stood paralyzed, staring in shocked disbelief at the blazing cottage.

*Go sabhala Dia sinn!** She launched into her native Gaelic for a swift prayer, then began to cry out Mackenzie's name. Panicking, she started to run, stopped, and turned in midstride, looking wildly upward to the second floor of the house. "Jess! Come quickly! Mackenzie's place is on fire!"

Jess, however, was already on his way. He shot through the door, dressed only in his pants and boots, throwing on a coat as he ran. Kerry was right behind him, struggling with the belt on her dressing gown as she ran outdoors.

"Stop your screaming, old woman!" Mackenzie roared at the housekeeper, grabbing her arm from behind which caused Molly to scream even louder. She whirled around to face Mackenzie, gave one final yelp, then hushed, looking from the caretaker to the burning cottage.

"You—you're not inside then!" she stammered blankly.

"Sure and I'm not!" Mackenzie growled acidly. "Get a bucket now! We must take the buckets to the pond!"

Kerry ran up to the caretaker and grasped his arm as if to reassure herself that he wasn't inside the burning building. "Mackenzie! Oh, Mackenzie—you're all right, then?"

"I'm perfectly fine, missus," he said gruffly, flustered and pleased by her concern. He turned from her and started for the pond with a bucket.

"Kerry, go back inside!" Jess ordered, grabbing a bucket for himself. "You'll catch cold out here!"

"No! You'll be needing me to help, too!" she shouted back at him.

For over two hours they worked furiously bailing water from the pond behind the cottage and flinging it onto the blaze. The smell of smoke and all the noise attracted several neighbors who came to help. A small volunteer fire company also showed up, too late to be of any real assistance.

The wind settled, and they finally succeeded in extinguishing the blaze, but the cottage was destroyed. Only a charred shell of one wall remained standing.

Much later, after they'd answered numerous questions from the firemen and the police, the four of them sat in the kitchen drinking coffee and talking in hushed, disturbed tones. Their faces were grimy, their hair and clothing saturated with the smell of smoke. But they were simply too tired to care.

Jess had no answer when both Kerry and Molly asked about the reason for the fire. A number of possibilities occurred to him, all of them troubling.

It was Mackenzie who finally made a terse reply. "I'm thinking we'd best take it as a warning," he said, his words dropping heavily into the silence around the large pine table.

"A warning?" Kerry asked, glancing uncertainly at Jess.

"Aye, and perhaps even more," Mackenzie replied, raising his head to look directly into Kerry's eyes. "I'm a known Irisher, missus—same as you." Without looking at her, he nodded toward Molly and added grudgingly, "Her, too."

Ignoring the housekeeper's glare, he continued. "The cottage is but a few feet from the house where you and the pastor were sleeping, don't you see?"

Kerry and Molly stared in bewilderment at Mackenzie. Jess, uncomfortable with his own suspicions, kept his eyes focused on the coffee cup in front of him.

"They likely thought I was inside," Mackenzie went on, his tone heavy with fatigue. "And that didn't bother them at all, now, did it?" He looked pointedly at Jess, who finally raised his head and met the caretaker's worried gaze.

"I'm thinking this bunch, whoever they may be, aren't a bit squeamish about harming an Irisher—especially one associated with the pastor."

Jess was unwilling—or afraid—to agree with Mackenzie, as if merely giving voice to his fears would make them more a reality. Still, he asked the question that had clawed at his mind since the terror of this night began: "You think this was meant as a threat against Kerry?" he asked quietly while reaching to cover her hand with his.

Mackenzie cocked his head and pursed his wide mouth. "I'd be inclined to think, Pastor," he said slowly, "that it was a threat against the two of you. Aye, that's what it looks like to me."

Kerry and Molly traded uneasy glances but said nothing. The four remained in unbroken silence for a long time. If any one of them had an opinion about Mackenzie's comment, no one voiced it. Occasionally, Jess looked over at Kerry sitting beside him, and once Molly narrowed her eyes and measured the caretaker with an appraising stare. But no one spoke until Jess asked Molly to prepare one of the bedrooms in the back of the house for Mackenzie.

"You can move into the house for now, Mack," he offered, "until we get the cottage rebuilt."

When the older man protested saying he could get a room in a boardinghouse, Jess firmly silenced him.

"I'd feel better, Mack, with another man in the house, especially since I'm gone so much. I'd really like for you to stay close."

Mackenzie searched Jess's eyes for a moment, then nodded his assent. Lifting his chin, he turned a defiant stare on Molly, as if he expected her to challenge Jess's suggestion.

Molly, however, simply curled her lip in an expression of resigned disgust, rolled her eyes toward heaven—and remained unexpectedly silent.

CHAPTER
NINE

The Sunday before Thanksgiving, Kerry sat on the edge of her pew and listened to Jess deliver a sermon which would, she suspected uneasily, ruffle a few feathers. *But only those who deserve to have them ruffled a bit,* she reminded herself.

He creatively threaded his message around the arrival of the pilgrims in America, the aid given them by the Indians, and the relationships—the friendships—that developed between many of the early settlers and the "savages" they had been taught to fear. He told how the descendants of those same pilgrims later plundered the lands of the very ones who had helped their ancestors, detailing a number of ways that "Americans abused Americans."

"And we're still doing it," he said quietly, with a sad, knowing smile. "What a shock it must be," he continued gravely, "to those who, for years, have thought of themselves as being decent, ordinary people—acceptable to God and presumably to the rest of the human race—to discover that they're not what they thought they were because the color of their skin is different or because there's a burr or a brogue in their speech or because their religion isn't what others think it should be. Imagine their astonishment when they realize that God must not consider them a part of his creation after all, even though they're strikingly similar to the rest of us who are walking around claiming to belong to him."

Kerry stared up at him, wide-eyed and a little surprised—as always—while her gentle-natured husband took on the mantle of power and eloquence he wore so easily once he faced a congregation. Though they had been married for nearly three years, and she had watched him and listened to him expound from his pulpit almost every Sunday during that time, she never failed to feel a sense of awe and wonder at the towering, black-robed figure he presented as he spoke to the people of his pastorate. Sometimes quiet-voiced, sometimes fiery; occasionally sorrowful, always sincere; frequently challenging, never condemning, Jess was a man who had dedicated himself to making a difference for God.

And he did make a difference, Kerry thought to herself with pride, allowing her mind to drift back to West Point. Most of the cadets at the Academy had thought of Jess as a rock, a stronghold. Rare was the man who graduated from West Point during the years Jess served as chaplain who didn't at least once, according to Molly, rely on his advice or assistance in some way.

And he was making a difference in Washington, too, Kerry believed, though it hadn't been easy for him. The Polk administration was known to be far more concerned about expansion and national power than the issue of human rights. Indeed, President Polk himself had been accused by some of the leading reformers in the country of being indifferent to the issue of slavery, the hardships of the factory workers, and the poverty of thousands of immigrants. Others regarded the stern-faced president as no more than a tool of the slave owners. Even Jess, usually quick to give every man the benefit of the doubt, admitted that the present chief executive seemed less than concerned about the country's social problems.

The current political regime's focus on the "manifest destiny" of the nation seemed to leave little time or energy to consider the plight of the laborers who were helping settle and build the country into the world power envisaged by the politicians. Consequently, Jess's crusade for a higher quality of life for the impoverished and enslaved was often ignored or viewed with disdain and anger by the majority of those with political influence.

But there were those who listened, and some were beginning to think for themselves. Opinions were changing, hearts were softening, and steps were being taken—although they were slow and often uncertain—to put into motion those laws that would eventually guarantee a better life for all Americans.

Kerry knew Jess was attempting to gain an audience with the Senate, hoping to inspire and encourage those who had the necessary influence and power to use it for the suffering, oppressed masses. But she also knew he had begun to despair of ever having his request granted. The few senators who agreed with Jess's views had strong opponents in most of the southern senators. Northcote, Forbrush, Calhoun, and others made no secret of the fact that they considered Jess to be hopelessly naive, even foolish.

Jess was a man ordinarily pleased with even the smallest signs of progress in his endeavors. Kerry often marveled at his seemingly bottomless reservoir of patience. Lately, however, she worried more than a little about his frequent fatigued appearance and occasional periods of brooding. He was given to long silences—which she'd grown used to. But this was different.

Ever since Mackenzie's cottage had burned down, Jess remained uncommonly quiet and heavy-spirited. When she questioned him, he would simply shrug off his melancholy and quickly make a cheerful effort to reassure her. She wasn't convinced, however. He was obviously troubled but apparently determined not to worry her.

Realizing that her thoughts had wandered far from the sermon, Kerry colored guiltily when a sudden, unusual silence jolted her back to the present. She returned her attention to the pulpit, only to see Jess staring out into the congregation with a peculiar frown of dismay.

A quiet stirring had begun throughout the sanctuary; heads turned and voices whispered as a number of people craned their necks to see what was happening. Jess's last few words died abruptly on his lips, and Kerry saw a flush shadow his face.

Uneasily, she turned her gaze in the direction of his disconcerted stare, catching her breath sharply when she saw that Senator Forbrush, the Northcotes, and Senator Calhoun and his wife had risen from their pews and were making their way up the center aisle, clearly intent on leaving the worship service.

John Calhoun, the tall, gray-haired senator from South Carolina, appeared to be pale with anger, his always severe features now hardened to a wintry mask. Not one of the departing group looked to either side of the aisle as they exited.

Once they were gone, every gaze returned to Jess in obvious anticipation of how he would deal with the blatant insult that had just been dealt him. Kerry swallowed with great difficulty and clutched her gloved hands so tightly they grew numb. She stared up at Jess. Her heart ached for his embarrassment; she desperately wanted to leave her pew and go to him.

While she sat there hurting for him, she saw his face settle into its familiar expression of quiet, controlled strength. In an even, steady tone, he continued, as if nothing out of the ordinary had taken place.

"Beloved brethren, these are not my words, but those of our Lord: 'Ye are all the children of God by faith in Christ Jesus. There is neither bond nor free. Ye are all one. God is no respecter of persons—have we not all one Father? Hath not one God created us? Why do we deal treacherously every man against his brother, by profaning the covenant of our fathers?' "

He leaned far across the pulpit, his face contorted with eloquent anguish. His voice was so quiet it could be heard only with effort.

"People, please hear me. God does not see race. He doesn't see the color of our skin. God does not see our nationality or our history or our legacy. God doesn't see kings or princes, prime ministers or presidents. He doesn't see rich or poor, wise or simple, great or small. God sees . . . the heart."

He paused, caught a breath, then continued in a voice hoarse with emotion. "He isn't looking for people who meet particular standards or specifications. He isn't looking for people to judge or condemn or punish. He's looking for people to love—people who will love him in return. That's all he wants. That's all he's ever wanted."

There was silence—a tense, waiting silence, heavy with expectation. Jess passed the back of his hand across his eyes then turned and stepped slowly down from the pulpit, exiting through the side door of the platform rather than going to the back of the sanctuary to greet the departing congregation as he usually did. After an awkward silence, the organist moved into a faltering postlude.

Kerry hurried from her pew, taking no notice of the excited whisperings and murmurings about her. She nearly stumbled in her haste to get out the side door and make her way to Jess's office at the rear of the building.

She found him standing at the large, narrow window behind his desk, still in his robe. When he turned to her, his shoulders were slumped and there was such an anguished look of defeat engraved upon his face she could have cried for him.

She went to him at once and stood on tiptoe to rest her hands on his shoulders; she kissed him lightly on the cheek. "I'm so terribly proud of you, dearest," she said softly. "That was a wonderful message."

He attempted a weak smile and touched one hand gently to her face. "Obviously, not everyone shared your enthusiasm, love."

"Don't let that blind bunch of bigots upset you a bit, d'you hear, Jess?" She put her arms around his middle and held him tightly, their positions reversed for once as she attempted to comfort him. Tipping her head back to gaze up at him, she added, "They're only a few, after all."

Jess shook his head ruefully. "But a most significant few, I'm afraid. I'm especially bothered by John Calhoun's attitude," he continued after a heavy sigh. "He's an intelligent man and an effective senator—one of the most powerful men in the Senate, as a matter of fact. We're at extreme odds with each other in what we believe—but I can't help but respect the man."

He sighed again, then wrapped his arms more tightly around her and rested his chin on top of her head. "Sometimes it all seems so . . . . futile. So much of the problem exists because of nothing more substantial than family custom or the tradition of a particular locale. I think that's one of the things I find the most discouraging: so many people believe in slavery because their parents upheld it or because of where they were raised. It would simply never occur to them to think for themselves."

"And they despise those who are different—the Irish included—for just as little reason," Kerry murmured with understanding. "But it's as you once told me, is it not, Jess?" she asked, putting her hands on his shoulders and drawing back just enough to look up at him. "A man can do no more than speak the truth. Only the good Lord can open the ears of those who need to hear it."

He smiled down at her. "Did I say that, wife?"

"Aye, that you did, my fine husband."

He stared at her for a moment, then tipped her chin upward with one finger, his expression brightening as he looked into her eyes. " Then it must be true, I suppose."

"I should think so, sir," she returned pertly.

"Ah, Kerry . . . let's go home," he said, dropping his hands from their embrace to shrug out of his robe. "I intend to do nothing else today but go home and stuff myself on whatever Molly's cooked up for Sunday dinner. And I don't want to think about anything more weighty than the extra two or three pounds I'm sure to put on this afternoon."

Relieved, Kerry took his robe from him and hung it in the closet. "That won't be difficult to do, dearest. I happen to know what Molly's planning for dinner."

His interest quickened as he turned back to her. "Oh? Something special?"

She shrugged and rolled her eyes mysteriously. "I'll not be spoiling her surprise. But it might just be something of which you're extremely fond."

"Dumplings?" he asked hopefully. "Did she make apple dumplings?"

With a smug smile, Kerry arched her brows, tucked her arm in his, and pulled him along behind her through the office door. "The sooner we get home, the sooner you'll be knowing, now isn't that right?"

After they finished dinner and Jess had moaned and protested enough about his overeating to please Molly, who had indeed prepared his favorite dish of apple dumplings, he and Kerry went into the library.

Kerry played with Brian Boru in front of the fire while Jess caught up on the mail and newspapers he hadn't had time to read for the past several days.

"I told you there was a letter here from John O'Sullivan, didn't I?" Jess asked, scanning the first page of several sheets of stationery.

O'Sullivan was the editor of a popular expansionist magazine; he had also been credited with first coining the phrase "manifest destiny," which had quickly gained popularity not only in Washington but throughout the entire country. Jess and O'Sullivan had become acquaintances, then friends, through their mutual contacts in publishing.

"Aye, you did," Kerry answered distractedly, laughing as she watched the rambunctious kitten tumble over his own feet and scoot across the hearth in pursuit of a catnip mouse. She was pleased to see that, true to her initial prediction for him, the tabby was growing up large and solid and brave—too brave for Molly, Kerry thought with amusement. Hardly a day passed that Brian Boru and the housekeeper didn't square off at least once. Overall, Kerry would have to judge Brian the definite winner in their contests.

"He confirms what we've been told about the potato blight in Ireland," Jess said in a low voice. "It's bad; very bad."

Alert to the note of concern in his tone, Kerry got up from the floor and went to sit beside him, perching on the arm of the sofa.

"How bad?"

He shook his head as he continued to read. "Someone in his family went over recently to check on their relatives. O'Sullivan says it would appear to be even worse than the crop failure in '39." He glanced up at her. "That's the year you left Ireland."

She nodded. "It was a terrible time. Da always tried to keep a few small crops in besides the potatoes to help us along, though the neighbors thought him odd for it. Mostly, the people live on their potatoes alone, you know."

"You can read this for yourself, but I'm afraid it's all bad news, love. John seems to think it means unavoidable disaster for Ireland, though the British government is already saying the facts have been exaggerated."

"Well, and they would," Kerry said indignantly. "Old Orange Peel* would no doubt like the country to starve to death before anyone could be knowing enough to help, disliking the Irish as he does."

Jess finished the letter then passed it to Kerry, who read it in silence. Finally, she dropped it into her lap and stared down at the floor for a long moment. "It will be famine again. And, from the sound of it, worse than ever before."

Jess reached for her hand. "I thank God you're here with me, love."

She turned her gaze onto him. "As do I, Jess. But I can't help thinking of all those who will starve to death or die in a ditch of the fever because they've no one to help them."

"England will simply have to help. She has too much invested in Ireland to ignore this."

"England's way of helping," Kerry replied with a small, bitter sound of derision, "will be to order the landlords to tumble the cottages around the very heads of starving children and send those who are still able to walk on their way to the poorhouse! That's always been the way of it, and most likely it won't be changing."

He studied her face, watching her eyes spark with anger as her brogue thickened. "John says it will be months before the full consequences of the blight are felt," he remarked, lifting another envelope from the stack on the table beside the sofa.

"That's true," Kerry agreed. "First there will be plenty. The people will be anxious to get rid of their potatoes while they can still be eaten. But after a few months, there will be nothing. That's when the hunger will start. I remember Da talking at night by the fire about other times of famine."

She handed the letter to him and rose from the arm of the sofa, walking across the room to scoop up Brian Boru from his stance in front of the window where he was appraising the drapes for possible climbing. The kitten flattened himself against Kerry's shoulder as she straightened to look out the window into the darkness of the early winter's evening.

Molly walked in just then with a fresh pot of coffee.

"Ah, Molly, how you spoil us," Jess said, leaning back against the cushion of the sofa with a broad smile.

"You can do with a bit of spoiling today, I'm thinking," the housekeeper muttered, placing the tray on the library table behind the couch.

"Kerry, have you extended our invitation to Cely for Thanksgiving dinner yet?" Jess asked, remembering their conversation of a few days before.

Kerry turned around, smiling at the purring kitten nestled against her shoulder. "Aye, I did." Her expression sobered as she set the kitten to the floor. "But she won't be coming."

"Why not?"

"Well, she didn't exactly say as much," Kerry replied with a small frown, "but I believe she thought it might cause trouble for us. She hemmed and hawed and finally thanked me but said she was going to fix a meal at the school for the students and their families."

Jess looked surprised. "Where will she find the means to do that? She can't possibly afford it on her own."

Kerry crossed her arms over her chest and sighed. "It will be meager at best, I should think. But I'm coming to learn that when Cely Johnson makes up her mind to do something, she'll somehow find a way to get it done."

Jess took the cup of steaming coffee Molly held out to him. "Would she let us help, do you think?"

"Help? How could we help, Jess?"

He took a sip of coffee, then set the cup on the lamp table beside him. "Well, if Molly's willing, we could help prepare some of the food, then deliver it to the school. In fact," he said thoughtfully, "we could join Cely and the others and have dinner with them, if you'd want."

"You'd do that, Jess?" Kerry's eyes lighted with pleased surprise.

"I'd enjoy it," he replied quickly. "And you'd like being with the children, wouldn't you?"

"Oh, yes, you know I would! But—"

"Molly, would you and Mack be willing to ignore the inconvenience and help out that day?"

Molly nodded firmly without hesitation. "'Twould be no problem at all for me, but I'd not be speaking for that sour old man. His mood changes with the hour, it does."

Kerry met Jess's grin with one of her own. Her expression quickly sobered, however, with her next question. "Could it bring trouble for you, though, Jess?" she asked, tugging anxiously at her fingers. "I wouldn't want to be doing anything to cause more problems than we've already had."

Seeing her eyes light with an uncertain glint of hopefulness, Jess promptly reassured her. "How could anyone fault me for helping to provide a Thanksgiving meal for a group of school children, Kerry? Besides," he added dryly, "it's not likely that we'll be running into any of the more prestigious members of the —"

His last few words died on his lips, interrupted by a cry of surprised alarm as the tall, spacious window directly behind Kerry suddenly shattered. Shards of glass flew inward, spraying the floor as a large rock sailed into the room and hit Kerry on the head with a sickening thud.

Jess lunged forward off the couch and hurled himself directly at Kerry, shouting her name. Molly, too, charged across the room. Both were too late. Kerry was down, first on her knees, then sprawled face forward on the floor.

Mackenzie came running into the library. "What happ—" He stopped dead when he saw Kerry on the floor with Jess and Molly bent over her.

Jess's face was a stricken mask when he raised his head and turned toward Mackenzie. "Mack, go for Dr. Marshall!" When he looked back at Kerry, he nearly strangled from the tight fist of fear clutching at his throat.

But Kerry raised one hand in weak protest, moaned, and started to turn over. "No . . . I'm all right . . ."

"Careful . . . careful, love . . . there's glass all around you," Jess cautioned in a shaky voice as he helped her turn over on her back.

His hand trembled as he smoothed her hair away from her forehead and studied her face. "Thank the Lord," he murmured with relief. "I was afraid you'd been cut." Carefully, he began to pick tiny slivers of glass from the skirt of her dress.

"No, I'm fine, really," Kerry assured him, her own voice unsteady. "Just . . . my knees, I think. I must have banged them when I fell."

"But your head—"

"It's only a bump." She made a weak dismissing motion with her hand. "I'm all right."

"Well, let's get you onto the sofa for now," Jess insisted, scooping her up into his arms with extreme care. "I still want to have George Marshall look at you."

"That's not necessary, Jess. I'm fine. Just let me rest a bit."

Mackenzie and Molly followed them to the sofa and continued to hover nearby. The big, awkward caretaker stared down at Kerry with dismay.

"You sure you don't need the doctor, missus? Maybe you're hurt more than you're knowing?"

Kerry managed a smile for him. "No, Mackenzie—really, I'm fine." She shuddered slightly. "Perhaps it frightened me a bit, but that's all."

"Molly, you stay here with her," Jess said. "We're going to have a look outside."

"*No, Jess!*" Kerry cried, thrusting herself upward to clutch his arm. "Someone might still be out there!"

"That's exactly what I intend to find out," Jess grated, gently but firmly removing her hand from his forearm. "Mack, get your club and go with me, please."

Whoever had thrown the rock was gone by the time Jess and Mackenzie reached the yard. They searched the area in front and back of the house; they even checked the carriage house. There was nothing to be found.

Mackenzie absently swung the shillelagh from his fingers and shook his head gloomily as they walked back into the house. "Do you suppose someone really meant to hurt the little missus, Pastor?" he asked, stopping in the reception hall. "Or is it just another threat, do you think?"

Jess felt extremely tired—tired and frightened and furious. He raked one hand through his hair in a gesture of frustration. "I don't know what to think anymore, Mack," he answered, dragging in a long, ragged breath, "except that perhaps I made a terrible mistake by coming here in the first place. Kerry's had nothing but misery and trouble ever since—" He stopped, unable to continue.

Mackenzie glanced at him. An uncommon warmth softened his features when he touched Jess lightly on the shoulder and mumbled reassuringly, "I'll help you take care of her, Pastor. I'll watch over her, too, just as closely as I can."

Jess searched the older man's gaze for a moment, then smiled weakly and nodded. "I know you will, Mack. And it helps me a great deal to know that."

But would it help Kerry? he silently asked himself. *Was anything other than leaving Washington going to help Kerry?*

CHAPTER
TEN

For the first time since their nightmare began, Jess and Kerry received word from the police that they might have a witness who could be of some help, at least in a minor way.

The day after the rock was thrown through the Dalton's window, all nearby residents were questioned. One of them, an elderly man who lived on the opposite side of the Square from the parsonage, thought he "might have seen something peculiar" the night before.

He had opened his front door to call his dog and was standing in the doorway, waiting, when he thought he saw a large, dark shadow fleeing the side yard of the parsonage.

He told the investigating officer he hadn't thought much about it, because he didn't see very well anymore and because "it's always so dark over there with all those big old trees." But he admitted that it might have been a person, and, yes, that person might have been running away from the Dalton house.

Jess agreed with the police that it wasn't much, but it was more than they'd had up until now. He told Kerry this much, and no more, although their neighbor had made one other ambiguous observation: "If what I saw was a man—and mind you, I'm not saying it was—then I can tell you this: he was big! In fact, now that I think about it, it went through my mind for just a second or two that it was Pastor Dalton, since he's such a big man himself, you know. But that wouldn't make any sense, now would it, because why in the world would the pastor be running away from his own house?"

It was the comment about a "big man" that bothered Jess most. He remembered clearly Kerry's description of the man who had abducted her: "a great, hulking lout," she had called him.

Not knowing how she might react to the possibility of the man having been close to her again, Jess chose, at least for the time being, to keep it to himself. He did, however, remind the police of the similarity of the descriptions.

More afraid than ever for her safety, Jess tried to talk Kerry out of going through with the plan to spend Thanksgiving Day at the school. With a feeling bordering on shame, he admitted to himself that, if he could, he'd lock her away from the outside world entirely until this whole ordeal was resolved. Lately, it seemed that he spent most of his waking hours in fear for her. The tension was wringing him dry.

That's why he now found himself faced with the undesirable choice of either reneging on his original suggestion about helping with the Thanksgiving dinner at the school or following through with it, knowing he would spend the entire day in the grip of anxiety simply because Kerry would be in an environment he couldn't control.

As was often the case in their marriage, though, she got her way. Widening her eyes in an innocent stare, she declared that since both he and Mackenzie—as well as a number of the children's fathers—would be around her all during the day, surely she'd be "adequately guarded."

The deciding factor, however, was when she twisted the knife just enough to remind him of the fact that all this had been his idea in the first place and she'd never known him to go back on his word.

Thus, Thanksgiving Day started before dawn for Molly and Kerry, and not long afterward for the men of the house.

A few minutes before seven that morning, Mackenzie made the mistake of walking into the kitchen. He grinned broadly at Adeline Corbett, who had asked to participate in the plans and was just tying the strings of a ruffled white apron around her slender waist. The caretaker went immediately to the stove and lifted the lids off various pans to inspect their contents. When no one so much as acknowledged his presence, he squared his shoulders, cleared his throat, and inquired about breakfast.

Bristling, Molly planted her hands on her hips and snapped

at him fiercely enough to make him jump away with a surly growl.

"Sure and you needn't be expecting to be waited on this morning, Murtagh Mackenzie!" With one forward move, she elbowed him out of the way, pushing between him and Kerry to lift a massive kettle of potatoes onto the large iron stove. After setting the kettle carefully in place, she turned on Mackenzie and waved a large cooking spoon at him with firm orders to "do for himself!"

Jess chose that moment to enter the kitchen, earning himself a dark glare of exasperation from Molly and an amused shrug from his wife. Assessing the situation, he wisely asked if he could help.

"Indeed you can!" retorted Molly without hesitation. "We'll be needing more wood, and the trap will have to be cleaned and padded a bit before we can load all this food onto it."

"Consider it done," he answered agreeably. Thinking he had sufficiently ingratiated himself, he ventured another question. "Ah . . . will there be breakfast today, Molly?"

Without turning from the stove, where she was pouring water over the potatoes, Molly gave him a short reply. "You'll have to be doing with leftover biscuits and curd cake this morning. I put a plate of each on the dining room table along with fresh coffee."

Mackenzie lifted his chin and snarled at the housekeeper. "And why wouldn't you tell me that when I asked, woman?"

The housekeeper raised her head from the kettle of potatoes, her dark eyes flashing dangerously. Again, she waved her spoon in Mackenzie's direction with a wild swipe.

"And have I recently been taken into your employ without my knowledge, old man? *Wirra!** Off with you now, the both of you!" she ordered, once more peeling the air with her spoon, this time aiming it at Jess.

Suddenly, she stopped and looked down at her feet where a playful Brian Boru was stepping off the distance to one plump ankle. She shrieked, "And get that *puca** out of my kitchen! *Now,* mind you!"

Smelling a good fight, the kitten started to circle Molly's feet, whirling faster and faster as the housekeeper turned and hopped from one foot to the other. Losing her balance, she dropped the large spoon. It clattered to the floor beside the kitten, who immediately leaped from one end of it to the other, creating a seesaw effect that obviously delighted him.

Molly's face went from amazement to fury to revenge as she classified the cat in descriptive Gaelic, relegating him to the category of disgrace formerly reserved for Oliver Cromwell, British landlords, and *gombeen men**.

For a split second, Kerry thought Jess was going to fall to his knees in a fit of laughter. He looked about to strangle and was foolish enough to laugh aloud—only for an instant, though. A covert glance at Molly, who appeared to be in the throes of a seizure, quickly sobered him.

Sensible Irishman that he was, Mackenzie didn't laugh, but merely stood watching, his face expressionless, his eyes dancing with keen enjoyment. Adeline Corbett turned discreetly away so Molly couldn't see the uncontrollable smile breaking across her features.

Momentarily reluctant to end all the fun, Kerry finally decided that, in the interest of saving all nine of Brian Boru's lives, she needed to act at once. She rushed across the room, grabbed the kitten with one hand and retrieved the now contaminated spoon with the other. Flashing a quicksilver, ingenuous smile, she offered the spoon to Molly and then hurried out of the kitchen with the disappointed kitten tucked safely under her arm.

By two o'clock that afternoon, the schoolroom had taken on the appearance of a banquet hall. The tables Jess and Mackenzie had improvised from planks and logs were covered with white dinner cloths Molly and Kerry had made from old sheets. Rich, enticing odors filled the entire room, emanating from the serving tables laden with roast turkey, dressing, baked ham, potato soup, soused herring, gravy, sweet potatoes, fruit loaves, assorted pies, and half a dozen different puddings.

Kerry had all she could do to keep Jess from tasting everything in sight; Mackenzie, too, did his fair share of sneaking small samples. Molly finally took over and chased both men away with a flap of her apron and a few words of warning.

Soon the little schoolhouse was crammed snugly with children and their parents. The adult guests were obviously uncomfortable and ill at ease at first, but not for long. Kerry watched with growing relief as Jess and Mackenzie moved among the men; eventually, they were all talking and laughing comfortably.

Molly, who didn't know the meaning of shy, matter-of-factly went about herding everyone to the tables, occasionally enlisting the help of some of the women. Continuing to hover and fuss, she made sure everybody ate twice as much as they needed—especially, Kerry noticed with fond amusement, the children.

Adeline Corbett was the surprise of the day. Throughout the afternoon she could be found with an infant on one side of her lap and a toddler on the other. After everyone was uncomfortably sated with food, the slim, attractive widow rolled up the sleeves of her frilly white shirtwaist and trooped outside to play ball with some of the older children.

Kerry noted with interest that Mackenzie seemed more than a little fascinated with their charming neighbor. Mrs. Corbett appeared to be the focus of his attention for a large part of the afternoon. Even more interesting, though, was the disgruntled glare she caught Molly casting at Mackenzie every few moments. *If I didn't know better,* Kerry thought, *I would be inclined to think that Molly is . . . jealous.* She immediately shook off the idea, suppressing a smile at her own foolishness. To her knowledge, the housekeeper and the caretaker never so much as offered a kind word to each other. *Molly, jealous? Hardly.*

Late in the afternoon, Kerry went looking for Jess. She found him outside, sitting Indian style under a large willow tree with a group of small, wide-eyed boys. A mixture of affection and sadness tugged gently at her heart as she stood watching him with the children. His hair windblown and his face smudged, he looked young, relaxed, and happy in his plaid flannel shirt and the canvas pants he had rolled up above his ankles to play leapfrog and kick-the-can.

She saw he was teaching the boys to make slingshots, combining his instructions with a fast-paced, colorful account of David's slaying of Goliath. When he looked up and saw Kerry watching, he grinned and waved before returning his attention to the circle of small admirers surrounding him.

He should have had a son . . . many sons, she thought sorrowfully. Her eyes misted, and she had to walk away from the scene. *Oh, dear Lord, he would have been such a wonderful father.*

She stood at the edge of the school yard, staring out across the river. When she felt Jess gently rest his hands on her shoulders, she rubbed quickly at her eyes. He said nothing for a time but simply let her lean back against him.

Like a great, aging queen determined to claim her throne to the very end, the late afternoon sun hovered above the dome of the Capitol Building in a bronze and golden arc before slipping slowly out of view.

"It's lovely, isn't it?" Kerry said softly.

"Glorious," he replied, turning her around in his arms. "I've seen only one thing in my lifetime that's more lovely than a sunset." His smile left no doubt whatsoever as to his meaning.

When she didn't answer, he searched her eyes for a long moment. "What is it, dear? What's made you sad?"

"It's nothing," she murmured, unwilling to spoil the moment.

He lifted one dark brow in gentle contradiction and absently tucked a silky curl behind her ear.

She shook her head and glanced down at the ground. "I suppose it was . . . seeing you with the children, seeing how good you are with them, how they enjoy you—and how you enjoy them."

With a gentle hand, he cupped her chin and tilted her head upward to look into her eyes. "Don't, sweetheart. Don't be hurt," he said quietly. "I enjoy them, yes. But I'm not wishing for anything other than what I have."

She was unable to believe his assurance, though she wanted to with all her heart. When she would have looked away from him, he framed her face between his hands and held her gaze. "Kerry, I'm telling you the truth. I've accepted our being childless—because of you, because of the way you fill my life. Please . . . don't be sad."

His love-filled gaze went over her face with concern. "It's going to be all right, little love. I've prayed and prayed that our Lord will give you . . . something . . . to help ease the loss, to help fill the emptiness. And I believe he will."

Her eyes reflected the plea of her heart. "You truly do believe that, Jess?" she asked with a husky catch in her voice.

With great tenderness, he pressed his cheek to hers. "Yes, *mavourneen,** I do," he told her softly. "As much as I love you, God loves you even more—and he's not going to let you grieve forever."

He smiled into her eyes. "Come along, now. Last I heard, Molly was insisting on a bit of music from you and Mack. And as you know, it doesn't do to keep Molly waiting."

In those first weeks of her convalescence after losing the baby, Kerry and Mackenzie had discovered a mutual love for the traditional Irish music. As soon as Kerry was able to be up and around, the caretaker shyly introduced her to his unusual collection of musical instruments—and his uncommon facility with each of them.

After learning that Kerry played the flute and the fife, he took it upon himself to teach her his *clairseach*—a small, wire-strung folk harp which he had made himself—and the concertina. The two of them, coaxed by Jess and Molly, spent numerous evenings playing their instruments after dinner.

Today, in addition to Kerry's flute, they had brought a fiddle and a *bodhran.** Mackenzie had brought his harp, too, which he played expertly in the ancient manner with his fingernails, using his left hand on the treble.

The children danced with delight, and the grown-ups stamped their feet and clapped as the two musicians regaled them with a number of traditional hornpipes, reels, and jigs. Even the few parents who had remained somewhat aloof throughout the day, as if they were unable to accept the sincerity of the Daltons' gesture of friendship, at last surrendered their reserve.

When Molly, in a rare moment of civility with Mackenzie, requested "The Minstrel Boy," everyone sat in hushed silence as the big Irishman rendered the poignant old ballad in a surprisingly clear, strong tenor.

The musicians closed the evening with a medley of the blind harper O'Carolan's tunes. As the last plaintive notes held and echoed across the room, Kerry glanced at Molly and saw that the housekeeper's eyes were clouded with seldom-seen tears. For one very special moment, she knew that the three of them—Molly, Mackenzie, and herself—had felt the bittersweet stirrings of a common memory, that ancient, age-less bond of the heart . . . *Erin remembered.*

In the middle of the night, Kerry awakened with the unpleasant awareness that she was about to pay for her overindulgence of the day's rich food. A minor rebellion seemed to be taking place in her stomach, and when the churning failed to subside after several moments, she decided to go downstairs and get some of Molly's stomach elixir, an unpleasant thought, at best.

Molly refused to reveal the contents of the foul-tasting stuff she kept in the kitchen pantry—but it never failed to work. Kerry had suffered a number of stomach upsets lately, probably because of strain and worry, and the elixir had proven surprisingly effective.

With a reluctant sigh, she eased herself out of Jess's arms, put on her dressing gown, and lighted a small candle. As she tiptoed out of the room, Brian Boru raised his head once, uttered a drowsy meow, then immediately nestled himself deeper into the plump cushion in his basket and closed his eyes.

The house was cold, and Kerry shivered as she reached the bottom of the stairs. Hurrying through the dining room into the kitchen, she bumped into a chair that had been pulled out from the table. With a muffled exclamation, she went into the pantry and rummaged through the cabinets until she found the elixir.

After swallowing two spoonsful of the mixture and drinking a small glass of milk to kill the taste of it, she retrieved her candle and left the kitchen. She got as far as the bottom of the stairway. With a puzzled frown, Kerry stopped and glanced about the reception hall, listening. As she stood there, a shroud of icy fear draped her entire body. Her heart lurched, skipped a beat, then began to bang wildly against her rib cage.

From somewhere in the cold, silent darkness came a whisper—then another. The pulse at Kerry's throat thudded even harder. Paralyzed with fear, she stared wide-eyed at the massive front door as if she expected someone to come charging through it at any moment. A dizzy feeling of approaching disaster caused her to reel slightly backward, grabbing onto the satin-smooth baluster to steady herself.

She glanced down at the candle in her hand, unable to decide whether or not she should extinguish it. Too frightened to face the total darkness of the hall, she let it be.

She heard the murmuring again, somewhat louder this

time. Swallowing with great difficulty, she took one cautious step forward, certain now that the sounds were outside, but close. *Very close,* she thought, as her heart gave another violent wrench.

Drawing in a deep, ragged breath, Kerry eyed the narrow panes of glass on either side of the front door. Fearful of being seen, she reluctantly blew out the candle, placed it on the second step from the landing, and began walking slowly toward the door.

She glanced from one side to the other with each step, moving as quietly as possible. The cold of the house mingled with the chill of her fear, and she began to tremble. The palms of her hands were wet with clammy perspiration, and she nervously wiped them on the sides of her dressing gown.

Just before she reached the door, she stopped. *Perhaps I should go upstairs and call Jess . . . perhaps I should cry out for Mackenzie . . . perhaps someone is trying to break into the house and if I am simply standing here in the hall when they—*

She jumped, nearly bolting from the room when she heard a cracking sound outside, followed by what sounded like the rustle of dry leaves. There was an abrupt shout, then the sound of departing hoofbeats. Quickly, she flattened herself against the wall by the door so she could peer out one narrow pane of glass.

It was a clear night, and most of the enormous old trees in the yard stood stripped of their leaves. But what foliage remained on the dense branches made it difficult to see anything but shadows.

Pressing herself even closer to the wall, Kerry craned her neck a little more. Puzzled, she stared at one of the trees closest to the house; somehow it looked different. One side appeared to be drooping from the weight of something, but it was impossible to make out what.

She glanced around the reception hall, her mouth dry, her eyes wet with hot, nervous tears of fright. Turning her gaze back to the glass partition, she caught a glimpse of a dark, shadowy form that appeared to be moving across a corner of the yard.

She stiffened, holding her breath as she watched. The shadow stopped suddenly, then once more began to sway back and forth. She cast an uncertain glance up the stairway, then looked back to the door; finally she decided to go upstairs after Jess.

With her pulse pounding painfully in her ears, she cautiously started to back away from the door. So intent was she at remaining perfectly quiet, she failed to realize that Brian Boru was padding softly down the stairs. The kitten stopped for a curious look at the heavy brass candlestick Kerry had left on the step. He took a playful swipe at it with one paw, then another, this time knocking it over. He watched with interest as it bounced off the bottom two steps and fell to the parquet floor with a clang.

Startled by the noise, Kerry whirled around, momentarily losing her balance. At the same time, the frightened kitten came bounding toward her, causing her to trip over him and step on his tail.

He screeched, and Kerry echoed it with a terrified scream of her own. Then, as though the sound of her voice had released a pent-up torrent of fear deep inside her, she screamed again.

Within seconds, Jess appeared at the top of the stairway, flinging on his dressing gown and rushing down the stairs. Molly appeared from her room off the kitchen, a fat beeswax candle flickering wildly in her hand. Mackenzie was no more than a moment behind her, his shillelagh raised for action.

"Kerry! What's wrong?" Out of breath and still dazed with sleep, Jess grabbed Kerry's shoulders, looking first at her, then glancing anxiously around the shadowed reception hall.

Mackenzie seemed to be everywhere at once, charging around the hall and peering into the adjoining rooms. Molly snapped angrily at the kitten, who, terrified by all the commotion, immediately ran and hid under a chair in the parlor.

Jess raised a hand to hush everyone, then turned back to Kerry, who was clutching the front of his dressing gown, her eyes round with fear.

"Jess! I heard voices—and someone was moving around outside—there's someone out there, I think—" Her words spilled from her in a tumble of meaningless gasps as she frantically tried to make herself understood.

Instantly alert, Jess clasped her firmly by the shoulders. "Kerry—slow down, love. Tell me what happened."

Kerry caught her breath, still running her words together in a hoarse whisper but now making more sense. "I came downstairs . . . to get some stomach medicine . . .When I came out of the kitchen . . . I heard noises . . . outside . . . like people talking . . . then I heard horses ride off—" She stopped, swallowed, and thought for a moment. "Brian knocked the candlestick off the step, and I accidentally stepped on him . . . I screamed . . . I was coming for you, but—"

Jess pulled her tightly against himself and glanced over her head at Mackenzie with a worried frown. "Are you all right, love?" he asked, his voice tight with anxiety.

Kerry nodded against his chest, trying to drag deep breaths of air into her constricted lungs, willing herself to stop her violent trembling. "I was afraid to look out."

Again Jess's gaze met the caretaker's. "Mack, would you get a lantern?"

Mackenzie was back in an instant. When Jess gently put Kerry away from him, she started to follow the two men to the front door. Jess turned and stopped her with a firm hand on her shoulder. "No," he said flatly. "You're to stay inside with Molly." He glanced at the housekeeper, who nodded and reached out to grip Kerry by the forearm.

As soon as Jess and Mackenzie walked outside, however, Kerry pulled away from Molly and started toward the door.

"Lass, you heard—"

Ignoring her, Kerry went out the door, stepping slowly and carefully onto the porch. Molly clucked her tongue, muttering in exasperation as she followed.

Kerry watched the two men move out into the yard, Mackenzie extending the lantern slightly outward to cast enough light for both of them to see a few feet in front of them.

They walked slowly and cautiously, not speaking. When Kerry saw them come to an abrupt stop, she inched her way to the edge of the porch so she could see better.

Molly immediately moved to her side. "Let's go back inside, lass! We'll both catch our death out in this cold with no coats!"

"Shhh! They've found something!"

Quickly lifting the hem of her dressing gown, Kerry raced down the steps and hurried over to where the men were standing. Molly quietly went after her, apprehensive but curious.

Pushing herself between Jess and Mackenzie, Kerry saw nothing at first but the stunned anger on the caretaker's face and the look of astonished horror that had settled over Jess. She squinted into the shadows of the trees, her eyes focusing slowly in the dim glow cast by the lantern. Following the direction of Mackenzie's gaze as he lifted the lantern slightly higher, she instinctively stepped forward, only to be stopped by Jess's firm, almost painful grasp on her arm.

"Kerry—don't! Go back to the—"

But it was too late. Kerry saw, in brutal clarity, what Jess would have spared her. Her eyes locked on the scene in front of her, her face contorting into an image of disbelieving revulsion. As if from a great distance, she heard a shuddering roar, quickly peaking in a thundering din somewhere inside her head.

Her mind clamored to retreat, unwilling to accept the awful, hideous reality in front of her. She squeezed her eyes shut and braced herself for what she knew would still be there when she opened them again.

It was real, sickeningly, dreadfully real. She wanted to scream in denial, but she had no voice. She was dimly aware that Jess had pulled her almost roughly against him and was trying to make her turn away, but she twisted in his arms, willing herself to confront, with deadly calm, the two effigies hanging from a massive limb midway up the largest oak tree in the yard. Behind her, she heard Molly gasp. Both Jess and Mackenzie tried to lead the women away from the scene, but Kerry stood rigidly firm, as if trapped in place by some invisible force.

The larger of the two forms swinging obscenely in the night breeze, obviously intended to be Jess, wore a black clerical robe. The robe was authentic, not a facsimile. The female effigy was dressed in a plaid gown, almost identical to many of the day dresses Kerry often wore. A shawl, again similar to those Kerry wore, had been tossed about its shoulders. Both faces had been crudely darkened to make them appear black, and a substance clearly meant to be blood had been splattered across the chest of each form. They dangled limply from the tree limb and swayed gently back and forth, looking incredibly, terrifyingly real.

Kerry felt her legs shake beneath her as she finally surrendered the little strength of will she had left. Numbly, she felt Jess pass her into Molly's arms. He then walked over to the tree and pulled off a scrap of paper that had been fastened onto the thick trunk with a large knife.

His face paled to an ashen mask, then seemed to go slack.

"What is it, Jess?" Molly asked harshly as she continued to mindlessly pat Kerry on the back.

Jess glanced at her, then at Kerry, before looking back to the paper in his hand. "A note," he answered in a strained, rough voice. He swallowed hard, moistened his lips, and began to read in a nearly inaudible monotone:

There won't be any more warnings, Dalton. He paused a moment and looked again at Kerry. *Take your Irish biddy—*his voice broke for an instant before he could continue—*and your darky-loving swill and get out of Washington. Or we'll carry the two of you out in matching coffins.*

The last thing Kerry saw was the dark and terrible pain—or was it fear—in Jess's eyes as he looked from her to Mackenzie, then to Molly. For an instant, she longed to go to him, to comfort him. *He looks so terribly stricken,* she thought, just before a softly lapping wave gently pressed her down and absorbed her into a black, peaceful pool of oblivion.

CHAPTER
ELEVEN

Late the next evening, two men faced each other across an immense, highly polished desk. The older of the two smiled coldly at the younger.

"I feel we need one more incident, just to be certain."

A small muscle at the corner of the younger man's mouth tightened, and he blinked his dark eyes nervously. "I don't think so, sir. I honestly believe he's about to quit. After last night, any rational man would give up and leave."

"I wish I could share your confidence," the man dressed in the expensively tailored suit replied. "But we're not dealing with just another hellfire-and-brimstone preacher here. Misguided as he may be, Dalton apparently believes everything he spouts from the pulpit. This man won't quit unless we push him right to the wall. And that," he said slowly with deliberate emphasis, "is exactly what I intend to do."

Pausing for only an instant, he continued in a hard, brittle voice. "I don't have much time left on the Hill. Before I leave, I intend to do everything in my power to insure the rightful place of slavery in this country. We're going right to the Pacific, make no mistake about it. If the abolitionists have their way, every territory added to the United States will be prohibited from owning slaves."

Abruptly, he dropped a fist onto the top of the desk with a loud, hammering thud. "That must not happen! I'm going to stop those nigra-loving northerners if it's the last thing I do. What's the good of expanding this country if we don't have the slave labor to people its industry?"

"Senator Calhoun would say that secession is the answer," the dark-haired young man suggested hesitantly.

"Senator Calhoun is a fool." The composed, intelligent face familiar to the public was now distorted and flushed with anger. "Destroying the union will only destroy the country. That's not the way."

Something savage and not entirely sane flared in his gaze, then disappeared. With noticeable effort, he calmed himself, smoothing the lapels of his suitcoat and checking his gold watch. "The other thing I intend to do is to get this country's deplorable immigration laws drastically tightened. At the rate we're bringing in the paddys and the rest of the foreigners, our labor structure is going to collapse totally within five years—ridiculous!"

The man across from him remained silent, accustomed to being used as a sounding board.

"Dalton's trying to wangle an invitation to address the Senate, you know," the man continued in an ugly tone. "And he'll most likely get it if I know that bunch of milksops!"

He half-rose from his chair, again pounding his fist on the desk. "I'm telling you, I want that rabble-rousing demagogue out of Washington! Do you understand? I want him out of this town." Seeing the surprised, somewhat speculative gaze of the younger man, he sat down abruptly, his agitation quickly replaced by an expression of impassive calm.

"It's not that I disagree with you, sir," the younger man finally spoke up. "But I can't help wondering how far we can go without all of us landing in trouble."

"Perhaps," the middle-aged man said with an edge of menace, "I need to remind you that you're not in a position to wonder about anything. Unless you want to spend the rest of your life hanging onto someone else's coattails, you'll do exactly as you're told. You have no choice—remember?"

The flash of anger in the younger man's eyes lasted only an instant before he paled and gained control of himself. "What exactly are your instructions for the others, then?" he asked tightly. "What should I tell them?"

For a long moment, the older man stroked his clean-shaven chin thoughtfully. "Tell them," he said in a chilling tone, "to go after the woman again. I don't want anything to happen to her, mind," he warned. "There's always the danger of driving Dalton too far and making him turn and fight—especially if he has nothing to lose. I detest the man, but I'd never make the mistake of underestimating him. Tell them to just . . . push the woman around a little. Perhaps give her a few bruises. That shouldn't be any problem," he drawled with a smile that made the younger man cringe. "They seem to enjoy their work immensely."

CHAPTER
TWELVE

"I don't want you to go to the school today, love. In fact, I'm asking you not to leave the house."

Surprised by Jess's remark, Kerry frowned and propped herself up against the pillows on their bed.

"But I must. I promised Cely. We have to clean the school and ready the desks and put the supplies back in order before Monday and—"

"I'll send a message to her and explain what happened," he said, glancing at her in the mirror as he buttoned the top button of his shirt.

He turned and went to sit beside her on the bed, extending one arm at a time for her to button his sleeves. She said nothing until she had finished and he had kissed her lightly on the cheek.

"Jess, please don't ask me to stay home today. That was two days ago. I rested all yesterday, just as you asked. But I'm fine now, truly I am." She laid one hand on his forearm. "I need to go, Jess. I need to be busy. I simply can't sit around here all day and think about . . . everything."

He avoided her eyes and pretended to straighten the quilt about her waist. "Surely you can keep busy here. And Molly and Mack are here to talk with—"

She stopped his words by framing his face with both hands and pulling his head down to hers. "You're afraid for me, and that's the truth of it, isn't it?"

When he didn't answer, she moved even closer to him,

forcing him to look at her. "Don't you see, Jess, that I'm even more worried for you?"

She pressed a finger to his lips to stop his protest. "It's you, after all, they're trying to intimidate. But I haven't asked you even once to lock yourself up inside the house and not go out, now have I?"

"No, but—"

"Because I know you won't—you can't. If you insist, though, you know I'll do as you ask. But I need to go about living, too, Jess—just as you do. I can't face day after day of shutting myself away from the world. There's so little I can do to help with your work, but the school—that's one thing I can do. Please don't ask me to give it up. I need it now more than ever."

"I'm not asking you to give it up," he protested quickly.

"Aren't you, now? And what about next week, Jess?" she asked him directly. "Won't you be wanting me to stay home then as well?"

"I'm—" He couldn't deny the truth of her words. "Kerry, I'm frightened—not for myself. For you. You've been a . . . target in this whole nightmarish assault from the beginning. Don't you understand?" A desperate plea brimmed in his gaze. "I can't even bear to think about something happening to you. I can't risk your being hurt any more than you already have been."

Gently, she coaxed his head onto her shoulder and combed the springy waves of his hair with her fingers. "I do understand, *avourneen** . . . aye, I do. But you must understand my feelings as well. Besides—what can happen? Mackenzie will take me to the school and come back for me, just as he always does. No one would expect Cely and me to be there today since school's not in session."

He raised his head and searched her eyes. His expression was somber, fear-edged, but resigned. "If it's that important to you, I won't ask you not to go."

"It is that important to me, Jess. But not so much that I'd see you hurt to have my way."

Kerry was almost ready to give in to his wishes, he looked so forlorn, exhausted, worried. *And he looks so much older,* she thought with a sudden stab of concern. *All this worry . . . and fear. It's done terrible things to him . . . and it just*

114

keeps happening, as though there will never be an end to it.

"Jess—"

"Kerry, I—"

They looked at each other, waiting. Jess gave her a rueful smile and said with resignation, "It's all right; I suppose I understand. Just . . . don't stay very long?"

She hugged him hard, "I promise. I'll probably be home long before you are."

"See that you are, little missus," he said softly, studying her dear, elfin face. "I confess that I like coming home to find a beautiful lass waiting for me."

"Thank you, dearest . . . for understanding," she said fervently, kissing him long and with aching tenderness.

By ten that morning, Kerry had dressed in one of her older, somewhat worn gowns—one she thought of as a work dress. She was tucking her hair back with combs when she heard Molly's voice loud and angry from the reception hall.

With a puzzled frown, she opened her bedroom door and stepped into the hallway to see what was going on downstairs. When she reached the upstairs bannister, she stopped dead, stunned to see Lowell Martin standing at the threshold of the open front door. Molly, her feet planted slightly apart and her hands braced firmly on her wide hips, was facing him.

"What nerve you have showing up at the front door of this home after your abysmal behavior!" The housekeeper made no effort to gentle her tone. Obviously infuriated with the young man at the door, she continued to rail at him, her brogue thickened by anger.

Kerry stared in astonishment as the impeccably dressed Martin twisted his mouth scornfully and silenced the housekeeper with a sharp retort.

"Remember your place, woman! Just give me a civil answer to my question and none of your sass."

Burning with anger, Kerry crossed the upstairs hall and raced down the steps to confront the tall, cold-faced man in the doorway.

Ignoring Molly's grasp on her arm as she pushed up beside her, Kerry snapped, "What are you doing here? What do you want?" She felt a quick blush of anger heat her face.

115

The ill-concealed contempt in Martin's raking gaze made Kerry even more furious.

"Mrs. Dalton—" his voice was smoothly correct, though Kerry could sense the scorn in his tone. "Senator Forbrush asked that I call to convey his regrets and those of the members of his household about what happened here Thanksgiving evening." He smiled ingenuously. "May I add that I, too, was outraged when I heard about the, ah . . . incident . . . that occurred on your front lawn. It must have been . . . most distressing . . . for you and the pastor."

Kerry knew he was boldly challenging her to doubt his sincerity. Hearing Molly's furious indrawn breath, she reached out a restraining hand and placed it on the housekeeper's plump forearm.

"Thank you very much, Mr. Martin," she said coldly. "I shall convey the senator's message to my husband."

Martin situated himself a few inches further inside the doorway before Molly could block him. "I wonder, Mrs. Dalton, if it would be possible for me to speak with your husband for a moment?"

"No, it would not," Kerry replied without explanation.

"I see. He's . . . out for the morning?"

Kerry nodded curtly. "If that's all—"

"Yes, of course," Martin slurred with forced politeness, glancing over his shoulder as Mackenzie brought the carriage to a halt out front. "I see you're preparing to leave. I shouldn't detain you any longer. Thank you for . . . receiving me so graciously, Mrs. Dalton." He smoothed the velvet collar on his coat, then stepped outside on the porch and lifted his gray top hat to his head. With a courteous nod to Kerry, he swaggered down the walkway, ignoring Mackenzie's narrow-eyed stare as he passed the carriage.

"Evil's own, that one!" Molly hissed. "You should have let me put Mackenzie on him with his shillelagh!"

Kerry shook her head. "I wonder what he really wanted," she murmured uneasily.

Later that afternoon, Kerry plopped down onto the teacher's chair in the schoolroom and moaned with fatigue. "I'm thinking we should have recruited some men to help us, after all." Her hair had long since escaped its combs and now fell in an unruly toss of tangled curls. Smudges of dust dotted her cheeks, and a spot of ink darkened one sleeve of her dress.

Cely glanced over at her from where she was shoving a box of wood onto the fireplace hearth. "You look like a little rag doll that's lost some of her stuffing," she remarked with an affectionate chuckle.

Kerry grunted and held her hands out in front of her for inspection. "Sure and wouldn't Mrs. Northcote crack her long nose if she were to see me now?"

"Well, at least we're ready for Monday." Cely rubbed her hands on both sides of her dress and cast a pleased look about the schoolroom. "I can't thank you enough for helping me with all this, Kerry. I'd have worked all weekend without you. Our new arrangement looks much better, don't you think? There's more room this way."

Kerry managed a weary nod. "Jess said the window glass will be put in before Christmas; did I tell you?"

"That soon?" Cely ran a slender hand through her short hair and stretched her arms above her head with a groan. "That's going to keep this place a lot warmer." She paused a moment, then added, "You and the pastor have helped us a lot, Kerry. I'm really grateful—and so are the parents."

"Well, now, you can thank Jess and Mackenzie for most of the ideas. Seems that one or the other of them is always coming up with something new."

"Mm. And then seeing that it gets done. There have been some real improvements this year, thanks to you and—" Cely broke off in midsentence, turning to glance toward the door. "I think I hear Mackenzie with your buggy."

Kerry hauled herself to her feet, sighing with the effort. She walked over to the door and bent to pick up a bucket of water and dirty cleaning cloths. "I'll empty this before I leave, and I'll see if Mackenzie will fix that broken leg on your desk before we go."

Kerry stuck her head out the doorway to look for Mackenzie. When she didn't see him, she went on outside and down the steps to the school yard.

After dumping the water and wringing out the rags, she put the bucket by the steps and walked around to the back of the building, thinking Mackenzie might have come that way to avoid the deep, treacherous ruts in front.

The afternoon was mild for late November, though it was as dark as early evening. The ground was spongy from the rain they'd had earlier in the week, and the low-hanging clouds promised more rain by nightfall.

Carefully sidestepping a number of deep pits in the yard, Kerry was surprised to find that Mackenzie wasn't there either; she wondered what Cely had heard. With a shrug, she turned and started back toward the front of the building.

When she first heard the sound of men's laughter, she thought perhaps some of the children's parents had come by. When she reached the front, however, and saw the riderless horses and Cely surrounded by a group of men in the open school yard, she felt her heart plummet with sick fear.

At first, they didn't see her. She put a hand up against the side of the building to steady herself, her mind reeling with panicked confusion. She desperately tried to think what to do. Four white men had Cely trapped and were circling her like predators, mocking her with suggestive remarks and obscenities.

Even from a distance, Kerry could see the fury in Cely's eyes and knew she wasn't about to cower to her tormentors. The tall black woman appeared to be rigid with anger, her chin thrust defiantly upward from the long, slender lines of her neck, her shoulders square and straight.

"Whooee—she's a fiery one, ain't she?" The voice belonged to a short, porcine man with a filthy shirt and vest. He was prodding Cely's abdomen with the barrel of his rifle.

"Ever see a savage that wasn't wild?" jeered a taller man behind him who was eyeing Cely with a look that held a frightening combination of contempt and lust.

Kerry felt her legs tremble and her mouth go dry with fear. She could almost feel the touch of the rifle herself as Cely tried to back away from the fat man, who only punched the gun that much harder into her middle.

She swallowed and clawed the wooden frame of the building, praying silently.

The large, burly man farthest away from her caught her attention—something about his head—his large, oddly shaped head and crooked, flattened nose.

"Merciful, Lord," she whispered in horrified disbelief.

It was him! The man who had abducted her that terrible day

when she first arrived in Washington. There couldn't possibly be two faces so deformed, so wretchedly revolting, in the same city.

At the sound of her gasp, the dull-witted man saw her and shrieked. "There she is! That's her!"

Every gaze turned to Kerry. Cely whirled around and shouted, "Run, Kerry!"

No one spoke for an endless moment. Kerry could feel herself paling under their mocking gazes. She couldn't run—she wouldn't leave Cely alone with them, even if there had been somewhere to go. *Where was Mackenzie? He should be here by now . . .*

Suddenly, the man closest to her, a thin, hard-looking man with black hair and peculiar silver eyes, moved to grab her arm. He yanked her away from the building and twisted her arm behind her so forcefully she cried out in pain.

The man shoved her against Cely, who immediately linked her hand with Kerry's. The fat man who had been goading Cely now turned his attention to Kerry, prodding her like an animal with the tip of his rifle.

To her horror, the dim-witted giant lumbered up and pulled furiously at her hair. "You hurt me! You hurt me and ran away!"

"Leave her alone!" Cely tried to protect Kerry by pushing in front of her, but, tall as she was, she was still no match for the hulking lout. It took no more than a quick jerk of his hand to tear her away from Kerry and send her sprawling to the ground.

When he turned back to Kerry, his face was scarlet with bewildered rage. "Why did you run away from me? I was supposed to take care of you!"

Kerry pushed a fist against her mouth to keep from crying out, unwilling to give these animals the satisfaction of seeing her terror.

"That's all right, Otis." The thin man with the odd silver eyes held the giant back with a firm hand. "She won't run away this time."

His voice was laced with mockery, his eyes cold with disdain as he flicked a glance over Kerry. "We have a message for you, Mrs. Dalton," he sneered. "And I'd advise you to listen to it very carefully."

Kerry's eyes blazed with incredulous anger and rising fear. She tried to go to Cely but was stopped by the large, beefy hand of the one called Otis.

The other two men stepped in closer and looked Kerry up and down with burning glints in their eyes that made Kerry's stomach churn with nausea. For an instant, she thought her legs would buckle under her.

The lanky, dark-haired man, who seemed to be the leader of the group, snapped her chin roughly upward and forced her to look directly at him. "Now pay attention, *ma'am*," he drawled contemptuously. "What we want you to do is to convince your nigra-loving husband that he has nothing more to say to the good people here in Washington. We figure he might be more inclined to listen to you than us—especially," his eyes narrowed in a nasty, threatening stare, "if we mess up your pretty little face just enough to let him know we mean business."

Kerry's blood froze at the raw evil she encountered in his eyes. Desperately, she struck out at him with her free hand, trying to twist away from his grasp. But he swiftly moved behind her and locked his arms around her waist, holding her in an iron vise.

"Let us help convince her, chief." The fat man sidled up in front of Kerry and, with absolutely no warning, he snaked out his hand and slapped her in the face.

Kerry gasped, her head reeling as much from the shock of being struck for the first time in her life as from the pain of the blow. From the ground, Cely cried out with furious protest and tried to scramble to her feet. But the hulking, disfigured Otis stopped her with a hard kick in the side from his enormous, boot-clad foot.

A young blond-haired man—in truth, he looked to be no more than a boy—stepped from behind the chief and sauntered up to Kerry. Until now, he had been silent, but Kerry saw with sick hopelessness that his eyes held nothing but malice and contempt.

"Don't be so hard on little Brigit, Sam," he said in an oily tone of voice, his gaze raking over Kerry with bold interest. "From what I hear, these Irish colleens don't understand rough stuff. They like to be sweet-talked. Isn't that right, Brigit?"

With a terrible smile, he tugged Kerry out of the chief's grasp and pulled her roughly to him, forcing his face down to hers in a crude kiss.

Kerry cried out, twisting away from him and wiping at her mouth with revulsion. He grabbed her again, this time passing her to the fat man with the offensive body odor. He, too, made a smacking motion against her face with his lips, laughing loudly when Kerry tried to rub away the foul taste of him from her mouth.

They continued to pass her back and forth, taunting her and handling her. The thin leader had no part in it but simply stood and watched with a cold, impassive stare.

So involved were they with their fun they failed to notice the carriage which pulled up in front of the school. Nor did they see the two large men jump from it—not until both were almost upon them.

They all whirled around, goggling in surprise as Jess roared with rage and hurled himself into their midst. At the same time, Mackenzie plowed his way into the huddle and cracked Otis's shoulder with a hard whack of his shillelagh. Bellowing with pain, the giant charged the Irishman with his head. In spite of his advanced years, however, the caretaker was more agile—and far more alert—than the mentally impaired Otis. He deftly stepped aside to avoid him, then whacked him once more, this time in the abdomen, sending him screaming to the ground. Immediately, he moved to help Jess, who had flattened the blond youngster against the side of the schoolhouse and was reaching for the porcine Sam with his free hand. Mackenzie snarled, charged the fat man with his shillelagh, and easily knocked him off balance into the mud.

A sudden gunshot exploded, stopping every one of them where they were. The man called chief held a rifle on Kerry while glancing coldly from Jess to Mackenzie. "Let my men go, Dalton—now! Or you can watch me make Irish stew out of your woman."

Jess stood unmoving, still holding onto the stunned, fair-haired boy. He looked from the man with the rifle to Kerry, then to Mackenzie, whose shoulders slumped in defeat as he reluctantly let go of the fat man. Slowly, Jess released his grasp on the boy, allowing him to slide free.

Kerry had never seen hatred in her husband's eyes—but

she saw it now. Hatred and a dark, terrible fury. *Please, Lord, don't let him do anything foolish. Don't let him be hurt . . . oh, merciful Father, won't you please, please stop this!*

Suddenly, another shot roared out in the school yard. All eyes turned to the form standing in the open doorway of the building. In the chaos of the moment, Cely had been forgotten. She now stood, tall and determined, a shotgun braced and aimed at the chief.

"Put it down." The command was ordered in a surprisingly calm tone of voice, while at the same time her eyes blazed with almost tangible rage.

The thin black-haired man aimed a speculative look at Cely, not moving his rifle even a fraction.

"I said put it down!"

With a look of pure menace, he lowered the rifle slowly and reluctantly, then dropped it to the ground in defeat.

Cely then turned the shotgun onto the fat man and the boy. "Move over by your boss," she instructed with a curt movement of her head.

They went without hesitation. She glanced for only an instant at Otis, still writhing in pain on the ground, then returned her attention to the other three men bunched closely together.

"What shall I do with them, Mr. Dalton?"

Jess hesitated, a question in his eyes.

She met his gaze and said dryly, "Oh, yes, Preacher—I know how to use it."

Jess still remained silent. Finally, with a look of reluctance, he shook his head back and forth and raised one hand in a gesture of restraint. "Keep them covered."

He moved quickly to Kerry, who was now hugging herself tightly, swaying back and forth as if she were trying to keep from crumbling into pieces.

"Kerry . . . are you all right?" he asked softly.

When she didn't answer, he felt a prickling of alarm. Gently, he gathered her into his arms and sheltered her closely against him, never taking his gaze from the men a few feet away. Feeling the violent trembling of her body, he held her even tighter.

"Mack—get that rifle," he said evenly, glancing down at Kerry in his arms. "Cely—bring me your gun. Mack and I will keep them here while you take the carriage and go for the police." He looked down at Kerry again, feeling his throat tighten at the way she was shaking in his arms. He wrapped her protectively against his side, extending his free hand to Cely.

Without blinking an eye, Cely walked calmly across the yard and handed Jess the shotgun. She paused only long enough to put a comforting hand on Kerry's shoulder and murmur something to her before going to the carriage.

It was midnight before Kerry finally cried. Jess had waited and worried while Molly bathed her silent mistress and helped her into a warm nightdress and bathrobe. Then, sitting down in the broad-bottom rocking chair by the fireplace in their bedroom, he pulled her onto his lap and began to talk to her in soft, gentle words of reassurance. He left her only once, to lay a fire and make certain it would burn for a while.

She trembled in his arms a long time, not speaking, not even looking at him. Finally, his loving tenderness penetrated her shock, and he felt her slender shoulders rise and fall as she began to shake uncontrollably with violent sobs.

Her hand clutched at his shirtfront, and he covered it gently with his own. "That's right, little love, you cry," he murmured into her hair. "Cry out all the ugliness, my darling. Cry it all away."

Throughout the long, silent hours of the seemingly endless night, Jess held Kerry in his lap like a small, grieving child. He rocked her slowly back and forth in the quiet warmth of their room, holding her close, humming songs without meaning, melodies without words. He listened to her hopeless sobs weaken, then finally cease. Even when she finally slept, he continued rocking and humming softly, as if he were determined to insure her peace, at least for a few hours.

Occasionally, he brushed a damp wave of hair away from her face or touched his lips gently to her temple. Sometimes, he simply looked at her and let his heart fill and overflow with love.

His shirt was wet from her tears, and his eyes were tired and scratchy from his own weeping; his thoughts were weary and confused. Why hadn't he taken her from this place before now? So much loss . . . so much suffering. Why had he even come? He had accomplished nothing.

The town is a wasteland, he decided bitterly. *On the surface it buzzes and clamors with important plans and activity, but its heart. . . its heart is desperate and uncaring, even ruthless. People are sacrificed for politics, and justice is exchanged for power. Nothing is allowed to stop the ambition of a few . . . nothing is sacred.*

Kerry moaned softly and burrowed deeper into the hollow of his shoulder. He felt the warmth of her even breathing against the pulse at his throat and he smiled, lightly resting his chin on top of her head so he could enjoy the sweet fragrance of her hair; he continued to rock and hum and cherish her.

I love her so, Lord. I love her so much it's a wonder my heart doesn't explode with it.

He raised his head enough to press a gentle kiss into the cloud of her hair, then resumed his prayer.

We've come to a crossing, haven't we, Father? I have to decide exactly what to do, where to go from here. And I can't be long in making up my mind. Too much is at stake. Oh, Lord, please speak to my spirit tonight. Give me at least enough of your wisdom, your guidance, to help me see what I'm to do about all this. And give me a way to keep my beloved safe and out of the reach of this evil. Please, Lord, keep her from any more pain. She's already been hurt so much because of me. Please—let it end. Let it end before it breaks her . . . before it destroys us.

Save us, Lord, I beg you. Save the both of us.

CHAPTER
THIRTEEN

By the next morning, Jess knew what he had to do; he also knew that Kerry would oppose him. Somehow, he would have to convince her that it was the only way.

Through the long dark hours of the night, he had considered every available alternative. The most drastic resolution, of course, would be to simply uproot his household and leave Washington. As soon as the idea entered his mind, however, he knew he couldn't possibly do it. In spite of all the problems and resistance he had encountered, he still had the responsibility of ministering to his congregation. At present, he was sure of very little, but he was certain it wasn't the Lord's will for him to desert the people he had promised to shepherd.

In addition, the invitation he'd hoped for from the Senate had arrived at the church only hours before the terrorizing incident at the school; he now had permission to address the Senate, as early as next week if he wanted. He had prayed for this opportunity for a long time; should he now turn his back on it?

If he were to ask for a temporary leave of absence from his pastorate—a few weeks—to take Kerry and Molly away and get them safely settled elsewhere before he returned, where exactly would he take them? Besides, what would it accomplish?

Finally, his eyes aching and his heart heavy, he wrote a letter which he intended to dispatch as soon as he talked with Kerry after the morning's worship service.

She was still sleeping when he left the house, and he gave

Molly instructions not to wake her. "I hate to ask you to miss Sunday worship, Molly, but if you would stay—"

"Never you fret about that, Jess. I'd not be able to keep my mind on the service anyway," the housekeeper quickly assured him.

Mackenzie insisted upon driving Jess to the church. A strong north wind with an accompanying sharp drop in temperature had stormed through the city in the predawn hours, and it was now bitterly cold. The caretaker returned home as soon as he left Jess, telling him he'd be back with the carriage later. Like Molly, Mackenzie was anxious about the little missus and chose to stay close to her that day.

After the service was over and Jess had greeted what he believed to be the last of the Sunday worshipers, he walked back into the sanctuary. He stopped in midstride when he saw Senator Calhoun, his wife, and his aide standing close to the pew where they had been seated earlier.

Jess had been surprised to see the famous southerner at the service that day. After the dramatic exit of the politicians and their families the week before, he had expected the withdrawals of several memberships. And, indeed, the Northcotes had done exactly that. Having had no word from the Calhouns or Preston Forbrush, he still did not expect to see either of them again. Now, it seemed that the tall, thin senator was obviously waiting for him.

Although he was aging, Calhoun was still a powerful, intimidating man in appearance and manner. As Jess walked up to the senator, it occurred to him that, had the two of them not been at such extreme odds politically, he would have greatly enjoyed Calhoun's friendship. He had long admired the man's strength of character and political brilliance.

"Senator?" Jess stopped and waited, wondering uncomfortably what to expect.

The older man said nothing for a moment but simply stared at Jess through measuring eyes. When he spoke, it was with some degree of awkwardness.

"Mr. Dalton—I want to express my regrets about the . . . incident involving your wife at the nigra school yesterday," he said stiffly.

Surprised that Calhoun even knew anything about the incident, Jess was even more astonished at his words. "Well . . .

thank you, Senator. Certainly, I appreciate your concern."

The tall, somewhat waspish South Carolinian pulled his heavy gray brows together in a frown. "There's something I want to say to you, sir. While I find your northern ties and your antislavery sympathies insufferable, I view what happened to Mrs. Dalton as an unforgivable outrage, a most regrettable experience. I want you to know that if I can help you discover who was behind that crowd of low-life rowdies, I shall be happy to do so."

Stunned by the senator's words, Jess almost failed to express his gratitude.

Calhoun started to move away, then stopped. "Have the police been able to get any information out of those thugs yet?"

Jess shook his head. "No—nothing. One of the investigating officers stopped here at the church earlier this morning. He said not a one of them would talk."

The senator thinned his mouth to a hard line. "Bad business, this. No one but a coward would attack a woman to gain his own ends." He stopped abruptly, glanced around as if embarrassed by his offer of assistance, then motioned to his wife and aide.

"Senator Calhoun—" Jess hesitated.

The older man turned and waited.

"I . . . thank you, sir. I'll convey your concern to my wife."

Calhoun nodded, squared his shoulders, lifted his chin, and marched out of the sanctuary, his wife and aide hurrying along beside him.

That afternoon, their usual large and sumptuous Sunday dinner was mostly a wasted effort on Molly's part. Kerry ate virtually nothing, and Jess was indifferent at best, though cherry-glazed baked ham was one of his favorites.

Molly shook her head and clucked softly to herself, uncommonly subdued as she removed their pie plates, each still holding a large wedge of uneaten custard pie. The housekeeper, sensing the tension in the room, worked quietly. Once the table had been cleared and she'd brought them fresh coffee, she immediately left Jess and Kerry alone.

"You scarcely touched your meal, love," Jess said softly,

reaching across the table to take her hand gently in his.

"Nor did you." Kerry stirred her coffee distractedly and stared down at the table. "How did this morning's service go?"

"Very well. I had a surprise, though. Senator Calhoun and his wife were there."

She glanced up. "You thought they wouldn't be back, didn't you?"

"I was afraid they might withdraw their membership along with the Northcotes, yes," he admitted. "Even more astonishing, they waited for me afterward—to deliver a message."

"A message? What sort of message?"

She looked surprised but pleased when he repeated Calhoun's words. "I was caught so unaware I'm afraid I barely responded." Rising from his chair, he came around the table to sit down beside her, bringing his coffee with him.

"We must talk, love," he said after lowering himself into the chair. "There are decisions that we have to make."

She searched his eyes, her gaze at first questioning, then wary. "What sort of decisions, Jess?"

"Kerry . . ." He knew he must be very careful of how he raised the subject. "I'm going to ask you to do something for me, something I'm afraid you won't like very well."

She sat quietly, studying his face with a worried look.

He drew in a steadying breath. "I want you to understand that if I could think of another solution, I would never suggest what I'm about to say. But—we have to do something, and I truly don't know what else to do."

She waited, saying nothing.

"Kerry, I've written to my Aunt Marian in New York. I've told you about her, remember? my mother's sister? I've asked her if you can stay with her for a short time."

"Stay with her?" Her expression was blank, uncomprehending.

"Yes, love. I . . . I want you to leave Washington . . . for now—just until I can find out who's responsible for this . . . attack that's been mounted against us. And until I can . . . perhaps locate another pastorate."

He avoided her gaze, although he knew her eyes were burning into him.

The room was silent for a long moment. Then, slowly and

distinctly, as though in a daze, Kerry said, "You want me to leave?"

He heard the note of disbelieving hurt in her voice and immediately reached for her hand, forcing himself to meet the pain in her eyes. "Don't say it like that, Kerry. Of course, I don't want you to leave. But . . . I don't know what else to do."

She jerked her hand away and drew back as sharply as if he'd struck her. "I won't!" She continued to stare at him incredulously. "Don't even think it."

"Kerry—" he reached for both her hands and clasped them securely in his. "Listen to me—please—we have to do something. We can't continue to live like this."

She shook her head in stubborn denial. "No—No! I won't listen to you. Not for a moment."

The vehemence in her voice made Jess realize that, if anything, he'd underestimated the intensity of her reaction.

"Love of my heart . . ."

"Don't!" She was close to shouting at him, and her eyes were on fire with anger and unshed tears. "Don't you dare do this with me, Jess Dalton! Don't you dare to be talking to me as if I'm a child! I'll not listen to you—I won't!"

She yanked her hands roughly out of his grasp and started to rise. Jess caught her, gently but firmly, and pressed her back onto the chair.

"You must listen to me, Kerry. I'm only talking about a short time, two or three weeks at most."

She sat down reluctantly, her eyes fixing him with a wounded, accusing glare.

"I just want to get you . . . out of harm's way, love, long enough to make some decisions—long enough to address the Senate."

At her look of surprise, he nodded. "The invitation came yesterday morning. That's why I was with Mack when he came for you at the school," he explained. "I couldn't wait to tell you, and when I got home and you weren't here, I decided to come along with Mack to pick you up." He glanced away from her for a moment, then added softly, "Thank the Lord I did come with him."

Her look softened only a little, but she allowed him to again envelop both her hands within his. "I'm glad for you, Jess—

about the Senate address," she murmured, lowering her eyes.

"Kerry . . . beloved . . . please try to understand. I can't think straight any longer," he said hoarsely. "I'm so afraid for you, so terrified that something awful is going to happen to you . . . because of me. I'm losing all sense of reason. I'm afraid for you to leave the house—and afraid for you to stay at home." He released one hand to rake it almost savagely through his hair. "Once I know you're safe . . . perhaps I can function rationally again."

He pulled her close to him and locked his eyes with hers. "Kerry . . . please do this for me. I swear to you, if the police don't get to the bottom of all this madness and do something about it within no more than three weeks—I'll leave my pastorate here. That will give me time to appear in front of the Senate, time to make some plans for us. Three weeks, Kerry," he promised again. "One way or another I'll come for you by then. If things are no better here, we'll go back to the Academy, if they'll have me, or somewhere else—anywhere besides Washington. I promise you, love."

Closing her eyes against the scalding tears fighting to break free, Kerry drew a long breath of despair.

"I don't want you to quit, Jess—not because of me."

"If I quit," he said bitterly, "it won't be because of you. It will be because of a group of unscrupulous madmen."

"Jess . . ." Her eyes clouded with dismay. "I don't want to leave you. Please don't ask me to do this." She hurried on when he would have protested. "Oh, I'm afraid sometimes, I can't pretend I'm not. Mostly I'm afraid for you though. You were so sure our Lord called you to this place, that you were led here. It's for me to stand with you now, don't you see?"

"Kerry—" He wiped at his red-rimmed eyes with the back of one hand, a tired gesture of frustration. "You don't understand what I'm thinking, what I—"

"I believe I do," she interrupted quietly. "You're thinking that you must quit, or I'll be hurt. You're basing your entire decision on me."

He stared at her, unable to deny her accusation. "I cannot . . . continue to exercise my own stubborn beliefs at your expense," he said, his voice rough with emotion. "I love you too much for that."

"Jess, *avourneen** . . ." Kerry gently framed his face between her hands and searched his gaze for a long time; neither of them spoke. It was the worry, the fine lines of fatigue and shadows around his eyes that finally made her lose her resolve to defy him. "Will it truly help you—if I do what you're asking? Is this really what you want?"

He attempted to memorize every line, every contour of her beloved face. "It will tear my heart out," he said softly. "But, yes. . .it's what I need you to do."

"Then. . .I'll go, Jess," she choked out. "If that's the only way. . .of course, I'll go."

Slowly, he rose from his chair and pulled her to her feet with him, wrapping her in his arms in a protective embrace.

"Molly will go with you."

"No!" She drew back and frowned at him with concern. "Molly must stay with you. I'll only worry myself sick if you're alone here with no one to do for you."

"Kerry, I'm capable of doing for myself, love," he insisted, attempting a weak laugh. "And Mack will be here, as well."

"No, Jess!" She gave a brusque, determined shake of her head. "Molly must stay with you. I won't go otherwise."

With a rueful smile, he gave in. "All right—all right, if it will make you feel better." He gathered her more closely against himself and dropped a light kiss on top of her head, wondering silently how he would ever survive the coming weeks without her.

"If you won't let me send Molly, I'm going to ask Charles to accompany you to New York and see you safely to my aunt's home."

Surprised, she protested. "You can't be without your secretary. Besides, it's entirely unnecessary."

"It is necessary, love, for my peace of mind. I won't rest until I know for certain that you've been safely delivered into Aunt Marian's care. Charles is a bit awkward and difficult to be with, I know. But he's a good lad and I've talked with him from time to time about what's been done to us. I'm sure he'll be glad to escort you."

He hesitated, then added, "I'd take you myself, but I have both the Caldwell wedding and the Senate address this week—"

She waved a dismissing hand. "You can't possibly leave

now. And if you're determined that I need someone with me, then I've no objection to Charles Payne. But I think you're being a bit foolish."

"When haven't I been a bit foolish, little love, where you're concerned?" he murmured, kissing her tenderly on her forehead. *Oh, Kerry, Kerry, love of my heart . . . how will I ever get through my days without your smile, without your touch . . . our love?*

CHAPTER
FOURTEEN

Kerry's good-bye to Molly and Mackenzie a few days later was a tearful prelude to her agonizing parting with Jess.

"You're doing the right thing, lass," sniffed the housekeeper. Molly had obviously been crying earlier; her face was puffy, her eyes swollen. She patted Kerry awkwardly on the shoulder, avoiding her gaze. "It's best, lass. I know you're heartsore—aren't we all. But something had to be done. It will be all right soon, see if it's not."

Mackenzie stood silently, staring down at the scuffed toes of his boots and holding a squirming Brian Boru close to his chest. Kerry stroked the kitten under his chin, biting furiously at her lower lip in an attempt to fight back a sob of pain. She looked up into Mackenzie's mournful face, then impulsively threw her arms around his neck and kissed him on his grizzled cheek. The big Irishman wiped one hand over his eyes in a hasty motion and muttered, "We'll be missing you something fierce, missus."

Kerry heard the choked catch in his voice. Oddly enough, the apparent grief of these two devoted friends supplied her with the needed incentive to pull her own emotions together. She lifted her head firmly and managed a smile for both of them.

"You'll take very good care of our Jess?"

"We'll see to him as best we can, you can be sure of that," Molly said, fighting to regain her composure.

"Aye, that we will," Mackenzie echoed. He hesitated a moment, then added gruffly, "We'll keep him safe and well for you, little missus. You're not to fret yourself about that."

"And Brian Boru as well?" she asked softly, casting an appealing look at Molly.

The housekeeper's lip quivered slightly, then she nodded. "He'll not be without proper feeding and a bit of attention, lass, rest your mind."

Giving each of them one last embrace, Kerry turned and fled down the walk to the carriage where Jess and Charles Payne waited for her.

They said little on the way to the train station. Charles drove the carriage while Jess kept one arm around Kerry, watching her out of the corner of his eye. She sat stiffly erect, clutching his hand tightly and looking straight ahead.

With a sick heaviness of heart, he wondered if she were afraid, knowing she would try to conceal it if she were. In her customary concern for him, she would attempt to make this day as easy as possible. Always, she put him first. *Dear little love . . . I am strangling with grief even as I sit here beside you. How can I possibly let you board that train? How can I bring myself to let you go?*

The shy, dark-haired secretary was swift to leave them alone when they reached the station, offering to see to Kerry's luggage so they could say their good-byes in private.

The few moments they had together before she had to board seemed to fly. All too soon, she was clinging to Jess to avoid the final, wrenching farewell.

"You must go, love—it's time," he murmured into the soft fragrance of her hair, making no move to release her from his embrace.

She nodded, locking her arms around his neck even tighter. "Jess . . ." Her voice broke, and she finished her question in a whisper. ". . . you're sure . . . that I must do this?"

He felt his shoulders heave, his heart sink, and he knew he was about to lose what little control he had left.

"Kerry . . . sweet . . . it's only for a little while, remember?" The lump in his throat grew and swelled to an unbearable agony. "I promised you, didn't I? Just . . . for a little while, love."

He felt the dampness of her tears mingling with his own, and he pulled in a ragged but determined breath. "Charles is waiting for you, love. Go now. I can't bear this any longer."

With great tenderness, he reached to loosen her hold around his neck and pushed her gently away from him.

Kerry gave him one last devastating look of anguish. Then, blinded with her own tears, she turned and ran to where Charles was waiting to help her board the train.

Jess stood, his hand upraised in a feeble wave, his desolate, unhappy gaze following the train as it gradually disappeared from view. Unexpectedly, the sight of the train moving off into the distance caused his thoughts to drift back to another day when Kerry had left him.

On that occasion, she had run away after convincing herself that she was no more to him than a troublesome thorn in his side. Half-crazed with fear and broken by her desertion, Jess found her in New York. There, they admitted their true feelings for each other and returned to West Point to be married.

But this was different; this time, he was sending her away. For a moment, he swayed on his feet. A faint roaring sound circled his head, and he suddenly felt extremely ill. His heartbeat fell apart, racing, then slowing with a jerk.

He shuddered and hugged his shoulders against an inexplicable chill spreading down the length of his spine. For one dark, agonizing moment, he saw Kerry's face—pale with fear, frozen in a silent scream of terror. The blood-freezing image disappeared as quickly as it had come, leaving him badly shaken and weak to the point of numbness.

He made his way to a bench and collapsed on it, drawing several curious glances from people rushing by. He didn't know how long he sat there, frightened, dazed, and desperately searching his mind to understand what had just happened to him. Finally, he leaned back wearily and closed his eyes. He wished with all his heart that he had gone with her, knowing he wouldn't draw an easy breath until Charles returned with word that she was safely ensconced at the home of his aunt. Already he was doubting the wisdom of what he'd done; already he was feeling the inconsolable desolation of her absence.

CHAPTER
FIFTEEN

The city was as crowded, noisy, and intimidating as Kerry remembered it. She felt dwarfed by the milling crowds pressing around them as Charles tried to find a hack. She had always found New York to be depressing; she thought it particularly so today.

The cobbled streets glistened with a cold rain that was no more than a degree or two away from being sleet. It wasn't evening, but the afternoon was gray and dismal. She shivered in her fur-trimmed cloak as the harsh wind pelted her face with stinging rain.

A dandy in an elegant coat and silk hat poked her rudely with his walking stick as he strolled by, only seconds before a vendor, hurrying along through the mob, stepped on her foot with enough force to make her cry out. The entire area was a teeming mass of laughter and bickering, peddlers and businessmen, velvet and canvas, the clatter of wagons, the shouting of children, and the language of uncounted nations. All was confusion and clamor, and Kerry, exhausted by an aching heart and a throbbing head, wanted nothing more than to get away and find some quiet.

She felt an enormous sense of relief when Charles led her to an enclosed carriage a few feet away and helped her inside. His instructions to the driver, however, puzzled her.

"Charles, are you sure that's the right address?" she questioned as he climbed into the carriage beside her. "That doesn't sound like the street name Jess wrote down for us."

Briskly rubbing his hands together to warm them, the boyishly slender young man frowned at Kerry blankly. "The right address?" His thin, deeply hollowed face then relaxed with understanding. "Oh, I'm sorry, Mrs. Dalton, I forgot to tell you. The pastor asked me to pick up some books and things for him before I return to Washington. I thought I'd just make a quick stop on the way if you don't mind."

Kerry did mind, not wanting to stop anywhere until she reached a warm house and a bit of peace and quiet. But she only nodded a silent assent and turned her attention to the scene outside the carriage as they began to move.

America . . . where the streets are paved with gold, she thought cynically, glancing out at the crowded, littered streets. The splendor of richly dressed pedestrians going merrily along their way was rudely marred by starving children, old men bowed by the indignity of begging, and young women dragging themselves along, looking half-alive, and trying to protect their small babies from the cold.

As the carriage clattered along for what seemed to be an interminable length of time, Kerry continued to stare dejectedly outside. At least fifteen or twenty minutes passed before she realized that their surroundings were undergoing a drastic change. The neighborhoods behind them appeared to be a combination of business districts and lower-class residential areas. Though gloomy and crowded, they had nevertheless looked respectable enough.

Now, peering out for a closer look, Kerry saw that a marked transformation had occurred. Without a doubt, they were in the midst of a slum area, and an incredibly deplorable one at that.

The street, rather than being cobbled, was no more than a rut of mud framed by dingy tenement houses, all alike and closely crammed together. Story after story rose above the ground, shutting out almost all that was left of the late afternoon light. Pigs ran loose in the streets, dilapidated breweries and dismal factory buildings hovered above ramshackle dwellings, and on every corner young toughs lounged indolently or shoved one another about. All the buildings were dingy red brick or rotting, unpainted frame. Kerry had an instant sense of squalor and congestion, and she caught a strong, unpleasant whiff of brewery odors mixed with rotting food and horse droppings.

She darted a quizzical look at Charles. The quiet young secretary appeared more tense than usual, but he seemed to be unaware of Kerry's growing dismay.

"Charles, are you certain you know where we're going?" she asked, her tone edged with doubt.

He looked at her and blinked. "Why . . . yes. Of course, Mrs. Dalton."

"Then perhaps we should learn whether our driver knows what he's about," Kerry snapped, her nerves frayed from fatigue and anxiety.

"Oh, I'm sure he does," Charles said soothingly.

Kerry, however, didn't miss the odd, somewhat anxious glint in his eyes. She looked out once more, then turned back to Charles, touching his forearm lightly. "Please, Charles—I think you should inquire. I can't imagine that this is the sort of neighborhood where you'd find what Jess ordered."

Charles appeared to consider her suggestion for a moment but did nothing. Nor did he offer a comment. Kerry studied him with growing bewilderment and vexation as he continued to stare straight ahead.

She felt her stomach begin to tighten and rebel at the thickening assault of offensive smells and her own growing alarm. This time when she spoke, her voice was sharp and far more authoritative.

"Charles—I want you to stop this carriage right now, please!"

He turned and stared at her, and Kerry swallowed hard at the look in his eyes. It suddenly occurred to her with a sickening sense of dread that there was something terribly wrong here.

Jess's secretary was ordinarily a quiet, retiring young man who went about his affairs with downcast eyes and very little display of emotion. But the hostile glare he now turned on her glistened with an unfamiliar slyness she had never seen before.

Kerry spoke his name once more, in a tight, apprehensive tone. "Charles?"

He ignored her. Kerry felt a chilling wave of panic seize her as she watched his chiseled, expressionless face. Her mind whirled, and for an instant she found herself unable to think or move. Somehow, she willed herself to swallow her

139

fear and act. Moving swiftly to lean against the door of the carriage, she hung her head out and shouted as loudly as she could. "Driver! Stop this carriage at once!"

Charles, stunned by her action, recovered quickly enough to snake his arm out and pull her roughly back inside, interposing his body over hers. Thrusting his head out, he shouted his own instructions to the driver. "The lady is ill, driver— just continue as you were. Take us to the address I gave you—as speedily as possible!"

Pulling himself back inside, he retained his grasp on her arm. "Please don't try that again, Mrs. Dalton. It'll be best if you simply cooperate."

"Cooperate!" Kerry stared at him with stunned disbelief. "Are you daft, Charles? What is this all about? Where do you think you're taking me?"

Instead of answering, he clamped his jaw rigidly shut and, still holding her arm in a painfully tight grip, he glanced from one side of the carriage to the other with wild, feverishly bright eyes. The driver, however, had heard Kerry call out and slowed the horses. Charles flicked his gaze to her face.

"Mrs. Dalton, tell the driver to go on," he rasped furiously.

"Indeed I won't!" Kerry retorted. She lifted her chin defiantly, her eyes blazing with anger. "And I'll thank you to let go of my arm at once, Charles Payne! I can't imagine what you're thinking of, but I can tell you that you're in trouble unless you—"

"Be quiet!" he hissed.

Seeing the enraged glint in his eyes, Kerry sensed, for the first time, how enormously disturbed the young man actually was. She felt a definite stab of fear as she looked away from him.

The carriage came to a complete stop, and Payne's face turned crimson. "Driver, come here, please! At once!" he called out.

Kerry held her breath, trying desperately to think what to do. When the driver approached the window of the carriage on Charles's side, she leaned forward with the intention of crying out. But Payne pushed her roughly back against the seat, still maintaining a relentless grip on her forearm as he turned to the driver.

"I'm afraid—the lady is quite beside herself," he said with

attempted smoothness. "She's had a terrible shock, you see, and it's caused her a great emotional disturbance."

The driver peered inside the carriage, his lined, weathered face suspicious and questioning.

"Please, driver, help me!" Kerry cried, her words spilling out in a rush.

"Say, what's going on here—"

Suddenly, Charles pulled a gun from inside his coat and shoved it close to the driver's face. "Now you listen to me—" he shouted in a high, shrill voice while the hand holding the gun trembled violently. "You get back up where you belong and take us to the address I gave you, or—"

Momentarily stunned by the sight of the pistol in Charles's hand, Kerry acted on instinct, sensing this might be her only chance to escape.

While Payne's attention was still diverted from her to the driver, she yanked herself free of his grasp, pushed the door open, and jumped from the carriage, taking off in a run.

Startled, Charles yelled after her, lunged from the carriage, and began to chase her. Kerry glanced back. When she saw him behind her, she increased her speed as much as possible on the slick, mud-pitted street. She ran like a wild animal, her heart pounding furiously as she darted between ragged children and tough, angry looking men.

At the entrance to a narrow alley, she stopped to look desperately around for a way to lose Charles, who was rapidly gaining on her. Making a split-second decision, she turned into the alley, clutching her purse against her chest with both hands as if to stop the pounding of her heart. She ran down the narrow alley and darted into a cobbled street lined with ramshackle tenements.

When she looked back and saw that Charles was no longer behind her, she nearly cried with relief. She slowed her pace for an instant and tried to catch her breath; she knew she had to keep running to put as much distance as possible between her and Payne. But the street was slick, and she slipped. Twisting her foot she fell sharply on one side of her ankle. The unexpected pain threw her completely off balance, and both feet went out from under her, causing her to fall face forward in the street.

By now Kerry was irrational with panic. She scrambled to

141

her knees, forcing herself by sheer strength of will to ignore her scraped chin and hands. Hauling herself to her feet, she once more began to run, all the while looking wildly around in search of a place to hide. Hot tears streamed down her cheeks as she half ran, half stumbled through the street. The pain in her foot made her feel faint and nauseous, and she was terrified she might pass out, knowing it would be the end of her if she did.

Suddenly she stopped, her eyes focusing on a drab tenement house directly across from her. The door was ajar, and a small boy stood in the doorway, staring curiously out at her.

Kerry locked her gaze with his for an instant, then glanced frantically back at the way she'd come. She had lost Charles, at least for the moment. But she had also lost her purse—most likely when she fell—and with it, the paper on which Jess had written his Aunt Marian's address. Now she had no idea where to go, even if she could remain free long enough to get there.

She wouldn't dare go back and look for the purse; Charles might turn into the alley any instant.

As she stood there, frantically trying to figure out what to do, the sound of a small, steady voice cut into her thoughts. "Is something wrong, missus?"

It was the little boy in the doorway. Kerry stared at him thoughtfully for a moment, then impulsively hurried over to him.

He studied her for a time before offering to move aside from the partially opened door so she could enter.

He was a peculiar little mite, Kerry thought as she stared down at him. He looked to be no more than six or seven years old, thin as a twig, but seemingly healthy. A thick mop of curls the color of a new copper coin topped his head like a jaunty cap, framing a narrow, somewhat delicate face. Eyes as green as a shamrock hill and sober with the wisdom of old sorrows carefully measured her. His muslin shirt was little more than a rag, his baggy trousers patched to the maximum. Yet, Kerry sensed she was being weighed by a formidable intelligence and a spirit of great depth.

"There's a man—" she gasped, barely able to get the words out. "—he mustn't catch me! Will you hide me, lad?"

He blinked. "Is he a bad man, then?"

Kerry nodded desperately. "Please—can you hide me?"

He considered her plea for only an instant, then nodded and closed the door. "Aye, you can come up to our place. Me Mum went to pick up the piecework, and I was watching for her. I'll take you to our room, then come back."

He led the way up a narrow, rickety staircase. Pausing at the landing of the third floor, he gestured for Kerry to follow him. At the end of a dark hall reeking of sour food odors and decay, he stopped, pushed open a badly warped door, and waited for Kerry to go inside.

"This is our room," he told her, following her over the threshold. "Me Mum says it's one of the best to have. Only the rooms in front and back have windows, you see," he explained with a slight note of pride in his voice.

He stood only inches away from her, as if he were waiting for something. Finally, he reached out his hands, and Kerry realized with surprise that he was offering to take her wrap.

"You can stay here while I go back downstairs and watch for me Mum," he said as he hung her wet cloak on a wall hook. " 'Tis not a neighborhood for a woman to walk alone in, don't you see, so I wait for her each day."

Panting heavily from her frantic race through the streets and the hasty ascent of the stairs, Kerry nodded with relief. "What's your name, lad?" *He's such a peculiar, serious little thing,* she thought.

"Casey Fitzgerald, missus. Mum calls me Casey-Fitz."

"An old name and one to be proud of," remarked Kerry automatically. "How long since you came?"

"Almost two months now."

"Your whole family?"

"There's only me and Mum. Nora Fitzgerald is her name." He paused a moment, then added, "Me Da started with us but he died on the way."

"I'm sad for you, Casey-Fitz. I, too, lost someone I loved aboard ship a few years ago. My only brother."

He nodded as if he had heard the story many times before. "There's a bit of a fire there in the cook stove, if you're cold," he told her, motioning to a small ancient stove in the corner of the room.

Kerry glanced about her surroundings with concealed dismay. The entire room wasn't as large as the smallest bedroom in the parsonage, and yet it was obviously the total living quarters for the boy and his mother. A rickety cot sat in front of the room's only window and apparently served as both bed and couch. In the middle of the room stood a rough-hewn table with two chairs, one of them with a broken back. A number of pieces of material and clothing were strewn across the table. A tattered upholstered chair cowered against one wall. Beside it sat a small oil lamp on a spindly legged table. The room was airless, dreary, and quite cold, but as clean and tidy as possible, given its furnishings.

Kerry turned back to the boy. "I'm extremely grateful to you, Casey-Fitz, for letting me come here. Oh, my name is Kerry, by the way—Mrs. Kerry Dalton."

"It's fine to be meeting you, I'm sure, Mrs. Dalton."

Kerry smiled at his attempt to be mannerly under the bizarre circumstances. "You may call me Kerry, if you like. Incidentally, Casey-Fitz, I'm from Ireland, too."

He nodded as if he had known it all along. He smiled then for the first time, only a hint of a softening around his mouth, but Kerry thought again that he had quite a remarkable face. It was a face that spoke of an ancient Celtic nobility, subtly touched with an earthiness and a sharp intellect far more developed than usually seen in one so young.

"I must go now," he said abruptly before turning to hurry from the room. "I'll be back soon with me Mum."

After the lad left, Kerry studied the room once more, then walked over to look out the window. There was nothing to see except a dreary brick wall a few feet away. As she stood staring woodenly outside, the hopelessness of her situation engulfed her.

Charles Payne, a man both she and Jess had trusted for months, had, for some inconceivable reason, attempted to abduct her. Had she not escaped when she did, he might even have harmed her, the way he waved that pistol around. Where had he intended to take her? and why?

Common sense told her that he was, in some way at least, implicated in the terrible nightmare of incidents that had been happening ever since their move to Washington. But she couldn't begin to fathom why.

Now, here she was, in this cold, dismal room, at the mercy of strangers who obviously had no means of helping her. She hadn't a prayer of finding her way to Jess's Aunt Marian without the address, which was written on a piece of paper in her lost purse. Nor had she any money to pay for assistance. Her valise was still in the carriage, so she had only the clothes on her back. She didn't know where she was or how to get away.

Merciful Father, how do I get out of this? She tried desperately to push down the coil of despair springing up inside her. She must keep her wits about her. Perhaps the boy and his mother could help, although she couldn't imagine how, seeing the dire straits they seemed to be in themselves.

Hearing footsteps on the stairs, she turned uneasily toward the door, holding her breath and wondering what kind of reception she might encounter from Nora Fitzgerald.

CHAPTER
SIXTEEN

The door opened on a small, frail-looking woman with frightened eyes. Casey-Fitz followed her inside, carrying a large basket heaped with pieces of material. The woman looked at Kerry for only a moment before turning to shut the door after her son.

With a tired sigh, she walked over to the table and cleared a place for Casey to set the basket, then raised her eyes to stare at Kerry with an anxious frown.

She wore a faded cotton dress and a ragged shawl, and her light brown hair was pulled into a careless knot at the nape of her neck. Her clothing was nearly threadbare, and she was far too thin. In spite of this, a quiet, understated loveliness and a hint of inner strength emanated from her.

Casey-Fitz took his mother by the hand and presented her as grandly as if she were a queen. "This is me Mum, Nora Fitzgerald. Mrs. Kerry Dalton is the lady's name, Mum."

The woman's gaze flickered from Kerry's face to the obviously expensive cloak hanging on the wall hook. "The boy says you're in trouble." Her voice was unexpectedly soft, but Kerry heard the definite note of apprehension in it.

She nodded quickly. "Your son was good enough to help me, Mrs. Fitzgerald. He's a fine lad." Nora Fitzgerald nodded as she pulled her shawl more tightly around her. "We can't have trouble here, Mrs. Dalton. It's only the boy and me, and I've nowhere else to be going. What is it you want from us, then?"

"Oh, I want nothing, Mrs. Fitzgerald!" Kerry assured her.

"There's a man, you see, who tried to—take me somewhere I didn't want to go. I had to get away from him and find my husband's aunt, for that's where my Jess thinks I am—" Kerry stopped in midsentence, realizing she was making no sense.

She drew in a steadying breath and attempted once more to explain slowly and clearly to Nora Fitzgerald the events that had brought her to the flat. Nora interrupted her only once, to indicate that she was to sit down at the table. "I have a bit of tea. I'll make us some while you talk."

Kerry sank gratefully onto the hard wooden chair and continued her explanation, stopping only long enough to take a deep sip of the tea Nora brought back from the stove.

"So you see, Mrs. Fitzgerald, I somehow have to find Jess's aunt so I can get word to my husband. He has no idea where I am or what's happened. I can't imagine what Charles Payne was about, but I'm terrified that all this is part of a scheme to do harm to Jess. I must make my way to his Aunt Marian's somehow—but I can't remember even a part of her address, except that the street had a number twenty in it."

The boy had come to stand beside his mother's chair as he listened. He said nothing while Kerry told her story, but simply stood quietly with a protective hand on his mother's thin shoulder. The small, unhealthy looking woman nodded when Kerry finished. "Sure and you've had a time of it, Mrs. Dalton." Her large, sober gray eyes searched Kerry's face for a long moment before she turned to look at her son.

It was Casey-Fitz who assumed the decision. "Couldn't we help Kerry, Mum?" he asked seriously.

"Mrs. Dalton, son," his mother corrected.

"She said I could call her Kerry."

"Did she now?" Nora gave him a soft smile. "Well, then, and I suppose you can. Do you have an idea how we can help, Casey-Fitz?"

"Not yet," he said matter-of-factly. "But perhaps by morning I'll think of a way."

Nora looked at the boy as if she had no doubt at all he would do just that. When she turned back to Kerry, her tired eyes held a steady light of warmth. "You're welcome to stay the night with us—or longer, if need be, Mrs. Dalton. But I fear I have no other means of helping you."

148

"To stay is enough—Nora. I'm more than grateful just for that." Kerry reached across the table to touch the young woman, disturbed by the frail, delicate texture of her slender hand.

"I'll fix us a bite to eat." Nora rose wearily from her chair. "Then I must be at my piecework."

Kerry quickly stood up. "Please—don't fix anything for me, Nora," she insisted, uncertain as to whether these two would have enough food for another mouth. Besides, she was far too upset to even think of eating. "I'm afraid I couldn't bear the taste of food right now."

The boy surprised her by coming around to her side and taking her hand. With a sober look of understanding, he said, "It's all right. We have enough."

She looked down at his small, dreamy-serious face for a moment, then tousled his curly hair affectionately. "Thank you, lad. But I'm afraid I simply couldn't eat right now."

He nodded acceptingly and went to help his mother. "You go ahead and start your work, Mum. I'll warm the soup."

"Is this your work, then, Nora?" Kerry asked, gesturing to the stacks of piecework on the table.

"Aye, it is for now. I go each morning to stand at the factory gate while they call the names. Eventually, I hope to get on inside. But for now, I do the piecework to keep us from going hungry."

"I'll help you tonight, then," Kerry told her, wanting to do something for this sad little woman who was being so kind to her. "Sure and I need something to keep my hands busy."

At first Nora looked doubtful, but then her gaze cleared as if she understood. "If you're certain you'd want to do that, Mrs.—Kerry—I'd be more than glad for the help."

They worked long hours into the night sewing trousers and trims, with Casey-Fitz helping them. The two women talked as they worked, trading stories of their homeland and families. Kerry told Nora about her own coming over, about her Da and Jess. She spoke longingly of their days at West Point, their courtship, and his ministry in Washington. She even revealed the terrible things that had happened to them, with the exception of losing the baby.

Nora in turn confided that her husband had been given a bit of money by his grandfather, whose farm had been prosperous before the potato crop failed. They used the small gift of money to pay their fare to America. Unfortunately, Casey's father sickened on the way and died on board the "coffin ship," leaving his wife and son alone and their money severely depleted by the time they reached New York.

"Thank the good Lord I had enough left to pay for this room for us," Nora said quietly, looking up from her piecework. "That plus the work I've been able to get has allowed us to live by ourselves here, rather than being cramped into a room with several others. Many in this building are living three or more families to a room, you see. I don't want that for Casey-Fitz, but I don't know how long I'll be able to avoid it, unless I get on at the factory."

Kerry's heart ached for them. They seemed so brave and fine, she thought, to be in such a desperate situation.

If I get out of this mess I'm in and back to Jess, somehow I'll repay the Fitzgeralds for their kindness.

After a few hours, Kerry saw Nora's head begin to nod and her shoulders sag even as she continued to work. Casey, who had worked indefatigably alongside the women, immediately got up and went to his mother. Quietly and gently, he removed the material from her hands and laid it on the table. Then he tugged Nora to her feet, very carefully draping her arm over his small shoulder.

"Come on now, Mum," he said softly, much as an adult would croon to a child. "You must be getting some rest."

He half-dragged his small mother over to the bed, eased her onto it, then very gently pulled a thin, shabby quilt over her still form.

Returning to the table, he resumed the work.

"Casey-Fitz," Kerry said softly, "don't you think you ought to get a bit of rest as well?"

His gaze met hers across the table. "I don't need as much sleep as Mum, you see. She's not a bit well. I'll just finish her quota first."

Kerry's throat tightened, and she quickly lowered her head so the boy wouldn't see the pity she was feeling. "It's a fine thing, Casey-Fitz, for a woman to have a noble son like yourself. You must be a great joy to your mother."

"Don't you have any children, then, Kerry?" He looked at her with compassion.

"I'm afraid not," she said quietly, unable to stop a thought of the tiny son she had never seen. Deliberately changing the subject, she looked up at him and asked, "Do you think about what you'd like to do when you're grown, Casey-Fitz? Have you a special dream for yourself?"

He glanced at her shyly, then looked away. "Aye, there are some things I'd like to do," he said solemnly. "First, I'd like to go home—back to Ireland. There are things there I want to see again, and some things I want to learn. Then I want to come back to America and help our people here. I'm going to be a doctor, you see."

"Ah, a doctor! That's lovely!" Kerry smiled across at him. "And what is it you want to learn about Ireland?"

He considered her question, coloring slightly. "You won't be laughing at me, if I tell you?"

"Of course I won't laugh at you, Casey-Fitz," Kerry assured him gravely.

He nodded, accepting her word. "I want to learn all the old stories and songs, and then bring them back here to keep for our people."

Kerry stared at him. What manner of child-man was this? "The hero legends and the tales of the Faery, you mean?"

He nodded his head enthusiastically. "Those, and the old songs." Something else seemed to occur to him then, and he added, "I think I'd like to be a harper, as well."

"That would be a fine thing, too. You like music, then?"

His smile was dreamy and distant, and his eyes took on a glow even as his hands continued to work the material. "More than anything. Me Da, he had such a voice. Mum said he could charm the birds from the bushes."

"I know a fine harper," Kerry told him, smiling at the memory of Mackenzie. "I should like you to meet him one day. He's a grand friend, and he plays the *clairseach** and the squeeze-box, and all sorts of instruments. He, too, has a big, fine voice."

"You told Mum that your husband is a preacher-man."

"Aye, he is," Kerry said softly, "and a wonderful man he is, Casey-Fitz." Her eyes glistened with pride and love. "Jess Dalton is a giant of a man, in stature and in heart, as much as any warrior of the *Fianna* * ever was," she said fondly.

Casey grinned at her. "Your face sparkles when you talk about him."

Surprised, Kerry laughed at herself. "Well, so does my heart, Casey-Fitz, and that's the truth of it."

For the next hour, she entertained the boy as they worked, telling him stories from her own collection of the old legends, adding to what he already knew of Cuchulain, Lugh of the Long Arm, Deirdre, and Queen Maeve. She recited a number of the exploits of Finn MacCuhal, the great leader of the *Fianna,** who was said to have eaten of the Salmon of Knowledge to gain all the wisdom of the world.

"And I think it's a wise thing for a lad like yourself to remember, Casey-Fitz, that no man—even a brave champion like Finn MacCuhal—could join the strong warriors of the *Fianna** unless they knew the old legends and poetry and could recite from them. Even the most famous warriors among the ancient ones, you see, were judged on more than their strength and bravery."

So fascinated he'd nearly forgotten his work, Casey asked with bright-eyed interest, "The *Fianna** were poets, too?"

"Oh, indeed they were—and isn't that the way of a true Irish hero, though? Part poet, part warrior, and part singer."

After two or three more stories, Kerry taught him the song "Drimeen" and some other old ballads. They sang softly together so they wouldn't wake Nora. The long night made them friends, and their love for the land they had left—its legends, its music, and its magic—brought the two of them together in a way time itself never could have.

CHAPTER
SEVENTEEN

The next morning, Jess paced impatiently back and forth in Senator Forbrush's waiting room, frequently glancing from the office door to the secretary's vacant desk.

His curiosity had been growing ever since the afternoon before, when Lowell Martin, Forbrush's aide, had brought a message from the senator requesting that Jess meet with him in his senate office at nine o'clock this morning.

At the moment, however, he was more apprehensive about Kerry than anything else. He couldn't understand why Charles wasn't back by now. He'd been certain the secretary would show up at the church office early this morning to report on the trip to New York. When he hadn't arrived by the time Jess had to leave for his meeting with Forbrush, he seriously considered canceling the appointment. Only the possibility that it was something of real importance spurred him to go.

While Preston Forbrush had never been openly hostile to him, he had made it painfully clear for weeks that he opposed every principle to which Jess had dedicated his life. For his part, Jess knew little about the famous senator other than what the Washington rumor mill had provided him: Forbrush was an awesomely wealthy man. It was thought that he had accumulated much of his wealth by questionable means. There were occasional whisperings of Forbrush's involvement in a number of practices Jess detested as immoral, even illegal.

Some of his more lurid dealings were said to include slave trading, prostitution, and vote buying. His facility for getting away with all of it was obvious since he was one of the most powerful and feared politicians in Washington.

Jess wasn't naive enough to think Forbrush had experienced a sudden change of heart about him. He was hoping, however, that perhaps the senator had at least decided to cease his recent defamation campaign against Jess and his ministry. He wondered, too, if this morning's meeting had anything to do with the upcoming Senate address.

The senator's office door opened suddenly; startled, Jess jumped and turned around.

"Ah, good morning, Pastor," Forbrush said cheerfully, making a sweeping motion with his arm to indicate that Jess should enter. "I'm pleased you were able to meet with me on such short notice."

The diminutive gray-haired senator appeared even smaller when he stepped back to allow Jess entrance to his office. Forbrush was often underestimated, Jess had heard, because of his small, almost delicate physical appearance; Jess suspected that it was a mistake one seldom made more than once.

Glancing around the massive, lavishly furnished office with its enormous monument of a desk, Jess was surprised to see Lowell Martin. The younger man nodded his head curtly and remained standing in front of the long, velvet-draped window.

"Please, sit down, Pastor," Forbrush offered, lowering himself gracefully into the large leather chair behind his desk.

The senator, Jess thought ruefully, had a way of making a man feel awkward and somewhat ponderous, no matter how correctly he might be dressed. His own sensible black suit suddenly felt poorly tailored and out of style on his large frame as he sat down in a comfortable leather chair opposite Forbrush. The much smaller man on the other side of the desk appeared fastidiously neat and impeccably groomed, his dark suit obviously expensive and custom-designed.

Jess felt a prickling of irritation when he realized Forbrush apparently intended to take his time in revealing the purpose of the meeting. Indeed, he ruefully admitted to himself, there was little that wouldn't irritate him this morning.

He hadn't slept at all during the night, his mind plaguing him with the memory of those last few moments with Kerry at the train station—the way she had clung to him, her tear-filled eyes begging him to change his mind. The sight of her petite, forlorn figure as she started toward the train, the way she had continued to glance back at him until she disappeared inside the passenger car, had haunted him hour after endless hour. The last thing he felt like doing right now was playing cat-and-mouse with Preston Forbrush.

A glance at Martin set him even more on edge. For some reason, the coldly handsome young man was virtually smirking at Jess, his light hazel eyes raking him with what could only be amused contempt. Unsettled, Jess transferred his gaze back to the senator. A disturbing needle of foreboding made the hair at the back of his neck tingle when he found Forbrush staring at him with the same expression of humorous scorn.

Finally, the senator broke the silence. "Well, Pastor, no doubt you're wondering why I asked you to come here this morning." His southern drawl was smooth and casual.

Jess inclined his head slightly, waiting.

"Of course you are," Forbrush said, his smile broadening. "Well, sir, the fact of the matter is that we have a proposition for you." He stared at Jess expectantly.

"What kind of proposition would that be, Senator?" With some effort, Jess kept his tone bland but courteous.

Forbrush rested his elbows on the desktop and laced his fingers together. "We have something . . . to trade . . . in return for your cooperation, Mr. Dalton."

Out of the corner of his eye, Jess saw Martin's sneer deepen. He remained silent, waiting for Forbrush to go on.

"Ah—of course. You're probably wondering what in the world I'm talking about, aren't you?" He hesitated, his smile fixed in place. "I've decided, Pastor, that it would really be in everyone's best interests—including your own—for you to resign your pulpit and leave Washington. Right away."

A strong wave of disappointment and surprise washed over Jess. Certainly he hadn't expected anything like this. "I think you know I won't do that, Senator," he said quietly.

"Well, now, that would have been true, I'm sure, until recently, you being the determined young man that you are," Forbrush remarked agreeably. "However, you're also known to be an intelligent, reasonable man as well, Pastor, so I'm positive you'll have a change of heart once you hear my proposition."

"I rather doubt that, Senator." Jess deliberately kept his voice even and steady, but his mind was racing. What was Forbrush up to?

"Oh, I wouldn't be too hasty to dismiss the possibility, if I were you, Mr. Dalton. At least, not until you've heard me out."

Jess made a small motion with his head to indicate his willingness to listen.

"Lowell, why don't you explain to the pastor why it's so important to us that he leave Washington?" Forbrush suggested slyly to his aide.

Martin took a step forward from his stance in front of the window. "Of course, Senator."

Jess wasn't a man easily intimidated, but he felt a definite stab of apprehension when he saw the undisguised hatred and contempt in Martin's gaze.

"What Senator Forbrush would like you to understand, Mr. Dalton," the aide said in a tone that dripped sarcasm, "is that you're simply not welcome in Washington any longer. Not," he added pointedly, "that you ever were. You're causing a great deal of undesirable confusion about issues that are really none of your business. You see, sir, to be brutally frank, you're a fool. Even worse, you're a dangerous fool. That's why you really must take your leave."

Jess started to his feet, but immediately forced down the rage boiling up in his throat at Martin's insult. He swallowed with difficulty and gripped the arms of his chair, but said nothing.

Forbrush studied Jess's face carefully before he spoke. "Forgive my aide's somewhat rash words, Pastor. The young do tend to be . . . indelicate at times, I'm afraid. Still, I must agree with Martin; you're simply not welcome in Washington."

"If you're finished, Senator—" Jess said heavily, again starting to rise from his chair, "I have other things to do."

"But I'm not finished," Forbrush snapped. "I offered you a proposition. Don't you even want to hear the rest of it?"

"There's absolutely nothing you could say to me that I'd be interested in hearing, Senator," Jess said with distaste, turning to leave the office.

"I wouldn't be too sure of that," Forbrush objected quickly. "Unless, of course, you no longer have any affection for that pretty little Irish wife of yours."

Jess whirled around, feeling his face burn with sudden anger and alarm. "What are you talking about?"

"Calm yourself, Pastor. It isn't seemly for a man of the cloth to show his temper, you know." Forbrush was obviously intent upon humiliating Jess.

"What about my wife?" Jess rasped. He moved swiftly to Forbrush's desk, bracing both hands on its smooth top as he leaned threateningly toward the mocking senator.

Forbrush blinked, wincing slightly. "Simply this," he answered after a slight hesitation. Meeting Jess's angry stare with an impassive glance, he stated flatly, "Your wife is now being held by some people who work for me in New York City. She is quite unharmed and will remain so if you cooperate. If you don't . . ." he let his words fall away meaningfully.

"That's a lie!" Jess shouted, knotting his hand into a sturdy fist and slamming the desk with a loud thud.

Forbrush stood abruptly; if he felt cowed by the immense, furious man across the desk from him, he concealed it well. His voice was even, his gaze level as he replied, "No, Pastor, it is not a lie. I realize that you have been, until this moment, unaware of the situation. But the fact of the matter is that your wife is not at the home of your aunt, as you believe. She has been taken captive and is in a location known only to me and a few select men who work for me."

Jess felt his hands and legs begin to tremble. *Kerry—they had Kerry? No! That was impossible. He'd seen her leave with Charles on the train, had seen the train leave the station on its way to New York. Charles was escorting her to his Aunt Marian's. Charles wouldn't let . . . Charles?*

He was unaware that he'd said his secretary's name aloud until Forbush answered with a cold smile. "Ah, yes. Another disappointment for you, I'm sure, Dalton. But you see, Charles does only what he's told to do. It's nothing personal, you understand."

His heart suddenly went crazy, his mind reeling with fear. *They had to be lying. Surely they were trying to bluff him. They couldn't possibly have Kerry . . . unless it were true, about Charles. . .*

157

Martin crossed his arms over his chest and gave a low, ugly laugh. The look of absolute cruelty on his face froze Jess's blood.

"Try not to worry, Mr. Dalton. The boys will take good care of your wife. Oh, it's true that they may be a bit crude sometimes, but they're not bad fellows. They may have a little fun with her, but they won't hurt her, I'm sure."

The sound that erupted from Jess could have been the roar of an enraged wild animal. He would have charged the younger man like an angry lion had the door to the office not exploded open on a wild-eyed, disheveled Charles Payne.

His attention diverted for the moment from Martin, Jess turned and lunged toward Payne. *"Where is she?"* he demanded furiously, catching the front of Charles's shirt in his hand. *"Where did you take her?"*

The secretary's face drained of all color as he stared up into Jess's burning eyes. "I . . . she . . ."

"Where?" Desperate beyond all endurance, Jess continued to clutch Payne by the shirt, blistering him with the heat of his anger.

"Let him go, Dalton!"

Martin's voice cracked like a rifle shot. For an instant, Jess ignored him, continuing to stare down into Charles's unshaven, terrified face.

"I said—let him go, Dalton, or I'll blow your head off."

Jess looked back over his shoulder to see Martin holding a gun on him. Slowly, he turned back to Charles, then dropped his hand. But his gaze never left the younger man's face. "How could you do this? Why?" His voice was rough with fear and ominously quiet.

Payne faltered, glancing from the gun in Martin's hand to the angry, wounded accusation in Jess's eyes. "They never told me I'd have to hurt anyone," he stammered, his look pleading for understanding.

Suddenly, he grabbed hold of Jess's arm. "It isn't as bad as you think. We never got there—to the place I was supposed to take her. She got away from me."

Forgetting the gun turned on him, Jess lowered his face so close to Payne's they almost touched. "What do you mean? Where is she?" he grated harshly.

"She ran away from me . . . in the streets. I wasn't . . .

able to find her." He cowered when he saw Forbrush start toward him, a look of disbelief and rage on his face.

"Are you saying you never got her to the inn?" the senator asked with incredulous fury, moving in beside Jess to impale the trembling secretary with his piercing stare.

Without warning, Charles's face began to crumble. He stared at Forbrush, then Martin, and finally Jess. Perspiration bathed his face as his entire body started to shake. "I couldn't help it," he muttered feebly. "I tried to stop her, but she ran. I searched for hours—I simply couldn't find her!"

Jess grabbed his arm. "But you remember where you were when she got away from you? You could take me there—"

Payne looked up at Jess with dazed eyes. "Take you? I—yes," he said distantly. Slowly, his gaze cleared.

"Yes—I'd remember, I think. Mr. Dalton, please believe me . . . I wouldn't have hurt her—I *wouldn't!*"

Jess glared down at the secretary with disgust. "It's been you all along? You and this bunch of madmen?" He made a wide, encompassing gesture with his arm. "Everything that's happened to us—to Kerry—you've been a part of it?" A mixture of disbelief and bewilderment marched across his face as he continued to search Payne's eyes.

"I—they never told me I'd have to hurt anyone. I didn't know it would lead to anything like this, I swear I didn't. They told me all I had to do was report your movements to them."

"But why, Charles?" Jess stared at him with undisguised hurt and disillusionment. "What ever possessed you to get involved with them in the first place? I've done nothing to you—you didn't even *know* me when I came here."

Charles hung his head in a silent gesture of shame.

"Go ahead, you sniveling little fool," Forbush's icy voice broke the quiet. "Tell him why you were so quick to accept our offer." When Payne said nothing, the senator rasped again, "Tell him!"

Charles turned his ravaged eyes on Jess as if he were about to beg for mercy. Instead, Jess saw defeat and total resignation settle over his thin face. Unable to meet the pastor's gaze, Payne stared down at the floor as he began to speak in an oddly calm and toneless voice.

"My mother—is Julia Shelton."

159

Jess lifted his brows with surprise. Julia Shelton was the most popular, renowned hostess in Washington. For years she had reigned as society's darling, a queen bee of incredible influence and power. At present, she was about to marry the wealthy, influential southern senator, John Caylor Waldo.

"Julia Payne Shelton," Charles said pointedly, now raising his gaze from the floor to look directly at Jess. "Both my father and her second husband, George Shelton, are dead."

Jess stared at him, still unable to comprehend the significance of his words.

"The lady Shelton has quite a secret," supplied Lowell Martin from where he was standing a few feet away. He leveled a mocking stare at Charles. "You see, she is about to marry one of the biggest slave holders in the South—and certainly one of the most virulent antinorthern politicians—and the poor man doesn't even know his intended is the granddaughter of a slave." He smiled, an ugly, contemptuous slash against his perfect features.

"They were going to give the story to the papers!" Payne cried. "They threatened to smear it all over Washington. I couldn't let them do that to her." He drew in a long, ragged breath, then continued, "Her entire life is wrapped up in this town. And she loves Senator Waldo, she truly does. They told me—if I'd cooperate with them—they'd keep her secret from becoming public. They even offered to set me up in a political career to make her proud of me." He glanced away from Jess's pitying gaze. "I've always been—a disappointment to my mother," he mumbled. "All I had to do was—"

"—betray me," Jess finished for him quietly, searching Charles's face.

Payne stared at him a moment, then nodded. "Yes. I wouldn't have done it just for the career," he protested. "But I had to do it . . . for her."

"Oh, Charles," Jess murmured with great sadness. "We could have found another way if you had only told me. I would have helped you—"

"This is all quite touching," Forbrush interrupted with a scathing sneer of contempt. "But quite pointless, I'm afraid. The two of you know far too much. I fear we have no choice but to —ensure your silence."

He half-turned to his aide. "It would seem that Payne had

some sort of mental collapse, wouldn't you say, Martin? Rushing in here like a madman, taking potshots at us, then shooting the famous abolitionist preacher and himself—" He clucked his tongue dramatically. "Such a shame, really."

With a curt nod of his head, he told Martin, "Do Payne first."

Martin darted an astonished glance at the senator. "Shoot him?" He hesitated, then added, "Your secretary—"

"Baker is in Virginia today, attending to some personal business for me. There is no one on the floor close enough to hear anything. Now do it!"

Martin still hesitated, looking from Payne to the senator. "There wasn't anything said about killing a man for you!"

"What did you expect, you simpleton?" Forbrush hissed. "That I'd sponsor you for nothing? Do as you're told!"

When Martin continued to waver, glancing nervously from Jess to Charles, Forbrush choked off an oath and grabbed the gun roughly out of his hand. "I should have known better than to take you on in the first place. Any offspring of a milk-sop like Thurman Martin couldn't have any backbone to him."

Forbrush angrily turned the gun on Charles and tightened his finger on the trigger.

Jess looked at the gun in Forbrush's hand, then at the expression in the senator's eyes. He knew he had no more than a second. Hunching one powerful shoulder, he shoved against Charles's side, pushing him out of the line of fire.

The force of Jess's move knocked Charles against the wall at the instant the gun exploded. Payne stared in horror as the big pastor took the bullet meant for him.

Jess weaved, staggered, and said only one word: *"Kerry . . ."*

As Charles watched Jess topple to the floor, he fumbled for his own gun. Managing to finally yank it from inside his coat, he slowly and deliberately aimed the pistol at Senator Preston Forbrush's heart.

CHAPTER
EIGHTEEN

A nagging feeling of dread settled over Kerry long before dawn, beginning with the eerie, blood-chilling howl that awakened her. *A stray dog,* she quickly told herself, *one of the alley scavengers that traipsed about the city streets in search of food.* But in those early, lonely hours before first light, she couldn't help but remember with a tingling of fear the stories of the banshee.

She'd grown up hearing about the warning wail in the night that foretold a death. But when her Da had disavowed the old superstitions as contrary to their Christian faith, Kerry had followed his example. She knew deep inside herself that this wave of foreboding was most likely due to the terror of the day before and the frightening, precarious position in which she now found herself. Still, in the cold, dark hours before morning, she'd been able to discard the disturbing tales of the unearthly, shrieking harbinger of death only with concentrated prayer and determined force of will.

As the morning wore on, with Nora gone to the factory and Casey-Fitz quietly working on cap trims, Kerry was again having uneasy feelings. Jess hadn't been out of her thoughts all morning. So strong was the pull of his dear smile and tender blue gaze that she had begun to wonder if something was wrong. Surely the bond between them was stronger than physical presence; she would know, wouldn't she, if things weren't right with him? And wouldn't he also know that things were not well with her?

She sighed, picked up a piece of material, and returned Casey's smile as she began to help him once more with the sewing. There was little she could do about the wild, implausible thoughts spinning through her mind. At least she would do what she could to keep her hands busy.

"You look happy this morning, Casey-Fitz," she observed, glancing at the boy working contentedly over a piece of material.

"True for you," he agreed. "I'm thinking Mum finally got on inside the factory. Otherwise, she'd have been back here long before now."

"That will make things better for the both of you, won't it?"

"Aye, Mum says it will. We're going to save every bit we can so we can have a proper house some day." A faint glimmer of hope lighted his eyes when he looked up at her.

"I'm glad for you, Casey-Fitz," Kerry said warmly. "Sure and the two of you deserve only good things."

He grinned at her, and Kerry thought he had quite the nicest smile she had ever seen, other than Jess's, of course.

"You like me Mum a lot, don't you, Kerry?"

"Well, I certainly do. And I like her son every bit as much."

Her words made his smile grow even wider. "Kerry, is your husband really a giant?" A frown creased his high forehead as he studied her face.

She laughed and reached over to ruffle his hair. "He is that, Casey-Fitz, but not one from the legends. My Jess is a great man in stature, but his heart is even bigger, don't you see?" Her eyes misted for a moment and her smile turned bittersweet. "He has a heart so big he sometimes tries to hold the pain of the world in it," she said softly, looking down at her hands.

Recognizing her sadness, the boy made no reply but simply reached across the table to touch her hand uncertainly. Kerry glanced at him with surprise, then forced herself to answer his smile.

By midmorning, her back had begun to ache, as much, she suspected, from sleeping on a thin pallet on the floor as from hunching over the piecework hour after hour.

She got up, rubbed her shoulders distractedly, and walked to the window—not that there was anything to see except the same depressing brick wall. At least the ribbon of light visible between tenement buildings helped to banish the bleak drabness of the room.

What was Jess doing now, right this minute? she wondered with longing. *Had Molly seen to it that he ate his breakfast? He was all too likely to go off without it if he was in a hurry. How would he manage to get his shirt-sleeves buttoned—he always fought them so—without her help? Was he missing her as sorely as she was missing him?*

Casey-Fitz abruptly ended her troubled reverie, pushing in beside her at the window and tugging upward on its warped, swollen frame in an attempt to raise it.

"D'you hear, Kerry?" he cried excitedly, finally managing to lift the window a few inches. "It's the fire wagons!"

Kerry craned her neck, trying to see into the street below, but the buildings were too close together. She heard the distant fire bells, however, and the sound of frightened, confused cries.

"Let's go downstairs and watch the wagons!" Casey shouted, turning away from the window.

"Get your coat, lad," Kerry ordered, grabbing her cloak off the hook. " 'Tis far too cold to stand outside without it."

By the time the two of them reached the downstairs doorway, horse-drawn fire wagons were racing through the street, followed by a mob of shouting people.

" 'Tis the factory! The Bowden Factory's burning!" someone cried.

Kerry turned to look in the direction the fire wagons were headed and saw a dark gray spiral rising into the sky. A strong smell of smoke filled the air.

Casey started to run, then turned to grab Kerry's hand to pull her along with him. "The factory, Kerry! 'Tis the factory where me Mum went!" he screamed. "Come on—we have to go to her!"

Panic struck her as she began to run with him through the street. The sound of snorting, excited horses and clanging bells led the shouting crowd. The two of them were shoved and pushed aside more than once, but they forced themselves back into the midst of the anxious mob and kept on running.

Kerry hadn't taken time to fasten her cloak, and now it fell from her shoulders. She left it in the street and continued to run. "Please, Lord, let her be all right!" she prayed desperately, ignoring the stitch in her side and forcing her legs to go even faster. Casey-Fitz kept a hold of her hand while his small feet flew over the cobbles. Eventually, they pulled away from the crowd and took the lead.

There was the sound of an explosion, then another, and behind them people began to scream and pray. Casey pointed up to the sky, not slowing his speed a fraction. "Look!"

Above the buildings Kerry saw thick black smoke, swirling debris, and shooting flames. They rounded a corner and stopped dead. The scene ahead of them was a hellish nightmare of exploding bricks and lapping flames. Firemen and police officers were trying to push back the crowd of stunned, panic-stricken people approaching the building, pressing closer and closer in an attempt to get to loved ones inside. Billowing smoke and flying embers were being picked up by the wind and whirled madly over the entire block.

The crowd behind them caught up with Kerry and Casey-Fitz; they were surrounded by loud keening and pleas for God's mercy. All was chaos, noise, and panic. Like a nightmare, sounds of pitiful screams came from inside the building. Kerry and the boy watched in silent horror as people began to jump to certain death. Many of them were already human torches when they plunged from the blazing inferno.

Still holding Casey's hand, Kerry started to move forward. The two of them were unable to take their terror-filled eyes off the burning brick building. Kerry heard a small voice beside her choke out one word—"Mum"—then he was gone.

Speechless, she watched the boy part the crowd and charge past spectators and through lines of firemen, their smoke-blackened faces wild with desperation as they worked furiously to halt the advance of the fire.

"Nooo . . . Casey . . . wait!"

Kerry panicked and froze for an instant, then began to run after him, crying his name as she raced into the crowd. She saw him slide by a burly fireman who tried in vain to block him; he then darted heedlessly into the burning building.

No longer conscious of what she was doing, Kerry plowed through the crowd, muttering mindlessly to herself as she forced her way to the gaping hole that had been the front entrance of the factory.

Merciful God, help me get him out of here, she prayed in desperation. A large hand reached out to stop her, and a hard block of a body tried to shove itself in front of her. But Kerry pushed on, choking on the dense, dark smoke, her eyes burning so fiercely she was almost blinded.

Inside the building, she screamed Casey's name and began looking aimlessly, wildly around to find him.

Suddenly she saw him, pinned behind a burning beam of wood, staring at her through enormous, terrified eyes. The smoke was worse, the heat was unbearable, and a path of flame snaked its way directly toward the boy. She stumbled forward across the floor, leaping over a mound of smoking rubble. Hoisting her skirt, she jumped the narrow lake of fire that threatened to engulf Casey-Fitz. Hurling herself at him, Kerry pushed him to safety only seconds before a blazing, falling timber would have crushed his small body beneath its deadly weight.

Staggering to keep her balance, she felt herself being quickly sucked into a spiraling tornado of smoke and flames. She heard a growing roar, a strange, whooshing sound above her, and finally a quiet hissing as something hit her head, then her shoulder. Her gaze stunned, she looked once at Casey before falling silently and limply to the floor.

CHAPTER
NINETEEN

"I'm going to New York today, George," Jess emphatically stated to his doctor. "I feel fine—and I'm leaving today."

George Marshall sternly frowned at his patient. "You may feel perfectly fine, but you aren't—not yet. You've lost a great deal of blood, Jess, and you need at least another two or three days' rest before you do anything—much less get on a train."

Paying little attention to the harried doctor, Jess sat on the side of the bed, shirtless, hair tousled, his eyes shadowed. His left arm was contained in a sling; with his free hand, he rubbed his beard as though he were deep in thought.

When he finally spoke, it was with an edge of stubbornness that made the doctor realize he might as well save his breath. "I intend to be in New York by evening, George—" he lowered his voice but the determination in his gaze never faltered—"I have to find Kerry. It's been three days now since she . . . disappeared. Three days—and I've done nothing but lie here in bed . . . and bleed."

He stood up, wincing slightly from the effort, then quickly clamped his jaw into the firm, strong line all too familiar to the doctor. "On your way out," he told the doctor pointedly, "would you tell Mack I could use his help, please?" He motioned to his wounded arm and smiled ruefully. "I find I badly miss having two hands."

Dr. Marshall raked one hand through his light hair in a gesture of frustration. "Surely you don't intend to travel alone. You could pass out."

"I won't pass out, George," Jess hesitatingly replied with

exaggerated patience. "How is Charles doing, by the way?"

Marshall twisted his mouth into a scowl of disapproval. "Better than he deserves. He'll be released from the hospital within the week. It's a lucky thing for him that Martin tried to shove the senator out of Payne's line of fire. Not only did his action save Forbrush's life, but it most certainly saved young Payne's as well. As it is, his rib cage may be extremely sore for a few days, but at least he's alive."

"Amazing," Jess said, going to the mirror to inspect his reflection, grimacing at what he saw. "At that close range, they could have easily killed each other."

Marshall nodded, watching Jess with clinical interest, as though he were waiting for some revealing sign of relapse.

"Well, Payne's bullet only winged the senator just as Martin knocked him to one side. And, of course, that shove was enough to throw off the senator's aim—so both of them got by with only superficial wounds. None of which might have been the case," added the doctor as he bent to open his medical bag, "if that senate guard hadn't heard all the ruckus and come by to check." Continuing to sort through the crowded contents of his bag, he added, "Forbrush wasn't so badly hurt he couldn't have killed both you and Payne had he not been stopped by the guard."

He walked over to Jess and said, "Sit down a moment and let me check that bandage." After satisfying himself that the wrapping on Jess's upper arm would do, he carefully replaced the sling.

When Jess again rose from the bed, Marshall studied him closely for a moment. "The police are going to be pressing you again soon to sign those charges against Payne, you know," he said slowly. "Forbrush is all taken care of; he'll be locked up as soon as he recovers. And Martin and the rest of those thugs are in jail, of course. But Charles Payne's fate is still hanging."

"I know, I know," Jess said evasively. "I'll get to it later."

The doctor narrowed his eyes. "Pastor, you are going to press charges against that man, aren't you?" When Jess made no reply, he prodded. "Surely you wouldn't let him get away with what he did."

Jess shook his head and crossed the room to open the top drawer of the bureau. "No," he answered, fumbling for a shirt and pulling it out from the drawer. "He has to pay for what he did. But I'd like to talk to Kerry before signing anything. She's the one who has suffered most from all this, after all." He hesitated, then added softly, "First I have to find her." He walked to the closet and began laying out clothing on the bed, one piece at a time.

"Pastor—Jess—would you please sit down for just a moment? If you're determined to go today, there's something you need to know."

Jess turned around and glanced at Dr. Marshall with an impatient frown. "George, you're not going to change my mind, so—"

The doctor sighed deeply and sank down onto the bed. "Your wife," he said, watching Jess carefully, "has been found."

For a moment, Jess simply stared at the doctor blankly. Then he took a step forward. A wild torrent of emotions battered his heart. He was almost afraid to hear the rest of what Marshall had to tell him. "When?" His voice caught and broke. "Is she all right?" He held his breath, waiting for the doctor's answer.

Marshall pulled in a deep breath, hesitating for a moment. Glancing away from Jess, he continued in a faltering voice. "Not . . . exactly, I'm afraid." A look at Jess's stricken face made him hastily add, "She's in a hospital in New York. There was a fire and she was injured."

"A fire—" Jess began to absently rub his wounded arm just above the bandage. "What kind of fire? where? how badly is she—"

Marshall held up a restraining hand. "I don't know very much, I'm afraid. A messenger showed up at the church office early this morning. Apparently a doctor at the hospital in New York sent him without knowing that you'd been wounded and were here at home. One of the deacons asked me to tell you." With an apologetic glance, he added, "I'm sorry I didn't tell you as soon as I got here, but I knew you'd insist on going to her right away, and I wanted to be sure you were able."

He shook his head in resignation, "You're not, of course, but I can see I might just as well save my breath."

Jess felt his pulse skip, then start to hammer crazily. "You don't know anything more about how she is?"

171

The doctor shook his head. "All I know is that she's alive. It seems she saved a boy's life in a factory fire. She must have been unconscious, at least for a time, because it was the boy who had the doctor send for you. The message said only that she'd been overcome by smoke and . . . hit by a falling cross beam."

Jess was unable to draw a deep breath. "Then . . . it could be serious," he said softly, more to himself than to the doctor.

Marshall held out his hands in a gesture of helplessness. "I wish I could tell you more, but I just don't know."

Jess walked quickly to the bedroom door, opened it, and called for Mackenzie; then he went to the clothes closet. He was surprised at how wobbly his legs were and hoped he didn't look as pale to the doctor as he felt.

Rising from the bed, Marshall walked over to him. "Here," he said, handing him a small white envelope. "Take these with you." When Jess looked down at the envelope in his hand, the doctor explained dryly, "Pain pills. Something tells me you may be glad for them later."

After he closed his medical bag and started toward the door, he turned back. "You have one of the doctors up there take a look at that arm if you're away for any length of time, do you hear?"

Jess nodded. "I will, George. Oh—do you happen to know the name of the boy, the one Kerry rescued from the fire?"

The doctor thought for a moment. "Fitzgerald, I believe. Little fellow, the messenger said. Lost his mother in the fire."

He took a few steps toward Jess, grasping his hand for a long moment. "You'll have my prayers, Pastor. God go with you."

Within moments after Marshall left, both Mackenzie and Molly came into the room. The anxious frown on the house-keeper's face and the expectant, half-smile on the caretaker's told Jess the doctor had already given them the news about Kerry.

"I see you've heard?"

Both nodded and started to speak in unison. Mackenzie, however, simply lifted his shoulders in resignation as Molly overrode his words. "I'll be packing a case for the lass while you get ready to leave, Jess. She'll be needing fresh clothes, no doubt, once she's . . . at herself again." She sniffed and

172

turned to Mackenzie. "You can pack for Jess, and be quick about it," she ordered, moving to leave the room.

"Molly—"

Jess's soft voice stopped her, and she turned back.

"Our girl will be all right," he said quietly. "I'm sure of it, aren't you?"

Molly studied his frightened eyes for a moment, then squared her shoulders and lifted her chin. "Of course she'll be all right, lad," she replied evenly. "She'll be perfectly fine in no time."

Jess smiled weakly at her, wondering if she realized how her mouth trembled when she answered.

CHAPTER
TWENTY

At the time Jess's train was nearing New York, Casey-Fitz was chewing his knuckles in a hospital room in the same city, watching the silent and frighteningly still Kerry. Her eyes were shut; her breathing sounded peacefully regular. The doctors said she was in a deep sleep—a coma, they called it.

Casey thought it must be something more than sleep, though, for she wouldn't open her eyes at all, even when he tried to talk to her. For two days, ever since the fire, he had held her hand, sometimes squeezing it ever so gently. He had sung to her, talked to her—indeed had done everything he could think of to awaken her. But still she slept.

The previous afternoon he finally asked the doctor if someone shouldn't let her husband, Mr. Jess, know about her being hurt. The doctor and his assistant promised they would. So far, though, Mr. Jess hadn't come—and surely if he knew, he would have been here by now.

Finally, Casey got up from the chair where he'd been sitting beside the bed for the last few hours. He leaned close to study her face, wanting to be certain she wasn't beginning to wake up. After a moment, he touched her lightly on the forehead and quietly tiptoed from the room.

He decided not to wait any longer. While she was still sleeping, he would go back to the flat. There was an envelope hidden in his Mum's Bible that contained a bit of coin they had been saving since the trip over. It was to be the start of their house fund. He would use it now to find help in locating Kerry's giant-husband.

As he walked up the cobbled street toward the flat, he decided to ask Mr. Flaherty for advice. He seemed a kind-hearted man. In fact, his Mum had once told him if he ever needed help when she wasn't about, to go see Mr. Flaherty. He was old, she had said, and a mite sick, so he was always in his room. Perhaps Mr. Flaherty could tell him what to do.

The thought of his Mum made his eyes burn. He rubbed them fiercely as he turned the last corner on the way to the flat. He mustn't think about her now. Mum was gone, and there was nothing he could do for her. But Kerry was still alive, and he must help her in any way he could. Later, he would think about his Mum. When he was sure he had plenty of time to cry, he would think about her.

He began to walk faster, then broke into a run.

Kerry wondered why she hurt so badly; her entire body seemed to be one tight ball of pain. Even her eyes ached with the effort of turning her head first to one side, then the other. Lying still, barely breathing, she waited for the room to stop swaying. Her stomach felt uneasy, as if she might be sick at any moment.

She closed her eyes again. It took too much effort to keep them open. Molly would be calling her a slugabed this morning for sure . . .

Molly. Her eyes flew open, this time focusing more clearly on the room. Molly wasn't here; no one was here. She glanced around, trying to remember, trying to identify her surroundings.

Casey-Fitz—and Nora. Where are they? Painfully, unwillingly, she remembered. There had been a fire . . . a burning building . . . Nora had been inside. Then Casey-Fitz . . . surrounded by flames, fire everywhere . . . a blow on her head and the lad's frightened eyes . . .

Where was he? "Casey-Fitz?" She whispered his name, pushed herself up, and leaned heavily on her elbows as she looked with bewilderment around the unfamiliar room.

Her head began to pound like a bellows, and she squeezed her eyes shut once more, only for a moment, willing herself not to be sick. She tried to sit up. Twisting herself to the side of the bed, she tightly hugged her shoulders while pulling in deep, ragged breaths.

The room spun slowly about her, then stopped. *A hospital room,* that's what it was. There were medicines on the table beside her, a pan, a pitcher, some towels—

The door was ajar and she could hear voices out in the hall. Men were talking. She started to call out to them but stopped when she heard their words.

". . . some famous northern preacher, the paper said. Shot him and his secretary both."

"Senator Forbrush, you say? He's the one rumored to be such a crook, you know."

"Apparently he deserved his reputation. He was wounded, too. The preacher used to be at West Point, did you see that?"

"Um-hm. The chaplain. Andrew Dalton's son—remember him, the labor union attorney? Wonder what it was all about. The paper didn't say much."

The voices moved on down the hall, leaving Kerry staring at the door, her eyes wild, her heart going crazy. *It had to be Jess. It couldn't be anyone else but Jess. He's been shot? By Senator Forbrush? And Charles—but Charles had been here with me in New York until—*

She forced her legs over the side of the bed, then waited for her head to clear and cease its relentless pounding. When the pain refused to go away, she gritted her teeth together and pressed her feet to the floor. Standing up, she nearly fell to her knees with the wave of nausea that assaulted her without warning. Grabbing of the table beside the bed, she closed her eyes, waiting.

I've got to get out of here . . . I've got to go to Jess. No, first I'll find Casey-Fitz and Nora. Nora. Nora is dead. How did she know that? She shook her head and began to walk toward a closet on the other side of the room. She would get dressed, then look for Casey-Fitz. They would go to Jess together.

The only thing in the closet was a scorched, foul-smelling dress, a blackened, torn remnant with part of the skirt ripped away. Her dress. Her shoes were there, but no cloak—not even a shawl. How could she go outside without a wrap? For that matter, how could she go anywhere in that dress?

Kerry turned and started back to the bed. She must think. She would sit down on the bed, wait for the pain in her head to go away, and then she would think what to do.

She got as far as the table before the room tilted. From very far away, she heard a buzzing sound which grew constantly louder until it exploded into a roar. She groped for the table, missed, tried to reach the bed, then fell into a heap on the floor.

Casey took the steps to the hospital entrance two at a time, patting the envelope inside his pocket to assure himself that the money was still there. Mr. Flaherty had been asleep, so he hadn't been able to get any advice from him. Unwilling to stay away from Kerry any longer, he had hurried from the flat and ran all the way back to the hospital, intent upon finding someone to help him get word to Mr. Jess.

A nurse tried to stop him as he sped down the hall, but he brushed her off and zigzagged away from her, darting toward Kerry's room.

As he entered, he saw the empty bed. Confused, he stopped and looked around. Then he saw her lying on the floor like a broken doll.

He cried out, ran to her, fell to his knees, and began tugging at her shoulder. When she didn't move, he hauled himself quickly to his feet and ran into the hall shouting for help.

At first he saw no one except a bearded giant of a man in a black suit with his arm in a sling. The man was walking toward him, but he wasn't Kerry's doctor so Casey continued to call for help.

He crossed the hall and peered into room after room, trying to find a doctor. Finally, he found a nurse and grabbed her hand to take her to Kerry.

At the same time, the big man in the black suit began walking faster and had almost reached Kerry's room. He stared hard at Casey and the nurse. When he got to the door of the room, reaching it the same time Casey did, he looked at the boy again, then glanced at the number of the room on the door. Casey saw him blink and thought he looked afraid. The boy instinctively stepped aside, and followed the man and the nurse into the room.

The minute Casey saw the man stop and stare at Kerry lying limply on the floor, he knew who he was. The giant man's face took on a terrible expression. For an instant, Casey thought the man would fall to the floor himself. Instead, he dropped to his knees beside her and with his free hand began to touch her hair, her shoulder, then her hair again, all the while murmuring her name.

"Kerry . . . beloved . . . It's all right now, Kerry . . . Everything is going to be all right now, little love . . ."

Casey heard the big man make an awful choking sound as he raised his desperate eyes to the nurse who knelt and took Kerry's hand to check her pulse. With a quick glance of alarm, she jumped up and ran quickly from the room, calling for the doctor.

Casey stood in silence, staring at Kerry and the man beside her, who continued to stroke her hair and murmur to her as if he thought she could hear him. When the doctor finally came running into the room, followed by the nurse, Casey watched them all hover about Kerry. Unnoticed, he then turned and quietly left the room to stand outside the door and wait.

CHAPTER
TWENTY-ONE

Jess supposed he had irritated the doctor—certainly he had offended the maidenly nurse's sensibilities—by his insistence that someone find him a rocking chair large enough to hold both himself and Kerry.

She had awakened once, but only for a moment. She hadn't even seen him, he was sure, since they'd banished him to the corner of the room so they could tend to her. The doctor assured him that she would be all right, that she was no longer in a coma but had simply passed out from weakness. She would probably sleep for several hours under the medication he had given her. It was then that Jess made his unusual request.

At first, the doctor gave him a look that plainly said he considered the young Mrs. Dalton's husband to be decidedly odd. Never one to be much concerned about how he appeared to others, Jess explained.

"She's been through—a nightmare. And we've been apart for days. At home, when she's upset, I always . . . rock her, by the fire. Please—I just want her to wake up knowing she's safe. She's been frightened for so long."

In the end, the nurse surprised Jess. She followed Dr. Rand out of the room without so much as a backward glance, and returned a few moments later accompanied by two young doctors who, between them, carried a large, extremely comfortable-looking rocking chair.

"If you'll just settle yourself and your wife there, Mr. Dalton," the nurse instructed in a no-nonsense manner, inclining her head toward the rocking chair, "I'll tuck a cover around her to keep her nice and warm. Oh—here, let's put this about her shoulders first." To Jess's great surprise, she produced a soft-looking, light blue shawl from beneath her arm. "Borrowed it from another patient," she said sheepishly.

She waited while Jess shrugged out of his suit coat and then helped him gently drape the shawl around Kerry's slim shoulders. After he gathered Kerry into his arms with great care and settled her onto his lap, the nurse tucked a large, warm blanket around her.

"Gracious, isn't she a little thing?" she clucked, standing back to admire her work.

Jess looked up into her plain, kindly face and smiled his gratitude. "I can't thank you enough for understanding."

The nurse studied the two of them for a moment with an unfathomable expression, then seemed to mentally shake herself back to business. "I'll be around most of the night if you should need me, Mr. Dalton," she said, turning and walking briskly out of the room.

Assuming the little boy he'd seen outside Kerry's room was the Fitzgerald lad, Jess now wondered where he'd gone and wished he had thought to ask the nurse about him. He wanted to talk with him, to learn more about the fire and what exactly had happened. But the boy disappeared shortly after they found Kerry passed out on the floor. Perhaps a relative had come to get him in the meantime.

He looked down at the elfin face he loved more than life. For what seemed like the first time in days, he was able to take a deep breath of relief. Pressing his lips gently against her cheek, he drew her as close as possible against his warmth, coaxing her head more comfortably onto his chest as he began to rock slowly and evenly. He rocked without ceasing for a long time, until he, too, fell asleep.

Kerry knew she was dreaming—dreaming that she was safely wrapped in Jess's arms, sitting on his lap in their rocking chair, warm, secure, and finally together again.

It was such a beautiful dream she wanted to keep it exactly as it was. She lifted one hand to be sure her eyes were closed, and when she realized they weren't, she blinked once, then again.

With the same hand, she touched his dear, beloved face, brushing her fingertips lightly against his beard and touching his lips, feeling his warm breath. Suddenly, his eyes opened, and he quickly caught her hand against his lips and kissed it ever so gently. His smile was soft with love and tenderness.

"Jess . . . is it a dream I'm having?"

He cherished her with his eyes. "No, little one, you're not dreaming. It's very real. You're safe, and I'm here, and everything is going to be all right now."

Kerry stared at him, afraid he might disappear any moment; she then looked around the darkened room. When she returned her attention to Jess, her gaze focused on his wounded arm with a soft little gasp of remembrance. "You were shot—I heard someone in the hall talking . . ."

He nodded quickly, then pressed a finger over her lips. "I'm all right, though. It was nothing serious."

She thought for a moment. "They said—Senator Forbrush shot you?"

Again he nodded his head. "It was him all the time, Kerry. He was behind—everything." He brushed one limp curl away from her face before going on. "He's quite mad. Apparently, he had some delusion about my usurping his power. He somehow concentrated all his hatred and prejudice on me; getting me out of Washington had become a kind of sick obsession with him, as though eliminating me would also eliminate any threat to him." He shook his head. "The rest of those—savages—worked for Forbrush."

"Charles"—she said suddenly. "Charles tried to take me somewhere—"

"Yes, love, I know," he quickly hushed her with a light kiss. "And I'll never forgive myself for trusting you to him. I might have lost you forever."

He looked so thoroughly miserable that Kerry couldn't bear it. She drew his head down and framed his face between her hands. "You only sent me away to protect me, Jess. You can't be blaming yourself for that."

He said nothing but simply savored her touch on his face.

"And Charles was working—for Senator Forbrush, too?" She didn't wait for him to answer, but let her thoughts tumble out in a confused rush of words. "Poor, awkward Charles. I shouldn't have thought he had a mean bone in him. He's always been odd, but I would have thought him only a weak man, at the very worst."

"He was being blackmailed by Forbrush and his henchmen," Jess told her. Seeing her look of astonishment, he nodded. "I'll tell you everything tomorrow, love," he promised quietly, "when you're stronger. You rest now."

"But it's truly over, Jess?" she asked worriedly, her eyes large and smudged with shadows.

"Yes, love. It's truly over. All of it. We can go home whenever you're well enough to travel." He thought for a moment, then added, "If you don't want to go back to Washington, though, I'll understand. We'll find another place."

"It doesn't matter, Jess," she said tiredly. "I don't care at all where I am, just so long as you're there with me."

"Molly told me how you were treated by some of the women, Kerry, and you don't have to go through that—"

She interrupted him with a small, dismissing motion of her hand. "Doesn't matter," she said groggily. "That all seems so unimportant now in light of everything else that's happened." She yawned, then made an effort to rouse herself. "Besides, I can deal with that in my own way." She gave him a sly little smile. "Perhaps I'll have a bit of help from Adeline Corbett, as well."

For a moment, she looked as though she were about to drop off to sleep again, and Jess attempted to make her as comfortable as possible in his embrace. Suddenly, she sat up and twisted in his arms. "Casey-Fitz!" she exclaimed, instantly alert. "Where is he, Jess?"

"Casey-Fitz?" he repeated with a puzzled frown.

She nodded, her eyes glinting with agitation. "The boy, the little lad—did you see him?"

"Oh—yes. Well, he's gone home, I suppose. Probably left during all the commotion after we found you lying on the floor. Don't you remember, darling? You fainted and fell."

She began to shake her head in distress. "But he saved my life, Jess! We must thank him—and help him somehow."

"Saved your life? I was told that you saved *his* life."

"Oh, no—that's not true. He ran into the building to find his mother, and I panicked and went after him. But something fell on me, I think, and that's the last thing I remember. It had to be Casey-Fitz, I'm sure, who got us both out of there." Her eyes clouded with sadness when she asked abruptly, "Nora's dead, isn't she?"

"His mother? Yes, I'm afraid she is, dear. Doesn't the boy have anyone else? What about his father?"

"No one," she answered softly. "His father is dead, too; he died coming over from Ireland. The poor mite is completely alone. Oh, Jess—think of what he did. He went into that burning building with the one thought of saving his mother— instead, because I needed help, he saved me."

"But, Kerry, he probably wouldn't have been able to get to his mother anyway." His gaze swept her face; seeing the pallor of her skin, he frowned with concern.

"Still, don't you see the terrible choice the lad had to make?" she insisted. "In the time it took to save me, he might have found his mother. Oh, Jess—if you knew Casey-Fitz, you'd know that possibility must have occurred to him. Yet, he stayed with me . . ." Her words drifted off as the enormity of her own statement settled over her.

Jess's countenance stilled, too, as his thoughts focused on the significance of what she'd told him. Something began to dawn at the back of his mind, a subtle, rising glint of understanding.

"Jess? What is it?"

He blinked, then said thoughtfully, "I think I could learn a thing or two from your young friend, love."

"What do you mean, Jess?"

He leaned his head against the back of the rocking chair for a moment, then sat forward again. "Casey-Fitz was faced with the choice of spending himself in search of a possibility—or reacting to the immediate need, that of saving your life—and his own, in the process."

He waited, thinking, then went on. "Sometimes, we drain ourselves trying to accomplish the impossible—or at least the unlikely—when what we need to do is take care of the need at hand." He nodded his head slowly, and a small, somewhat rueful smile touched his lips. "Your Casey-Fitz did the immediate thing. That's a lesson that comes hard to me—but one I most desperately need to learn, I fear."

At her puzzled glance, he touched his index finger lightly to the tip of her nose and said, "Let's just say that in the future, instead of concentrating on that distant mountain I'm always

185

trying to move, I'm going to see about clearing the road of a few small stones that are in the way."

She nodded slowly with understanding. "I wish we could start with the boy. Oh, Jess—you should see the place he's living in. It's only a little hole of a room—dark and cold and hardly furnished at all. And he has barely enough to eat."

She clenched her hands together in despair. "They were so kind to me, Jess—the two of them, Nora and the boy. I was so frightened, and they took me in and shared the little they had with me. And now—"

Tears misted her eyes, but when he tried to comfort her, she sat up even straighter, a frown of dismay creasing her forehead. "Oh, Jess, whatever will he do? And he's such a treasure of a child. Did you see him, did you see his eyes? He loves the old stories and he sings like an angel . . . and do you know, he wants to be a harper, and a doctor, and—"

"Whoa, whoa!" Jess cupped her chin in his hand, smiling at her outburst. "Do you know, Kerry Shannon, that for the very first time since I married you, I do believe I'm jealous?"

She stared at him blankly, then laughed a little. Her expression quickly sobered, however. "Oh, Jess—please try to find him right away. He shouldn't be alone, not now, so soon after losing his mother. And . . . I don't know why I'm so sure, but I believe he's been here with me, ever since the fire."

His eyes questioning, he studied her face for a long moment. "You're really taken with the boy, aren't you, love?"

She nodded eagerly. "You'd understand why if you could spend a bit o' time with him, Jess. He has a way about him. I don't know exactly what it is . . . but he's—special."

He pulled her close to him, wrapping her hand in his and brushing his lips tenderly across her fingers. "Must be the Irish in him," he murmured. "They definitely have a way of stealing one's heart, I'm told."

They sat quietly for a long time, Kerry resting against his warmth, drawing from his strength and his love, each thinking their own thoughts. It was Jess who finally broke the silence.

"Kerry—" he stopped, seemed to make a decision, then went on. "You say the boy's alone?"

Kerry turned to look at him. "Yes—he has no one."

"Perhaps when you're stronger, we could think about—"

She didn't let him finish. "What, Jess?"

"Not now, dear. You have to rest. Later, we'll talk about what we might be able to do for your Casey-Fitz."

She sat up in his arms. "What are you thinking?" Her eyes took on a childlike glint of anticipation. "Jess?"

He pursed his lips thoughtfully and gave her an uncertain look. "Well, you're obviously—fond of the boy. And if he's been hanging around you as much as you think, he must be—attached to you, as well. Perhaps . . ." He left the thought unfinished, and for a moment Kerry thought he was about to drift into one of those mind-wandering, distant moods of his.

Anxious to keep his attention, she prompted, "Perhaps what, Jess?"

His eyes cleared. "Perhaps—later, of course—we could talk with him about—living with us."

She opened her mouth in surprise, then quickly clamped it shut. "Why do we have to wait until later? Why couldn't we talk to him right away?"

"Well, I told you, love, we need to wait until you're stronger."

"I'm perfectly strong enough now," she insisted. "Jess—are you suggesting what I think you are? Are you saying we could take Casey-Fitz back with us—that is, if he wants to go—that he could stay with us and be . . . our own?"

As always, her quicksilver mind threatened to leave him in the dust, and he found himself mentally groping to catch up with her. "Ah . . . yes . . . yes. I suppose that's what I'm saying, love. If the boy has no one else, perhaps he'd be willing to—adopt us as his parents. What do you think?"

She stared at him for only an instant, then threw her arms around his neck, surprising him with her strength as she kissed him soundly. "I think," she declared fervently, "that you are the most wonderful man alive, Jess Dalton. And I think I love you more than everything."

"I see. Ah . . . does that mean you approve of my idea?"

She nodded her head vigorously. "Will you try to find him now, Jess? Please?"

"Kerry, I don't think the boy is here. Surely he is exhausted and has probably started on his way home by this time.

"But will you just look, Jess?"

He sighed, pretending exasperation, then nodded. "All right. If you'll promise to get back into bed and stay there this time. I'll see if I can find this—treasure of a lad who has so thoroughly charmed you."

Obediently, she started to remove herself from his lap. Just as quickly, he tightened his embrace. "Not so fast, Mrs. Dalton," he said softly. "You'll not start bouncing out of my arms again so soon after finding your way back into them."

He stood then, lifting her and nestling her closely against him, staring down into her face as if he were trying to frame every lovely line of it for his memory.

Finally, he smiled and whispered, "I love you . . . more than everything, Kerry, *mavourneen.*"* Then he kissed her breathless and put her gently back to bed.

Casey thought he might as well go back to the flat. Earlier, he had left his hiding place just long enough to peep into Kerry's room. When he saw she was awake and that Jess was holding her on his lap, he quietly though somewhat reluctantly, returned to the dark little niche around the corner from the supply closet and sank to the floor.

He could leave now, there was no need to hang around. She wouldn't need him to watch over her any longer. Still he delayed, thinking about how it had been for a while to have someone who needed him. His Mum had depended on him, of course, but she was gone now. And since Kerry had needed him so soon after losing his Mum, there hadn't been time to feel alone—or lonely.

But Kerry was obviously fine now, so he could be on his way. He needed to go back to the flat and think about what to do. He would have to find work soon. There would be no more piecework from the Bowden factory, of course, since it had been demolished by the fire.

It was just as well. He had always hated doing the piecework. He'd never said anything to his Mum, for she was sad enough without his adding to her pain. But he had promised himself that he would never touch a needle again if he were ever finished with this business.

He thought about going to sea. Perhaps he could get a job on a ship and have a look at other countries. He might even end up back in Ireland for a bit.

He patted his pocket. Sure and there was enough to get him by until he found work that suited him. He tried to think about it, but the thought of his Mum's thin, worried face kept getting mixed up with all the other thoughts in his head. He gave it up for the present.

He propped up his legs, folded his arms on them, and put his head down to rest. He let himself think about his Mum. He spent a long time remembering her; finally, he allowed himself to cry.

That was how Jess found him—huddled in a damp, dark corner, his tear-streaked, dirty face propped on his knees, his thin, bony shoulders heaving with sobs.

Casey looked up, his large, brave eyes widening at the sight of Kerry's giant husband standing over him. They studied each other in silence for a long time before Jess reached out a hand to help the lad to his feet. "Will you come with me, son? Kerry and I would like to talk with you . . . about something very important."

Casey looked at the immense hand and then glanced up into the giant's smiling eyes. He hesitated a moment before grasping the outstretched hand and rising from the dark corner.

The giant draped his free arm around the boy's thin, narrow shoulders, and together they walked down the dimly lighted corridor. Once, when the giant glanced down to find the boy's solemn eyes studying him with enormous interest, he smiled an odd little smile and said, seemingly to himself, "Ah, Lord, it seems you went to the trouble of handpicking him, didn't you? Complete with copper curls and shamrock eyes."

He chuckled softly, gave the boy's shoulder a gentle squeeze, then shook his head in wonder as they walked on.

EPILOGUE

April 5, 1865
Richmond, Virginia

Dear Dad and Little Mother . . .

I'm writing this on my birthday, blessed by the assurance that today, as I'm thinking lovingly of you, you are thinking of me and wondering if your roaming boy is alive and well.

Rest yourself, Little Mother, for I'm perfectly fine. I have good news. Though you may hear it long before you read this letter, I want the pleasure of writing down the words to those I love best. The war, you see, is at last about to end.

President Lincoln is in Richmond today, and all the boys are trying for a look at him, yours truly included of course. Word has it that Lee is ready to surrender; his forces are depleted, and his men are starving. It's over—finally over. But, oh, haven't we paid a price.

I've been with General Grant for several weeks now. Somehow, he learned that I'm your son, and we sat for hours one night talking about the years you were together at West Point. You should hear him speak of you, Dad; what respect. And he asked if you're still as pretty and saucy as you were years ago, Little Mother. I told him, of course, that you are! Didn't my eyes bug to learn that our famous Union general was the very same cadet who drove your carriage the day you two were married.

Some say the general had no mind for the military when he was a cadet at the Academy, that he only cared about the horses. Perhaps you'd know about that, Dad; I intend to ask you all about him when I get home, for he's a fascinating fellow. I also sense that he's a sorrowful, lonely man—a man with a bottomless, gentle spirit and a sad, haunted soul.

But no more talk of war. Today is for our memories, especially mine of you. Always, my heart is filled with the two of you and the rich, happy life you've given me. What an incredible, wonderful legacy is mine, thanks to both of you.

I'm remembering that long ago night in New York City when I saw you striding toward me, Dad, down that hospital corridor. I thought you were the biggest man I'd ever seen, and the years have made it abundantly clear that you are every bit the giant I believed you to be.

One of my favorite memories is of the day I stepped off the train in Washington when you and Little Mother took me home with you as your own son. I can still feel the soft wool of my new gray suit and my stiff black shoes and that ridiculous hat I kept for years. Most of all, though, I remember Grandma Molly wrapping me up in her arms as if she'd ordered me special from New York—and Grandpa Mack handing me my own shillelagh, which he said no self-respecting Irishman should ever be without.

Will any of us ever forget the day those two dear souls were wed to each other in your church, Dad, with you reading the service—as best you could, that is, over the sounds of Little Mother's weeping?

Oh, how I loved the both of them—and how endlessly patient they were with me . . . even when I ruined Grandma Molly's shiny waxed floors by chasing Brian Boru across them at top speed . . . or when I filled Grandpa Mack's pipe with nutmeg to see his mustache flap up and down.

And didn't Grandma do exactly what she always told Grandpa Mack she intended—going to the Lord ahead of him to be sure the angels were forewarned that he was on his way. How I miss them now that they're gone.

What a rich man I am, loved ones. Today, I am twenty-seven years old, and I've never lived a day without the security of knowing somebody loves me, more than anything.

I owe both of you so much. You've given me a fine education at West Point, medical school, a grand home, a good life, love—so much love.

And how, Little Mother, could I go searching among my dearest memories without being ever so keenly aware of all the gentle, lovely ways you have fed my Celtic soul? The songs you sang throughout my childhood, the stories you told me, the legends you breathed life into, the poetry and the music—ah, that grand and glorious music.

What a pair the two of you are. I can still see you, Dad, tossing our Little Mother into a snowdrift—just to watch her emerald eyes flash. And never, ever, will I forget the sight of her snuggled on your lap as the two of you rocked in front of the fire, drawing strength and comfort from each other, always so completely, wonderfully, in love.

Pity me, though, when I begin to search for my own love. For how could I ever settle for less than what I've seen between the two of you? May the good Lord bless me with such a love, and I'll never ask for more.

God willing, I'll be home soon, loved ones. For now, at least, I'm tired of doctoring, tired of blood, pain, hopelessness, and death . . . tired of being tired. I have it in my mind to live my dream and go to Ireland once I rest for a bit. I have to go back or I'll never really know myself. I have a need to see where I came from and what it was like. I want to get to know the land and the people so I can choose what to bring home with me and what to finally leave behind.

But first, I'm coming home—coming home to be healed by your love, for nothing but love can heal the wounds this war has inflicted upon me and so many others like me.

Growing up in the circle of such a vast, enormous love—only that has enabled me to walk these battlefields of misery and remain a whole man while keeping a bit of hope for when it's over.

I thank God every day of my life for you, Dad, and you, my adorable Little Mother. I thank you both for the wonderful memories that will forever be a part of me . . . for the shelter of a love as big as all eternity.

I am now and always will be—

Your devoted son,

Casey Fitzgerald Dalton

The Dalton Saga concludes with the story of Casey-Fitz, Jess and Kerry's adopted son, in *A Lamp Unto the City*. In the aftermath of the Civil War, Casey-Fitz exchanges one battleground for another as he takes his own fight for freedom— and his medical practice—to the streets of New York, streets teeming with the misery of impoverished immigrants. Here he finds his destiny and the love of his life—Brianna Mackay— only to learn that he may be forced to surrender one for the other.

GLOSSARY

avourneen/mavourneen: my darling

alannah: endearment for young child

asthore: my love; my beloved

bodhran: drum made of goat skin stretched over a wooden frame

clairseach: ancient wire-strung harp

cuisle mo chroid: pulse of my heart

fianna: legendary band of professional Irish warriors bound by rules of chivalry, sworn to fight for the king against foreign foes and for peace among the clans within the realm

gombeen men: unscrupulous money lenders

go sabhala Dia sinn: God save (help) us

mavourneen/avourneen: my darling

ochone: exclamation of distress; "Oh, dear!" "Goodness!" "Alas!"

Orange Peel: nickname Daniel O'Connell gave to the British prime minister, Sir Robert Peel

puca: goblin

wirra: exclamation; "Oh!"

About the Author

The inspirational texts of B.J. HOFF have appeared for many years on Abbey Press greeting cards, plaques, calendars, and in gift books. She is also the author of a number of inspirational novels. *A Whisper in the Wind* is the second book of a trilogy, *The Dalton Saga*. The story will be continued in *A Lamp Unto the City*, to be published during the coming months. The first book of *The Dalton Saga*, *To Love and to Honor* is presently available in bookstores everywhere.

Abbey Press has also published a book featuring a variety of B.J. Hoff's best-selling inspirational texts, *Meetings With the Master*.

A former music teacher and church music director, B.J. lives in Lancaster, Ohio, with her husband and two daughters.